Test Bank

Anatomy & Physiology

Elaine N. Marieb

Benjamin
Cummings

San Francisco   Boston   New York
Cape Town   Hong Kong   London   Madrid   Mexico City
Montreal   Munich   Paris   Singapore   Sydney   Tokyo   Toronto

Publisher: Daryl Fox

Managing Editor, Editorial: Kay Ueno

Associate Project Editor: Mary Ann Murray

Publishing Assistant: David Stalder

Managing Editor, Production: Wendy Earl

Production Supervisor: David Novak

Production Editor: Bettina Borer

Composition: The Left Coast Group, Inc.

Manufacturing Buyer: Stacey Weinberger

Marketing Manager: Lauren Harp

Adapted by Temma al-Mukhtar, San Diego Mesa College, from Test Bank for
Human Anatomy & Physiology, Fifth Edition, by Wayne Siefert.

Benjamin
Cummings

ISBN 0-8053-6475-7
2 3 4 5 6 7 8 9 10–VG–05 04 03 02 01
www.aw.com/bc

Preface

This Test Bank was developed to accompany *Anatomy & Physiology*, First Edition, by Elaine N. Marieb. Each chapter contains a variety of questions, including:

Fill-in-the-Blank Questions
Short-Answer Questions
Matching Questions
True/False Questions
Multiple-Choice Questions
Clinical Questions

Since it is often difficult to measure student understanding of conceptual ideas, especially in physiology, emphasis is placed on the proper design of multiple-choice questions. Because multiple-choice questions test comprehension as well as recall, a large number of these questions are provided. Additionally, objective questions lend themselves well to machine scoring, which is often necessary with large classes.

For each question in this Test Bank, the following information is provided:

Answer: Correct answer. The essay questions include short answers that may be expanded upon by the instructor or student.

Diff: Level of difficulty. Noted as 1 (simple recall), 2 (more difficult detail recall), 3 (some analysis), 4 (more difficult analysis), 5 (analysis and conceptual answers).

Page Ref: These page numbers reference relevant content in the main textbook.

This Test Bank is intended as a complete question source to accompany the text, but it can also be used to supplement any existing questions an instructor may already be using. The Test Bank is formatted so that an instructor can cut and paste questions for preparation of an exam. An interactive Macintosh and Windows CD-ROM version of this Test Bank is available, which will allow you to easily alter the questions provided or add new questions to fit your class.

Since testing is an integral part of any course, and science courses in particular are an ideal arena in which to explore logical thought processes, this Test Bank will serve as a nucleus for developing critical thinking in students and will enhance the learning experience for both students and instructors.

Comments and suggestions are always welcome. They may be sent care of Anatomy and Physiology, Benjamin Cummings, 1301 Sansome Street, San Francisco, CA 94111.

Contents

CHAPTER 1   The Human Body: An Orientation

Fill–in–the–Blank/Short Answer Questions

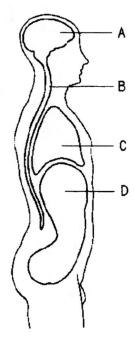

Figure 1.1

Using Figure 1.1, identify the following:

1) Thoracic cavity.

   Answer: C
   Diff: 1   Page Ref: 18

2) Cranial cavity.

   Answer: A
   Diff: 1   Page Ref: 18

3) Abdominal cavity.

   Answer: D
   Diff: 1   Page Ref: 18

4) Vertebral cavity.

   Answer: B
   Diff: 1   Page Ref: 18

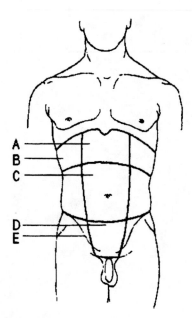

Figure 1.2

Using Figure 1.2, identify the following:

   5) Umbilical region.

      Answer: C
      Diff: 1   Page Ref: 20

   6) Right hypochondriac.

      Answer: B
      Diff: 1   Page Ref: 20

   7) Hypogastric (pubic) region.

      Answer: D
      Diff: 1   Page Ref: 20

   8) Epigastric region.

      Answer: A
      Diff: 1   Page Ref: 20

   9) Right iliac (inguinal) region.

      Answer: E
      Diff: 1   Page Ref: 20

Fill in the blank or provide a short answer:

   10) _____ consist of similar cells that have a common function.

      Answer: Tissues
      Diff: 1   Page Ref: 4

11) The _____ system secretes hormones that regulate growth processes and nutrient usage by body cells.

Answer: endocrine
Diff: 2   Page Ref: 6

12) _____ is a term that describes the back of the elbow.

Answer: Olecranal
Diff: 1   Page Ref: 14

13) _____ is a term that describes the heel region.

Answer: Calcaneal
Diff: 1   Page Ref: 14

14) The elbow is _____ to the wrist.

Answer: proximal
Diff: 1   Page Ref: 16

15) The _____ cavity contains tiny bones that transmit sound vibrations to the organ of hearing in the inner ear.

Answer: middle ear
Diff: 1   Page Ref: 20

16) The _____ cavity contains the bladder, some reproductive organs, and the rectum.

Answer: pelvic
Diff: 1   Page Ref: 18

17) _____ peritoneum is the serous membrane that covers the intestines.

Answer: Visceral
Diff: 1   Page Ref: 19

18) _____ physiology concerns urine production and kidney function.

Answer: Renal
Diff: 1   Page Ref: 4

19) _____ is a broad term that covers all chemical reactions that occur within the body cells.

Answer: Metabolism
Diff: 1   Page Ref: 9

20) What is the function of the serous membranes?

Answer: They act to reduce friction and allow the organs to slide across cavity walls.
Diff: 2   Page Ref: 19

21) Fully describe the anatomical position for the human body.

Answer: The body is erect, arms hanging at the sides, palms forward, and thumbs pointed away from the midline.
Diff: 2   Page Ref: 15

Matching Questions

Match the following:

1) Column 1: Directly causes mechanical motion.

Column 2: Muscular

Answer: Muscular
Diff: 1   Page Ref: 6

2) Column 1: Responds to environmental changes by transmitting electrical impulses.

Column 2: Nervous

Answer: Nervous
Diff: 1   Page Ref: 6

3) Column 1: Provides support and levers for muscles to work on.

Column 2: Skeletal

Answer: Skeletal
Diff: 1   Page Ref: 6

4) Column 1: Protects underlying organs from mechanical damage and synthesizes vitamin D.

Column 2: Integumentary

Answer: Integumentary
Diff: 1   Page Ref: 6

Match the following:

5) Column 1: Controls the body with chemical molecules called hormones.

Column 2: Endocrine

Answer: Endocrine
Diff: 1   Page Ref: 6

6) Column 1: The thyroid gland is part of
          this system.

   Column 2: Endocrine

   Answer: Endocrine
   Diff: 1   Page Ref: 6

7) Column 1: Delivers oxygen and nutrients
          to the tissues.

   Column 2: Cardiovascular

   Answer: Cardiovascular
   Diff: 1   Page Ref: 6

8) Column 1: Removes and filters excess
          fluid from tissues.

   Column 2: Lymphatic

   Answer: Lymphatic
   Diff: 1   Page Ref: 7

Match the following:

9) Column 1: Breaks down ingested
          foodstuffs so they can be
          absorbed.

   Column 2: Digestive

   Answer: Digestive
   Diff: 1   Page Ref: 7

10) Column 1: Rids the body of
           nitrogen–containing wastes.

    Column 2: Urinary

    Answer: Urinary
    Diff: 1   Page Ref: 7

11) Column 1: Site of fetal development.

    Column 2: Female Reproductive

    Answer: Female Reproductive
    Diff: 1   Page Ref: 7

12) Column 1: Breaks down ingested food
           into its building blocks.

    Column 2: Digestive

    Answer: Digestive
    Diff: 1   Page Ref: 7

13) Column 1: Site of gas exchange between
the atmosphere and the body.

Column 2: Respiratory

Answer: Respiratory
Diff: 1   Page Ref: 7

Match the following:

14) Column 1: Arteries, veins, heart.

Column 2: Cardiovascular

Answer: Cardiovascular
Diff: 1   Page Ref: 6

15) Column 1: Trachea, bronchi, alveoli.

Column 2: Respiratory

Answer: Respiratory
Diff: 1   Page Ref: 6

16) Column 1: Adrenal glands, pancreas,
pituitary.

Column 2: Endocrine

Answer: Endocrine
Diff: 1   Page Ref: 6

17) Column 1: Esophagus, large intestine,
rectum.

Column 2: Digestive

Answer: Digestive
Diff: 1   Page Ref: 7

18) Column 1: Kidneys, bladder, ureters.

Column 2: Urinary

Answer: Urinary
Diff: 1   Page Ref: 7

Match the following:

19) Column 1: Stomach.

Column 2: Abdominopelvic

Foil: Spinal

Answer: Abdominopelvic
Diff: 1   Page Ref: 20

20) Column 1: Intestines.

Column 2: Abdominopelvic

Answer: Abdominopelvic
Diff: 1   *Page Ref: 20*

21) Column 1: Heart.

Column 2: Thoracic

Answer: Thoracic
Diff: 1   *Page Ref: 18*

22) Column 1: Uterus.

Column 2: Abdominopelvic

Answer: Abdominopelvic
Diff: 1   *Page Ref: 18*

23) Column 1: Brain.

Column 2: Cranial

Answer: Cranial
Diff: 1   *Page Ref: 18*

24) Column 1: Bladder.

Column 2: Abdominopelvic

Answer: Abdominopelvic
Diff: 1   *Page Ref: 18*

25) Column 1: Lungs.

Column 2: Thoracic

Answer: Thoracic
Diff: 1   *Page Ref: 18*

Match the following:

26) Column 1: Arm.

Column 2: Brachial

Answer: Brachial
Diff: 1   *Page Ref: 14*

27) Column 1: Buttock.

Column 2: Gluteal

Answer: Gluteal
Diff: 1   *Page Ref: 14*

28) Column 1: Head.

   Column 2: Cephalic

   Answer: Cephalic
   Diff: 1   Page Ref: 14

29) Column 1: Knee (anterior aspect).

   Column 2: Patellar

   Answer: Patellar
   Diff: 1   Page Ref: 14

30) Column 1: Chest.

   Column 2: Thoracic

   Answer: Thoracic
   Diff: 1   Page Ref: 14

Match the following:

31) Column 1: The bridge of the nose is ____
          to the left eye.

   Column 2: Medial

   Answer: Medial
   Diff: 1   Page Ref: 16

32) Column 1: The upper arm is ____ to the
          forearm.

   Column 2: Proximal

   Answer: Proximal
   Diff: 1   Page Ref: 16

33) Column 1: The heart is ____ to the
          stomach.

   Column 2: Superior

   Answer: Superior
   Diff: 1   Page Ref: 16

34) Column 1: The fingers are ____ to the
          wrist.

   Column 2: Distal

   Answer: Distal
   Diff: 1   Page Ref: 16

35) Column 1: The stomach is ____ to the
            spine.
   Column 2: Anterior

   Answer: Anterior
   Diff: 1   Page Ref: 16

True/False Questions

1) Positive feedback mechanisms tend to increase the original stimulus.

   Answer: TRUE
   Diff: 1   Page Ref: 13

2) Ausculation is listening to organ sounds with a stethoscope.

   Answer: TRUE
   Diff: 1   Page Ref: 3

3) The principle of complementarity of structure and function means that the structure of a part reflects its function.

   Answer: TRUE
   Diff: 1   Page Ref: 4

4) The elbow is proximal to the shoulder.

   Answer: FALSE
   Diff: 1   Page Ref: 16

5) The serous membrane that lines the peritoneal cavity is called visceral peritoneum.

   Answer: FALSE
   Diff: 2   Page Ref: 19

6) A major function of serous membranes is to increase friction.

   Answer: FALSE
   Diff: 1   Page Ref: 19

7) The right hypochondriac region contains the majority of the stomach.

   Answer: FALSE
   Diff: 1   Page Ref: 20

8) Embryology concerns the structural changes that occur in an individual from conception through old age.

   Answer: FALSE
   Diff: 1   Page Ref: 3

9) A tissue consists of groups of similar cells that have a common function.

   Answer: TRUE
   Diff: 1   Page Ref: 4

10) It is important to any organism to maintain its boundaries, so that its internal environment remains distinct from the external environment surrounding it.

Answer: TRUE
Diff: 1   Page Ref: 8

11) Although oxygen and water are essential to life, atmospheric pressure is really not important to sustain life.

Answer: FALSE
Diff: 1   Page Ref: 10

12) Regardless of the variable being regulated, all homeostatic control mechanisms have at least three interdependent components.

Answer: TRUE
Diff: 1   Page Ref: 10

13) The control of blood glucose levels by pancreatic hormones is an example of a negative feedback mechanism.

Answer: TRUE
Diff: 1   Page Ref: 12

14) The epigastric region is located superior to the umbilical region.

Answer: TRUE
Diff: 1   Page Ref: 20

15) The ovaries are part of the endocrine and reproductive systems.

Answer: TRUE
Diff: 1   Page Ref: 6, 7

Multiple-Choice Questions

1) Histology could be defined as a study of:
A) cells.   B) tissues.
C) cell chemistry.   D) the gross structures of the body.

Answer: B
Diff: 1   Page Ref: 3

2) A structure that is composed of two or more tissues would be:
A) a complex tissue.   B) an organ system.
C) an organ.   D) a complex cell.

Answer: C
Diff: 1   Page Ref: 4

3) Which of the following would not be functional characteristics of life?

    A) movement
    C) maintenance of boundaries

    B) responsiveness to external stimuli
    D) decay

Answer: D
Diff: 2   Page Ref: 8-9

4) Which statement is not true concerning characteristics of life?

    A) All body cells exhibit irritability to some extent.

    B) Each organ system is isolated from all other body systems.

    C) Growth can be an increase in size due to an increase in the number of cells.

    D) Reproduction occurs on both the cellular level and the organismal level.

Answer: B
Diff: 2   Page Ref: 8-9

5) The single most abundant chemical substance of the body, accounting for 60% to 80% of body weight, is:

    A) oxygen.   B) protein.   C) water.   D) hydrogen.

Answer: C
Diff: 1   Page Ref: 9

6) The posterior side of the patella would be called:

    A) sural.   B) crural.   C) antecubital.   D) popliteal.

Answer: D
Diff: 2   Page Ref: 14

7) Which of the following statements is true concerning feedback mechanisms?

    A) Positive feedback mechanisms always result in excessive damage to the host.

    B) Negative feedback mechanisms tend to increase the original stimulus.

    C) Negative feedback mechanisms work to prevent sudden severe changes within the body.

    D) Blood glucose levels are regulated by positive feedback mechanisms.

Answer: C
Diff: 2   Page Ref: 10-13

8) The anatomical position is characterized by all the following except:

    A) body erect.
    C) palms turned posteriorly.

    B) arms at sides.
    D) thumbs pointed laterally.

Answer: C
Diff: 1   Page Ref: 15

9) A good example of a positive feedback mechanism would be:

    A) body temperature regulation.

    B) regulating glucose levels in the blood.

    C) enhancement of labor contractions by oxytocin.

    D) blood calcium level regulation.

Answer: C
Diff: 1   Page Ref: 13

10) A parasagittal plane is:

    A) a transverse cut just above the knees.

    B) two cuts dividing the body into left and right halves.

    C) any sagittal plane except the median.

    D) any cut dividing the body into anterior and posterior.

Answer: C
Diff: 1   Page Ref: 15

11) Which of the following organs or structures would be found in the left iliac region?

    A) appendix   B) stomach   C) liver   D) intestines

Answer: D
Diff: 2   Page Ref: 20

12) The parietal pleural would represent a serous membrane:

    A) covering individual lungs.   B) lining the thoracic cavity.

    C) covering the heart.   D) lining the abdominal cavity.

Answer: B
Diff: 2   Page Ref: 19

13) Choose the anatomical topic and definition that is not correctly matched.

    A) Gross anatomy: study of structures visible to the eye.

    B) Microscopic anatomy: study of structures too small to be seen by the naked eye.

    C) Developmental anatomy: study of the changes in an individual from birth through old age.

    D) Embryology: study of the changes in an individual from conception to birth.

Answer: C
Diff: 1   Page Ref: 3

14) Homeostasis is the condition in which the body maintains:

    A) the lowest possible energy usage.

    B) a relatively stable internal environment, within limits.

    C) a static state with no deviation from preset points.

    D) a dynamic state within an unlimited range.

Answer: B
Diff: 2   Page Ref: 10-11

15) The lungs are located in the following cavities:

   A) pleural, ventral, and thoracic.   B) mediastinum, thoracic, and ventral.

   C) pleural, dorsal, and abdominal.   D) pericardial, ventral, and thoracic.

   Answer: A
   Diff: 1   Page Ref: 18

16) Choose the following statement that is not completely correct regarding serous membranes.

   A) Serosa are very thin, double-layered structures.

   B) Serous membranes are divided into parietal and visceral membranes with a potential space between the two.

   C) Visceral pericardium covers the surface of the heart, and parietal pericardium lines the walls of the heart.

   D) Serous membranes secrete a watery lubricating fluid.

   Answer: C
   Diff: 2   Page Ref: 19

17) Place the following in correct sequence from simplest to most complex:

   1. molecules
   2. atoms
   3. tissues
   4. cells
   5. organ

   A) 1-2-3-4-5   B) 2-1-4-3-5   C) 2-1-3-4-5   D) 1-2-4-3-5

   Answer: B
   Diff: 2   Page Ref: 5

18) Which of the following are true functional characteristics of humans or other complex life forms?

   A) Distribution of tasks to different organ systems creates true independence of all body cells.

   B) The digestive system breaks down food to simple molecules for distribution to all body cells.

   C) The reproductive system works independently of all other systems.

   D) The external boundary is a limiting membrane that encloses its contents.

   Answer: B
   Diff: 2   Page Ref: 8

19) Which of these is not part of the dorsal cavity?

   A) cranial cavity   B) thoracic cavity   C) spinal cord   D) vertebral cavity

   Answer: B
   Diff: 1   Page Ref: 18

20) The spleen is located in which abdominopelvic quadrant?

    A) right upper   B) right lower   C) left upper   D) left lower

Answer: C
Diff: 1   *Page Ref: 20*

21) Which of the following statements is most correct of homeostatic imbalance?

    A) It is considered the cause of most diseases.

    B) The internal environment is becoming more stable.

    C) Positive feedback mechanisms are overwhelmed.

    D) Negative feedback mechanisms take over.

Answer: A
Diff: 2   *Page Ref: 19*

22) Subdivisions of anatomy include:

    A) gross, macroscopic, visual, and microscopic.

    B) gross, regional, dissection, and surface.

    C) regional, surface, visual, and microscopic.

    D) gross, regional, systemic, and surface.

Answer: D
Diff: 1   *Page Ref: 3*

23) The term *pollex* refers to the:

    A) great toe.   B) calf.   C) fingers.   D) thumb.

Answer: D
Diff: 1   *Page Ref: 14*

24) The dorsal body cavity is the site of which of the following?

    A) intestines   B) brain   C) lungs   D) liver

Answer: B
Diff: 1   *Page Ref: 18*

25) One of the functional characteristics of life is irritability. This refers to:

    A) indigestible food residues stimulating the excretory system.

    B) sensing changes in the environment and then reacting or responding to them.

    C) the nervous system causing all living things to sometimes experience anger.

    D) the necessity for all organisms to reproduce.

Answer: B
Diff: 2   *Page Ref: 8*

26) Survival needs of the body include:

A) nutrients, water, movement, and reproduction.

B) nutrients, water, growth, and reproduction.

C) water, atmospheric pressure, growth, and movement.

D) nutrients, water, atmospheric pressure, and oxygen.

Answer: D
Diff: 2   Page Ref: 9

27) The pancreas and liver work together to maintain homeostasis through:

A) positive feedback.   B) negative feedback.

C) both negative and positive feedback.   D) neither positive nor negative feedback.

Answer: B
Diff: 1   Page Ref: 12

28) The anatomical position is used:

A) rarely, because people don't usually assume this position.

B) as a standard reference point for directional terms regardless of the actual position of the body.

C) only when a body is lying down.

D) as the most comfortable way to stand when dissecting a cadaver.

Answer: B
Diff: 2   Page Ref: 15

29) A horizontal section through the body is called:

A) frontal.   B) regional.   C) sagittal.   D) transverse.

Answer: D
Diff: 1   Page Ref: 15-17

30) A vertical section through the body, dividing it into left and right, is called:

A) frontal.   B) regional.   C) sagittal.   D) transverse.

Answer: C
Diff: 1   Page Ref: 15-17

31) A vertical section through the body, dividing it into anterior and posterior, is called:

A) frontal.   B) median.   C) sagittal.   D) transverse.

Answer: A
Diff: 1   Page Ref: 15-17

32) Which body cavity contains the pleural and pericardial cavities?

A) abdominal cavity   B) pelvic cavity

C) thoracic cavity   D) dorsal cavity

Answer: C
Diff: 1   Page Ref: 18

Clinical Questions

1) A small family was traveling in its van and had a minor accident. The children in the back seats were wearing lap belts, but still sustained numerous bruises about the abdomen, and had some internal organ injuries. Why is this area more vulnerable to damage than others?

   Answer: The abdominal organs are the least protected in the body because they are not surrounded by a bony covering such as the ribs, pelvis, or cranium.
   Diff: 4   *Page Ref: 18–20*

2) A surgeon removed a section of tissue along a transverse plane for microscopic examination. What two names would the section be called?

   Answer: A cross section or a transverse section.
   Diff: 3   *Page Ref: 17*

CHAPTER 2   Chemistry Comes Alive

Fill-in-the-Blank/Short Answer Questions

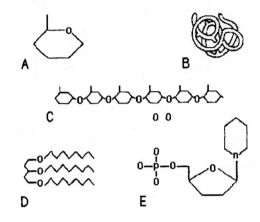

Figure 2.1

Using Figure 2.1, identify the following:

1) Lipid.

   Answer: D
   Diff: 2   Page Ref: 41

2) Functional protein.

   Answer: B
   Diff: 2   Page Ref: 45

3) Nucleotide.

   Answer: E
   Diff: 2   Page Ref: 49

4) Polysaccharide.

   Answer: C
   Diff: 2   Page Ref: 40

5) Monosaccharide.

   Answer: A
   Diff: 2   Page Ref: 40

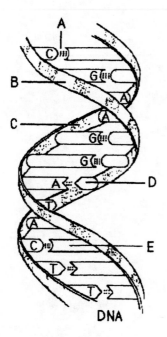

Figure 2.2

Using Figure 2.2, identify the following:

    6) Deoxyribose sugar.

        Answer: B
        Diff: 2   Page Ref: 50

    7) Thymine.

        Answer: D
        Diff: 2   Page Ref: 50

    8) Guanine.

        Answer: E
        Diff: 2   Page Ref: 50

    9) Phosphate.

        Answer: C
        Diff: 2   Page Ref: 50

    10) Hydrogen bond.

        Answer: A
        Diff: 2   Page Ref: 50

Fill in the blank or provide a short answer:

11) The atomic number is equal to the number of _____.

Answer: protons
Diff: 1   Page Ref: 25

12) Molecules such as methane that share electrons have _____ bonds.

Answer: covalent
Diff: 1   Page Ref: 30

13) An atom with three electrons would have a valence of _____.

Answer: one
Diff: 2   Page Ref: 28

14) AB D1→ A + B is an example of a _____ reaction.

Answer: decomposition
Diff: 1   Page Ref: 33

15) _____ have a bitter taste, feel slippery, and are proton acceptors.

Answer: Bases
Diff: 1   Page Ref: 37

16) Polysaccharides with long chains of similar units are called _____.

Answer: polymers
Diff: 2   Page Ref: 39

17) A holoenzyme is composed of an apoenzyme and a _____.

Answer: cofactor
Diff: 1   Page Ref: 47

18) In a DNA molecule guanine would connect to _____.

Answer: cytosine
Diff: 1   Page Ref: 49

19) The _____ molecule directly provides energy for cellular work.

Answer: ATP
Diff: 1   Page Ref: 50

20) Explain the difference between potential and kinetic energy.

Answer: Potential energy is the energy an object has relative to position. Kinetic energy is energy associated with a moving object.
Diff: 3   Page Ref: 23

21) How can phospholipids form a film when mixed in water?

Answer: Phospholipids have both polar and nonpolar ends. The polar end interacts with water, leaving the nonpolar end oriented in the opposite direction.
Diff: 4   *Page Ref:* 42

22) What properties does water have that make it a very versatile fluid?

Answer: High heat capacity, high heat of vaporization, polarity and solvent properties, reactivity, and cushioning.
Diff: 3   *Page Ref:* 35

23) What advantages does ATP have in being the energy currency molecule?

Answer: It is easy to store; it releases just the right amount of energy for the cell's needs so it is protected from excessive energy release. A universal energy currency is efficient because a single system can be used by all the cells in the body.
Diff: 4   *Page Ref:* 50-55

24) Explain why chemical reactions in the body are often irreversible.

Answer: Chemical reactions that release energy cannot be reversed unless energy is put back into the system. Also, the body may use the chemicals solely for its energy, such as glucose, or some reactions produce molecules in excessive quantities (like CO_2 and NH_4) that the body needs to discard.
Diff: 3   *Page Ref:* 34

25) When a set of electrodes connected to a lightbulb is placed in a solution of dextrose and a current is applied, the lightbulb does not light up. When the same unit is placed in HCl, it does. Why?

Answer: HCl ionizes to form current-conducting electrolytes. Dextrose does not ionize, and therefore does not conduct current.
Diff: 3   *Page Ref:* 36

26) Describe the factors that affect chemical reaction rates.

Answer: Temperature increases kinetic energy and therefore the force of molecular collisions. Particle size: smaller particles move faster at the same temperature and therefore collide more frequently; also, smaller particles have more surface area given the same concentration of reactants. Concentration: the higher the concentration, the greater the chance of particles colliding. Catalysts increase the rate of the reaction at a given temperature. Enzymes are biological catalysts.
Diff: 5   *Page Ref:* 34

Matching Questions

Match the following:

1) Column 1: A bond in which electrons are shared unequally.

   Column 2: Polar covalent bond

   Answer: Polar covalent bond
   Diff: 1   Page Ref: 39

2) Column 1: A bond in which electrons are completely lost or gained by the atoms involved.

   Column 2: Ionic bond

   Answer: Ionic bond
   Diff: 1   Page Ref: 29

3) Column 1: A bond in which electrons are equally shared.

   Column 2: Nonpolar covalent bond

   Answer: Nonpolar covalent bond
   Diff: 1   Page Ref: 39

4) Column 1: A type of bond important in typing different parts of the same molecule together into three-dimensional structure.

   Column 2: Hydrogen bond

   Answer: Hydrogen bond
   Diff: 1   Page Ref: 32

5) Column 1: An atom with one electron in its outer orbit would form which type of bond?

   Column 2: Ionic bond

   Answer: Ionic bond
   Diff: 1   Page Ref: 29

Match the following:

6) Column 1: Electrically charged particle due to loss of an electron.

   Column 2: Cation

       Foil: Electron

   Answer: Cation
   Diff: 1   Page Ref: 29

7) Column 1: Neutral subatomic particle.

   Column 2: Neutron

   Answer: Neutron
   Diff: 1   Page Ref: 24

8) Column 1: Smallest particle of an element
             that retains its properties.

   Column 2: Atom

   Answer: Atom
   Diff: 1   Page Ref: 29

9) Column 1: Smallest particle of a
             compound that still retains its
             properties.

   Column 2: Molecule

   Answer: Molecule
   Diff: 1   Page Ref: 27

Match the following:

10) Column 1: Beer.

    Column 2: Mixture

    Answer: Mixture
    Diff: 1   Page Ref: 27

11) Column 1: Water.

    Column 2: Compound

    Answer: Compound
    Diff: 1   Page Ref: 27

12) Column 1: Carbon.

    Column 2: Element

    Answer: Element
    Diff: 1   Page Ref: 24

13) Column 1: Potassium.

    Column 2: Element

    Answer: Element
    Diff: 1   Page Ref: 24

14) Column 1: Blood.

    Column 2: Mixture

    Answer: Mixture
    Diff: 1   Page Ref: 27

Match the following:

15) Column 1: Can be measured only by its
effects on matter.

Column 2: Energy

Answer: Energy
Diff: 1   Page Ref: 23

16) Column 1: Anything that occupies space
and has mass.

Column 2: Matter

Answer: Matter
Diff: 1   Page Ref: 23

17) Column 1: Although a man who weighs
175 pounds on Earth would
be lighter on the moon and
heavier on Jupiter, his
_____ would not be
different.

Column 2: Mass

Answer: Mass
Diff: 1   Page Ref: 23

18) Column 1: Is a function of, and varies
with, gravity.

Column 2: Weight

Answer: Weight
Diff: 1   Page Ref: 23

Match the following:

19) Column 1: Legs moving the pedals of a
bicycle.

Column 2: Mechanical energy

Answer: Mechanical energy
Diff: 1   Page Ref: 23

20) Column 1: When the bonds of ATP are
broken, energy is released to
do cellular work.

Column 2: Chemical energy

Answer: Chemical energy
Diff: 1   Page Ref: 23

21) Column 1: Energy that travels in waves. Part of the electromagnetic spectrum.

Column 2: Radiant energy

Answer: Radiant energy
Diff: 1   Page Ref: 23

22) Column 1: Represented by the flow of charged particles along a conductor, or the flow of ions across a membrane.

Column 2: Electrical energy

Answer: Electrical energy
Diff: 1   Page Ref: 23

Match the following:

23) Column 1: Heterogeneous, will not settle.

Column 2: Colloids

Answer: Colloids
Diff: 1   Page Ref: 27

24) Column 1: Heterogeneous, will settle.

Column 2: Suspensions

Answer: Suspensions
Diff: 1   Page Ref: 28

25) Column 1: Homogeneous, will not settle.

Column 2: Solutions

Answer: Solutions
Diff: 1   Page Ref: 27

26) Column 1: Will not scatter light.

Column 2: Solutions

Answer: Solutions
Diff: 1   Page Ref: 27

True/False Questions

1) A synthesis reaction always involves bond formation.

Answer: TRUE
Diff: 1   Page Ref: 33

2) Emulsions and colloids are the same thing.

Answer: TRUE
Diff: 1   Page Ref: 27

3) Chemical properties are determined primarily by neutrons.

Answer: FALSE
Diff: 1   *Page Ref: 24*

4) A charged particle is correctly called an ion.

Answer: TRUE
Diff: 1   *Page Ref: 29*

5) Isotopes differ from each other only in the number of electrons contained.

Answer: FALSE
Diff: 1   *Page Ref: 27*

6) About 60% to 80% of the volume of most living cells consists of organic compounds.

Answer: FALSE
Diff: 1   *Page Ref: 24*

7) Lipids are a poor source of stored energy.

Answer: FALSE
Diff: 1   *Page Ref: 42*

8) Oxygen is present in proteins but not fats.

Answer: FALSE
Diff: 1   *Page Ref: 41–42*

9) The suffix –ase usually indicates an enzyme.

Answer: TRUE
Diff: 1   *Page Ref: 48*

10) Glucose is an example of a monosaccharide.

Answer: TRUE
Diff: 1   *Page Ref: 39*

11) A base may be described as a proton acceptor.

Answer: FALSE
Diff: 2   *Page Ref: 37*

12) The farther away from the nucleus an electron is found, the less potential energy it possesses.

Answer: FALSE
Diff: 1   *Page Ref: 28*

13) A molecule consisting of one carbon atom and two oxygen atoms is correctly written as CO_2.

Answer: TRUE
Diff: 1   *Page Ref: 27*

14) The lower the pH, the higher the hydrogen ion concentration.

Answer: TRUE
Diff: 1   Page Ref: 37–38

15) Covalent bonds are generally weaker than ionic bonds.

Answer: FALSE
Diff: 1   Page Ref: 30

16) Hydrogen bonds are strong bonds.

Answer: FALSE
Diff: 1   Page Ref: 32

17) The fact that no chemical bonding occurs between the components of a mixture is the chief difference between mixtures and compounds.

Answer: TRUE
Diff: 1   Page Ref: 28

18) The substances making up a mixture can be separated by physical means.

Answer: TRUE
Diff: 1   Page Ref: 28

19) Elements are unique substances that cannot be broken down into simpler substances by ordinary chemical means.

Answer: TRUE
Diff: 1   Page Ref: 24

20) The number of electrons in an atom is always equal to the number of neutrons.

Answer: FALSE
Diff: 1   Page Ref: 24

Multiple-Choice Questions

1) Which of the following is necessary for proper conduction of nervous impulses?
   A) Fe   B) I   C) P   D) Na

Answer: D
Diff: 1   Page Ref: 36

2) A phospholipid is usually:
   A) partially hydrophilic and partially hydrophobic.
   B) hydrophobic.
   C) hydrophilic.
   D) neither hydrophilic nor hydrophobic.

Answer: A
Diff: 2   Page Ref: 43

3) In general, the category of lipids that we refer to as oils have:

   A) a high water content.   B) long fatty acid chains.

   C) a high degree of saturated bonds.   D) a high degree of unsaturated bonds.

   Answer: D
   Diff: 2   Page Ref: 41

4) Which of the following is not true of proteins?

   A) May be denatured or coagulated by heat or acidity.

   B) Some types are called enzymes.

   C) Appear to be the molecular carriers of the coded hereditary information.

   D) Function depends on the three–dimensional shape.

   Answer: C
   Diff: 2   Page Ref: 32

5) The single most abundant protein in the body is:

   A) DNA.   B) hemoglobin.   C) collagen.   D) glucose.

   Answer: C
   Diff: 1   Page Ref: 47

6) Carbohydrates are stored in the liver and muscles in the form of:

   A) glucose.   B) triglycerides.   C) glycogen.   D) cholesterol.

   Answer: C
   Diff: 4   Page Ref: 39

7) Coenzymes are:

   A) organic molecules derived from vitamins.

   B) two enzymes that perform the same function.

   C) metal ions.

   D) enzymes that work together.

   Answer: A
   Diff: 2   Page Ref: 47

8) The speed or rate of a chemical reaction is influenced by all of the following except:

   A) the concentration of the reactants.   B) the temperature.

   C) the presence of catalysts or enzymes.   D) the presence or absence of carbon.

   Answer: D
   Diff: 2   Page Ref: 35

9) A chemical reaction in which bonds are broken is associated with:

   A) the release of energy.   B) the consumption of energy.

   C) a synthesis.   D) forming a larger molecule.

   Answer: A
   Diff: 2   Page Ref: 34

10) Salts are always:

A) ionic compounds.   B) single covalent compounds.

C) double covalent compounds.   D) hydrogen bonded.

Answer: A
Diff: 1   Page Ref: 36

11) The numbers listed represent the first, second, and third energy levels, respectively. On this basis, which of the following is an unstable or reactive atom?

A) 2, 8, 8   B) 2, 8   C) 2   D) 2, 8, 1

Answer: D
Diff: 2   Page Ref: 29–30

12) A solution that has a pH of 2 could best be described as being:

A) acidic.   B) basic.   C) neutral.   D) slightly acidic.

Answer: A
Diff: 1   Page Ref: 37–38

13) Which of the following would be regarded as an organic molecule?

A) H_2O B) NaCl   C) NaOH   D) CH_4

Answer: D
Diff: 1   Page Ref: 38

14) A chain of 25 amino acids would be called a:

A) peptide.   B) nucleotide.   C) protein.   D) starch.

Answer: A
Diff: 1   Page Ref: 42

15) A long chain of simple sugars would be a:

A) monosaccharide.   B) polysaccharide.

C) protein.   D) nucleic acid.

Answer: B
Diff: 1   Page Ref: 39–40

16) The coiling of the protein chain backbone into an alpha helix is referred to as the:

A) primary structure.   B) secondary structure.

C) tertiary structure.   D) quaternary structure.

Answer: B
Diff: 1   Page Ref: 45

17) Carbohydrates and proteins are built up from their basic building blocks by the:

   A) addition of a water molecule between each two units.

   B) addition of a carbon atom between each two units.

   C) removal of a water molecule between each two units.

   D) removal of a nitrogen atom between each two units.

   Answer: C
   Diff: 1   Page Ref: 40–42

18) Which statement about enzymes is false?

   A) Enzymes raise the activation energy needed to start a reaction.

   B) Enzymes are composed mostly of protein.

   C) Enzymes are organic catalysts.

   D) Enzymes may be damaged by high temperature.

   Answer: A
   Diff: 2   Page Ref: 47–48

19) The differences between mixtures and compounds include:

   A) Chemical bonding does not occur between the components of a mixture.

   B) Components forming a mixture can be separated by physical means.

   C) Compounds are formed from two atoms, while mixtures are formed from three or more atoms.

   D) Mixtures are homogeneous—samples taken from any part are identical to ones taken from any other area.

   Answer: A
   Diff: 2   Page Ref: 28

20) Select the statement that is most correct regarding chemical bonds.

   A) Covalent bonding involves the transfer of one or more electrons from one atom to another.

   B) Multiple bonds are not possible with covalent bonding.

   C) Hydrogen bonds are very weak and often involve water.

   D) Ionic bonds involve the sharing of electrons between two atoms.

   Answer: C
   Diff: 2   Page Ref: 28–32

21) _____ is a suspension.

   A) Cytoplasm   B) Seawater   C) Rubbing alcohol   D) Blood

   Answer: D
   Diff: 1   Page Ref: 28

22) Select the correct statement about isotopes.

A) Isotopes of the same element have the same atomic number but differ in their atomic weights.

B) All the isotopes of an element have the same number of neutrons.

C) All the isotopes of an element are radioactive.

D) Isotopes are rare and occur only in the heavier elements.

Answer: A
Diff: 1   Page Ref: 26–27

23) The four elements that make up about 96% of body matter are:

A) carbon, oxygen, phosphorus, calcium.   B) nitrogen, hydrogen, calcium, sodium.

C) carbon, oxygen, hydrogen, nitrogen.   D) sodium, potassium, hydrogen, oxygen.

Answer: C
Diff: 2   Page Ref: 24

24) Isotopes of the same element have the same:

A) number of neutrons but different numbers of protons.

B) number of protons but different numbers of neutrons.

C) atomic weight.

D) mass number.

Answer: B
Diff: 2   Page Ref: 26

25) An example of a coenzyme is:

A) copper.   B) riboflavin (vitamin B_2).

C) iron.   D) zinc.

Answer: B
Diff: 1   Page Ref: 47

26) _____ is fat–soluble, produced in the skin on exposure to UV radiation, and necessary for normal bone growth and function.

A) Vitamin K   B) Cortisol   C) Vitamin A   D) Vitamin D

Answer: D
Diff: 1   Page Ref: 43

27) In liquid XYZ, you notice that light is scattered as it passes through. There is no precipitant in the bottom of the beaker, though it has been sitting for several days. This liquid must be a _____.

A) solution   B) suspension   C) colloid   D) mixture

Answer: C
Diff: 2   Page Ref: 27

28) Atom X has seventeen protons. How many electrons are in its valence shell?

    A) 3   B) 5   C) 7   D) 10

Answer: C
Diff: 2   *Page Ref: 29*

29) If an atom were to have two protons, then it would:

    A) have a valence of 0.   B) be very stable.

    C) be chemically active.   D) have three electrons.

Answer: B
Diff: 2   *Page Ref: 28–29*

Clinical Questions

1) Since a doughnut contains a large quantity of energy that can become available for our metabolism when eaten, why isn't the doughnut "jumping" all over the counter or hot to the touch?

    Answer: Doughnuts contain large quantities of energy, but it is chemical potential energy locked in the form of carbohydrates (simple and complex) and fats. Only when the carbohydrates and fats are broken down and enter the cell's metabolic pathways can the energy be converted to mechanical kinetic energy.
    Diff: 3   *Page Ref: 23*

2) Mr. Martinez read that cholesterol was bad for his health, so he eliminated all foods and food products containing this molecule. He later found that his cholesterol level dropped only 20%. Why did it not drop more?

    Answer: Cholesterol is produced by the liver, in addition to being ingested in foods.
    Diff: 3   *Page Ref: 42*

3) How can DNA be used to "fingerprint" a suspect in a crime?

    Answer: The DNA of a person is unique to that individual. By obtaining the DNA from nucleated cells from the crime scene (e.g., tissue, sperm), heating it gently to separate the strands, combining it with the suspect's DNA, and allowing it to reanneal, the relatedness can be determined by the amount of base pairing.
    Diff: 4   *Page Ref: 48–50*

4) Why is it possible for us to drink a solution that contains a mixture of equal concentration of a strong acid and a strong base, either of which, separately, would be very caustic?

    Answer: When an acid and base of equal strength are mixed, they undergo a displacement reaction to form a water and a salt.
    Diff: 3   *Page Ref: 37*

CHAPTER 3   Cells: The Living Units

Fill-in-the-Blank/Short Answer Questions

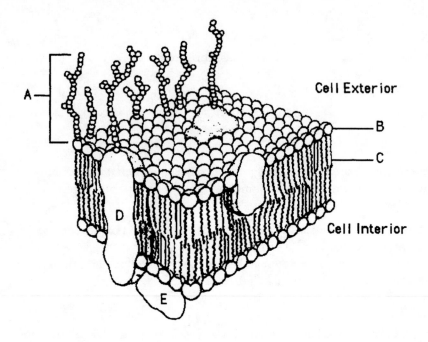

Figure 3.1

Using Figure 3.1, identify the following:

    1) Nonpolar region of phospholipid.

        Answer: C
        Diff: 2   Page Ref: 58

    2) Glycocalyx.

        Answer: A
        Diff: 2   Page Ref: 58

    3) Polar region of phospholipid.

        Answer: B
        Diff: 2   ·Page Ref: 58

    4) Peripheral protein.

        Answer: E
        Diff: 2   Page Ref: 58

5) Integral protein.

Answer: D
Diff: 2   *Page Ref: 58*

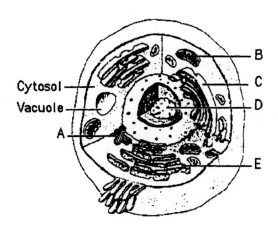

Cytosol
Vacuole
A
B
C
D
E

Figure 3.2

Using Figure 3.2, identify the following:

6) Found in a centrosome.

Answer: A
Diff: 1   *Page Ref: 57*

7) Packages proteins.

Answer: C
Diff: 1   *Page Ref: 57*

8) rRNA is synthesized here.

Answer: D
Diff: 1   *Page Ref: 57*

9) Produce most ATP molecules.

Answer: B
Diff: 1   *Page Ref: 57*

10) "Membrane factory."

Answer: E
Diff: 1   *Page Ref: 57*

Fill in the blank or provide a short answer:

11) The RNA that has an anticodon and attaches to a specific amino acid is _____ RNA.

Answer: transfer
Diff: 1   *Page Ref: 94*

12) Water may move through membrane pores constructed by transmembrane proteins called _____.

Answer: aquaporins
Diff: 2   *Page Ref: 64*

13) _____ is the division of the cytoplasm.

Answer: Cytokinesis
Diff: 1   *Page Ref: 87*

14) The metabolic or growth phase of a cell life cycle is called _____.

Answer: interphase
Diff: 1   *Page Ref: 85*

15) In order for the DNA molecule to get "short and fat" to become a chromosome, it must first wrap around small molecules called _____.

Answer: histones
Diff: 1   *Page Ref: 85*

16) _____ are hollow tubes made of spherical protein subunits called tubulins.

Answer: Microtubules
Diff: 1   *Page Ref: 79*

17) Aerobic cellular respiration occurs in the _____.

Answer: mitochondria
Diff: 1   *Page Ref: 74*

18) Two very important second messengers used in the G protein–linked receptor mechanism are cyclic AMP and _____.

Answer: ionic calcium
Diff: 1   *Page Ref: 73*

19) The most common extracellular ion is _____.

Answer: sodium
Diff: 1   *Page Ref: 67*

20) The process of discharging particles from inside a cell to the outside is called _____.

Answer: exocytosis
Diff: 1   *Page Ref: 68*

21) A red blood cell would swell if its surrounding solution were _____.

Answer: hypotonic
Diff: 1   *Page Ref: 65*

22) A _____ is a channel between cells.

Answer: connexon
Diff: 1   *Page Ref: 61*

23) Describe two important functions of the Golgi apparatus.

Answer: To modify, sort, and package proteins.
Diff: 3   *Page Ref: 77*

24) Why can we say that a cell without a nucleus will ultimately die?

Answer: Without a nucleus, a cell cannot make proteins, nor can it replace any enzymes or other cell structures (which are continuously recycled). Additionally, such a cell could not replicate.
Diff: 4   *Page Ref: 83*

25) Are Brownian motion, diffusion, and osmosis seen only in living tissue?

Answer: No. Since they are passive processes that do not require energy, they can occur in the absence of any cellular processes.
Diff: 3   *Page Ref: 62–66*

26) What forces maintain a steady state "resting" membrane potential?

Answer: Both diffusion and active transport mechanisms operate within the cell membrane to maintain a resting membrane potential.
Diff: 3   *Page Ref: 71*

27) Briefly describe the glycocalyx and its functions.

Answer: The glycocalyx is the sticky, carbohydrate–rich area on the cell surface. It helps bind cells together and provides a highly specific biological marker by which cells can recognize each other.
Diff: 5   *Page Ref: 60*

28) Explain the term *genetic code*. What does it code for? What are the letters of the code?

Answer: The genetic code is the information encoded in the nucleotide base sequence of DNA. A sequence of three bases, called a triplet, specifies amino acid in a protein. The letters of the code are the four nucleotide bases of DNA designated as A, T, C, and G.
Diff: 3   *Page Ref: 92*

29) Why are free radicals so dangerous to cells, and how are they dealt with by the body?

Answer: Free radicals are highly reactive chemicals that cause havoc in any cellular environment by reacting with things they should not. Cells with peroxisomes have enzymes specific to reducing free radicals into less reactive chemicals.
Diff: 3   *Page Ref: 79*

Matching Questions

Match the following:

1) Column 1: Forms part of the protein
synthesis site in the
cytoplasm.

Column 2: Ribosomal RNA

Answer: Ribosomal RNA
Diff: 1   *Page Ref: 56*

2) Column 1: Act as "interpreter" molecules
that recognize specific amino
acids and nucleotide base
sequences.

Column 2: Transfer RNA

Answer: Transfer RNA
Diff: 2   *Page Ref: 92*

3) Column 1: Attaches the correct amino
acid to its transfer RNA.

Column 2: Synthetase enzymes

Answer: Synthetase enzymes
Diff: 1   *Page Ref: 94*

4) Column 1: Provides the energy needed for
synthesis reactions.

Column 2: ATP

Answer: ATP
Diff: 1   *Page Ref: 94*

5) Column 1: Found in the cytoplasm, this
structure specifies the exact
sequence of amino acids of the
protein to be made.

Column 2: Messenger RNA

Answer: Messenger RNA
Diff: 1   *Page Ref: 94*

6) Column 1: May be attached to the ER or
scattered in the cytoplasm.

Column 2: Ribosomal RNA

Answer: Ribosomal RNA
Diff: 1   *Page Ref: 94*

Match the following:

    7) Column 1: Chromosomes decoil to form chromatin.

    Column 2: Telophase

    Answer: Telophase
    Diff: 1   Page Ref: 89

    8) Column 1: Chromosomal centromeres split and chromosomes migrate to opposite ends of the cell.

    Column 2: Anaphase

    Answer: Anaphase
    Diff: 1   Page Ref: 89

    9) Column 1: Nuclear membrane and nucleolus disintegrate.

    Column 2: Prophase

    Answer: Prophase
    Diff: 1   Page Ref: 89

    10) Column 1: Chromosomes align on the spindle equator.

    Column 2: Metaphase

    Answer: Metaphase
    Diff: 1   Page Ref: 89

    11) Column 1: Centrioles move to opposite ends of the cell.

    Column 2: Prophase

    Answer: Prophase
    Diff: 1   Page Ref: 88

Match the following:

    12) Column 1: The outermost boundary of the cell; confines cell contents and regulates transport of substances into and out of the cell.

    Column 2: Plasma membrane

    Answer: Plasma membrane
    Diff: 1   Page Ref: 56

13) Column 1: Essentially sacs of digestive enzymes; often called "suicide sacs" because they have the ability to destroy the cell itself.

Column 2: Lysosomes

Answer: Lysosomes
Diff: 2   Page Ref: 68

14) Column 1: Powerhouses of the cell; the most important site of ATP production.

Column 2: Mitochondria

Answer: Mitochondria
Diff: 2   Page Ref: 56–57

15) Column 1: The cellular "packaging site" for substances that are to be exported from the cell.

Column 2: Golgi apparatus

Answer: Golgi apparatus
Diff: 2   Page Ref: 56–57

16) Column 1: Serve as "seeds" from which microtubules sprout.

Column 2: Centrioles

Answer: Centrioles
Diff: 2   Page Ref: 56–57

Match the following:

17) Column 1: Plays a role in the synthesis of steroid–based hormones and proteins.

Column 2: Endoplasmic reticulum

Answer: Endoplasmic reticulum
Diff: 1   Page Ref: 56–57

18) Column 1: The actual site of protein synthesis.

Column 2: Ribosomes

Answer: Ribosomes
Diff: 1   Page Ref: 56–57

19) Column 1: Hollow cytoskeletal elements that act as organizers for the cytoskeleton.

Column 2: Microtubules

Answer: Microtubules
Diff: 2   *Page Ref: 56–57*

20) Column 1: Dense spherical bodies in the nucleus that are the synthesis site for ribosomal RNA.

Column 2: Nucleoli

Answer: Nucleoli
Diff: 1   *Page Ref: 56–57*

21) Column 1: Houses DNA and RNA.

Column 2: Nucleus

Answer: Nucleus
Diff: 1   *Page Ref: 56–57*

True/False Questions

1) Each daughter cell resulting from mitotic cell division has exactly as many chromosomes as the parent cell.

Answer: TRUE
Diff: 1   *Page Ref: 87*

2) The spindle is formed by the migration of the chromatin.

Answer: FALSE
Diff: 1   *Page Ref: 88*

3) Final preparation for cell division is made during the cell life cycle subphase called G_2.

Answer: TRUE
Diff: 2   *Page Ref: 86*

4) Chromatin consists of DNA and RNA.

Answer: FALSE
Diff: 1   *Page Ref: 84–85*

5) The "cell theory" as stated by Schleiden and Schwann indicated that membranes form the basis of all cell structure.

Answer: FALSE
Diff: 1   *Page Ref: 55*

6) In osmosis, movement of water occurs toward the solution with the lower solute concentration.

Answer: FALSE
Diff: 1   Page Ref: 64

7) The genetic information is coded in DNA by the regular alternation of sugar and phosphate molecules.

Answer: FALSE
Diff: 1   Page Ref: 91

8) A process by which large particles may be taken into the cell for protection of the body or for disposing of old or dead cells is called phagocytosis.

Answer: TRUE
Diff: 1   Page Ref: 69

9) The orderly sequence of the phases of mitosis is prophase, metaphase, anaphase, and telophase.

Answer: TRUE
Diff: 1   Page Ref: 88–89

10) Diffusion is always from areas of greater to areas of lesser concentration.

Answer: TRUE
Diff: 1   Page Ref: 63

11) Facilitated diffusion always requires a carrier protein.

Answer: TRUE
Diff: 1   Page Ref: 63

12) Pressure caused by gravity is necessary for any filtration pressure to occur in the body.

Answer: FALSE
Diff: 2   Page Ref: 67

13) DNA transcription is another word for DNA replication.

Answer: FALSE
Diff: 1   Page Ref: 87, 92

14) The glycocalyx is often referred to as the "cell coat," which is somewhat fuzzy and sticky with numerous cholesterol chains sticking out from the surface of the cell membrane.

Answer: FALSE
Diff: 2   Page Ref: 60

15) Places on the membrane surface that look as though they have been "spot welded" are called tight junctions.

Answer: FALSE
Diff: 1   Page Ref: 60

16) In their resting state, all body cells exhibit a resting membrane potential ranging from –50 to about +50 millivolts.

Answer: FALSE
Diff: 1   *Page Ref: 71*

17) Microfilaments are thin strands of the contractile protein myosin.

Answer: FALSE
Diff: 2   *Page Ref: 80*

18) Interstitial fluid represents one type of extracellular material.

Answer: TRUE
Diff: 1   *Page Ref: 96*

19) A principle of cell theory is that continuity of life has a cellular basis.

Answer: TRUE
Diff: 1   *Page Ref: 55*

20) Mitochondria contain their own DNA.

Answer: TRUE
Diff: 1   *Page Ref: 74*

21) The cell (plasma) membrane normally contains substantial amounts of cholesterol.

Answer: TRUE
Diff: 1   *Page Ref: 56*

22) The plasma membrane is more than 90% phospholipids by weight.

Answer: FALSE
Diff: 1   *Page Ref: 55*

23) The function of gap junctions is to regulate the passage of chemical substances between adjacent cells.

Answer: FALSE
Diff: 1   *Page Ref: 61*

24) Most organelles are bounded by a membrane that is quite different in structure from the lipid bilayer of the plasma membrane.

Answer: FALSE
Diff: 1   *Page Ref: 74*

25) It is widely believed that mitochondria may have arisen from a type of bacterium that took up residence in the ancient ancestors of modern cells.

Answer: TRUE
Diff: 1   *Page Ref: 74*

26) Only one cell type in the human body has a flagellum.

Answer: TRUE
Diff: 1   Page Ref: 82

27) Microtubules are hollow tubes made of subunits of the protein tubulin.

Answer: TRUE
Diff: 1   Page Ref: 79

28) Telomeres are the regions of chromosomes that code for the protein ubiquitin.

Answer: FALSE
Diff: 1   Page Ref: 96

Multiple-Choice Questions

1) Which of the following is true regarding the generation of a membrane potential?
   A) Both potassium and sodium ions can "leak" through the cell membrane due to diffusion.
   B) In the polarized state, sodium and potassium ion concentrations are in static equilibrium.
   C) The maintenance of the potential is based exclusively on diffusion processes.
   D) When the sodium-potassium pump is activated, potassium is pumped into the cell twice as fast as the sodium is pumped out, thus causing the membrane potential.

Answer: A
Diff: 2   Page Ref: 67

2) The RNA responsible for bringing the amino acids to the "factory" site for protein formation is the:
   A) rRNA.   B) mRNA.   C) tRNA.   D) ssRNA.

Answer: C
Diff: 1   Page Ref: 94

3) A red blood cell placed in pure water would:
   A) shrink.
   B) swell initially, then shrink as equilibrium is reached.
   C) neither shrink nor swell.
   D) swell and burst.

Answer: D
Diff: 1   Page Ref: 65

4) The plasma membrane (cell membrane) is:
   A) a single-layered membrane that surrounds the nucleus of the cell.
   B) a double layer of protein enclosing the plasma.
   C) the phospholipid bilayer surrounding the cell.
   D) a membrane composed of tiny shelves or cristae.

Answer: C
Diff: 1   Page Ref: 58

5) Which of these is not a function of the plasma membrane?

A) It is selectively permeable.

B) It prevents potassium ions from leaking out of the cell.

C) It acts as a site of cell–to–cell interaction and recognition.

D) It contains the cell contents.

Answer: B
Diff: 1   *Page Ref: 56*

6) Which structures are fingerlike projections that greatly increase the absorbing surface of cells?

A) stereocilia   B) microvilli   C) cilia   D) flagella

Answer: B
Diff: 1   *Page Ref: 60*

7) Which of the following statements is correct regarding diffusion?

A) The rate of diffusion is independent of temperature. ✕

B) The greater the concentration of gradient, the faster the rate of diffusion. ✓

C) Molecular weight of a substance does not affect the rate of diffusion. ✕

D) The lower the temperature, the faster the diffusion rate. ✕

Answer: B
Diff: 2   *Page Ref: 62–63*

8) Cell junctions that promote the coordinated activity of cells by physically binding them together into a cell community include all of the following except:

A) gap junctions.   B) desmosomes.   C) peroxisomes. ✕   D) tight junctions.

Answer: C
Diff: 1   *Page Ref: 79*

9) If cells are placed in a hypertonic solution containing a solute to which the membrane is impermeable, what could happen?

A) The cells will swell and ultimately burst.

B) The cells will lose water and shrink.

C) The cells will shrink at first, but will later reach equilibrium with the surrounding solution and return to their original condition.

D) The cells will show no change due to diffusion of both solute and solvent.

Answer: B
Diff: 2   *Page Ref: 65*

10) Once solid material is phagocytized and taken into a vacuole, which of the following statements best describes what happens?

    A) A ribosome enters the vacuole and uses the amino acids in the "invader" to form new protein.

    B) A lysosome combines with the vacuole and digests the enclosed solid material.

    C) The vacuole remains separated from the cytoplasm and the solid material persists unchanged.

    D) Oxygen enters the vacuole and "burns" the enclosed solid material.

Answer: B
Diff: 1   *Page Ref: 69*

11) Microtubules do not:

    A) affect motility.   B) affect the arrangement of the organelles.

    C) participate in cell division.   D) help form the cell's cytoskeleton.

Answer: D
Diff: 1   *Page Ref: 79*

12) Which of the following is a function of a plasma membrane protein?

    A) circulating antibody

    B) molecular transport through the membrane

    C) forms a lipid bilayer

    D) oxygen transport

Answer: B
Diff: 1   *Page Ref: 60*

13) Which of the following statements is correct regarding RNA?

    A) Messenger RNA, transfer RNA, and ribosomal RNA play a role in protein synthesis.

    B) If the base sequence of DNA is ATTGCA, the messenger RNA template will be UCCAGU.

    C) There is a specific type of mRNA for each amino acid.

    D) rRNA is always attached to the rough ER.

Answer: A
Diff: 2   *Page Ref: 91–95*

14) Which of the following would not be a constituent of a plasma membrane?

    A) glycolipids   B) messenger RNA   C) glycoproteins   D) phospholipids

Answer: B
Diff: 1   *Page Ref: 56*

15) Mitosis is:

    A) formation of sex cells.   B) nucleus replication.

    C) to create diversity in genetic potential.   D) division of a cell.

Answer: B
Diff: 1   *Page Ref: 87*

16) The electron microscope has revealed that one of the components within the cell consists of microtubules arranged to form a hollow tube. This structure is a:

    A) centrosome.   B) centriole.   C) chromosome.   D) ribosome.

Answer: B
Diff: 2   *Page Ref: 81*

17) Which of these is an inclusion, not an organelle?

    A) melanin   B) lysosome   C) microtubule   D) cilia

Answer: A
Diff: 1   *Page Ref: 73*

18) Cholesterol is used in the cell membrane to:

    A) help make the membrane more rigid.

    B) help make the membrane more fluid.

    C) assist in cell recognition by the immune system.

    D) allow carbohydrates to pass through the membrane.

Answer: B
Diff: 1   *Page Ref: 59*

19) If the nucleotide or base sequence of the DNA strand used as a template for messenger RNA synthesis is ACGTT, then the sequence of bases in the corresponding mRNA would be:

    A) TGCAA.   B) ACGTT.   C) UGCAA.   D) GUACC.

Answer: C
Diff: 2   *Page Ref: 95*

20) Which of the following is true regarding cells in humans?

    A) Organelles are independent life forms.

    B) Maximum cell diameter is limited to 2 micrometers.

    C) Cells can be as long as 1 meter.

    D) Most cells of an adult have a very short life span.

Answer: C
Diff: 1   *Page Ref: 55*

21) Phospholipids:

    A) are exclusively hydrophilic molecules.

    B) contain polar tails and nonpolar head groups.

    C) are both hydrophilic and hydrophobic in nature.

    D) form the lipid bilayer, with tails directed to the outside.

Answer: C
Diff: 1   *Page Ref: 58*

22) Passive membrane transport processes include:

  A) movement of a substance down its concentration gradient.

  B) movement of water from an area of low concentration to an area of high concentration.

  C) consumption of ATP.

  D) the use of transport proteins when moving substances from areas of low to high concentration.

Answer: A
Diff: 1   Page Ref: 62

23) Select the most correct statement regarding the glycocalyx.

  A) It involves highly specific biological markers on the surface of the cell.

  B) It is responsible for egg–sperm recognition.

  C) It is involved with all immune system functions.

  D) It is composed of mostly proteins.

Answer: A
Diff: 1   Page Ref: 60

24) Mitochondria:

  A) are always the same shape.

  B) are single–membrane structures involved in the breakdown of ATP.

  C) contain some of the code necessary for their own duplication.

  D) synthesize proteins for use outside the cell.

Answer: C
Diff: 1   Page Ref: 74

25) Peroxisomes:

  A) also called microbodies, contain acid hydrolases.

  B) are able to detoxify substances by enzymatic action.

  C) function to digest particles ingested by endocytosis.

  D) sometimes function as secretory vesicles.

Answer: B
Diff: 1   Page Ref: 79

26) DNA replication:

  A) can also be called mitosis.

  B) is spontaneous, not requiring enzyme action.

  C) takes place during interphase of the cell cycle.

  D) occurs only in translationally active areas.

Answer: C
Diff: 1   Page Ref: 86

27) Which statement is the most correct regarding transcription/translation?

   A) The nucleotide sequence in a mRNA codon is an exact copy of the DNA triplet that coded for it.

   B) The nucleotide sequence in a mRNA codon is an exact copy of the DNA triplet that coded for it except that uracil is substituted for thymine.

   C) The nucleotide sequence in a tRNA anticodon is an exact copy of the DNA triplet that coded for it.

   D) The nucleotide sequence in a tRNA anticodon is an exact copy of the DNA triplet that coded for it except that uracil is substituted for thymine.

Answer: D
Diff: 2   *Page Ref: 92*

28) In the maintenance of the cell resting membrane potential:

   A) extracellular sodium levels are high.

   B) cells are more permeable to Na^+ than K^+.

   C) the steady state involves only passive processes.

   D) the inside of the cell is positive relative to its outside.

Answer: A
Diff: 1   *Page Ref: 71*

29) Which of the following is a concept of the cell theory?

   A) Simple cells can arise spontaneously from rotting vegetation.

   B) A cell is the basic structural and functional unit of living organisms.

   C) The subcellular organelle is the basic unit of life.

   D) Only higher organisms are composed of cells.

Answer: B
Diff: 1   *Page Ref: 55*

30) Which of the following is a principle of the fluid mosaic model of cell membrane structure?

   A) Phospholipids form a bilayer that is largely impermeable to water–soluble molecules.

   B) Phospholipids consist of a polar head and a nonpolar tail made of three fatty acid chains.

   C) The lipid bilayer is a solid at body temperature, thus protecting the cell.

   D) All proteins associated with the cell membrane are contained in a fluid layer on the outside of the cell.

Answer: A
Diff: 1   *Page Ref: 58*

31) Which of the following statements is most correct regarding the intracellular chemical signals known as "second messengers"?

A) Second messengers act through receptors called K-proteins.

B) Second messengers usually inactivate protein kinase enzymes.

C) Cyclic AMP and calcium are second messengers.

D) Second messengers usually act to remove nitric oxide (NO) from the cell.

Answer: C
Diff: 1   Page Ref: 72

32) The main component of the cytosol is:

A) proteins.   B) sugars.   C) salts.   D) water.

Answer: D
Diff: 1   Page Ref: 73

33) Which of the following is not a type of cytoplasmic inclusion?

A) glycogen granules   B) lipid droplets

C) pigment granules   D) ribosomes

Answer: A
Diff: 2   Page Ref: 73

34) Lysosomes:

A) are used mainly for the cell to "commit suicide."

B) contain acid hydrolases that are potentially dangerous to the cell.

C) maintain a highly alkaline internal environment.

D) are the major site of protein synthesis.

Answer: B
Diff: 2   Page Ref: 78

35) The endomembrane system is:

A) a system by which cells are riveted together by desmosomes.

B) an interactive system of organelles whose membranes are physically or functionally connected.

C) the process by which bacteria took up residence in ancient cells.

D) a system of hydrophilic lipid monolayers that surround cell organelles.

Answer: B
Diff: 1   Page Ref: 79

36) The functions of centrioles include:

    A) organizing the mitotic spindle in cell division.

    B) providing a whiplike beating motion to move substances along cell surfaces.

    C) serving as the site for ribosomal RNA synthesis.

    D) producing ATP.

Answer: A
Diff: 1   Page Ref: 81

37) A gene can best be defined as:

    A) a three-base triplet that specifies a particular amino acid.

    B) noncoding segments of DNA up to 100,000 nucleotides long.

    C) a segment of DNA that carries the instructions for one polypeptide chain.

    D) an RNA messenger that codes for a particular polypeptide.

Answer: C
Diff: 1   Page Ref: 91

38) Extracellular matrix is:

    A) composed of strands of actin protein.

    B) the most abundant extracellular material.

    C) a type of impermeable cell junction found in epithelia.

    D) not present in connective tissue.

Answer: B
Diff: 1   Page Ref: 96

39) Crenation is an example of:

    A) blood cells in an isotonic solution.   B) blood cells in a hypotonic solution.

    C) blood cells in a hypertonic solution.   D) blood cells in blood plasma.

Answer: C
Diff: 1   Page Ref: 65

40) Some hormones enter cells via:

    A) exocytosis.   B) endocytosis.

    C) pinocytosis.   D) receptor-mediated endocytosis.

Answer: D
Diff: 1   Page Ref: 69

41) If a tRNA had an AGC anticodon, it could attach to a(n) _____ mRNA codon.

    A) AUG   B) UCG   C) TCG   D) UGA

Answer: B
Diff: 1   Page Ref: 95

Clinical Questions

1) Since the placement of red blood cells in distilled water would be detrimental to their health due to the water's hypotonic effects, why it is possible that drinking distilled water can have no ill effect on our intestinal cells?

   Answer: The intestinal lining is still considered outside of the body and the distilled water is rapidly mixed with mucus and other substances.
   Diff: 3   *Page Ref: 65*

2) A small boy received a cut on his arm and his mother applied hydrogen peroxide. The wound bubbled! Why?

   Answer: The hydrogen peroxide was degraded to water and oxygen (which bubbled off) by the action of cellular and bacterial enzymes (catalases).
   Diff: 4   *Page Ref: 79*

3) The antibiotic streptomycin binds specifically to the small subunit of the bacterial ribosome, interfering with several steps in the functioning of those ribosomes. What process is being affected, and why does this kill the bacteria?

   Answer: Streptomycin inhibits bacterial protein synthesis. Cells die if they are unable to synthesize new proteins for enzymes and for cell division.
   Diff: 3   *Page Ref: 91–96*

CHAPTER 4   Tissue: The Living Fabric

Fill-in-the-Blank/Short Answer Questions

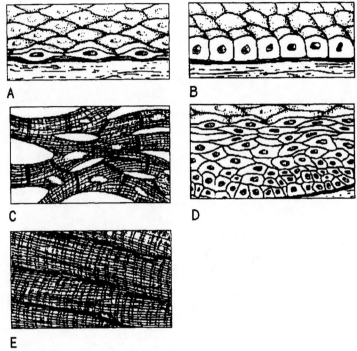

A

B

C

D

E

Figure 4.1

Using Figure 4.1, identify the following:

1) Simple cuboidal epithelium.

   Answer: B
   Diff: 2   Page Ref: 102

2) Cardiac muscle.

   Answer: C
   Diff: 2   Page Ref: 123

3) Simple squamous epithelium.

   Answer: A
   Diff: 2   Page Ref: 101

4) Stratified squamous epithelium.

   Answer: D
   Diff: 2   Page Ref: 104

5) Skeletal muscle.

Answer: E
Diff: 2   Page Ref: 122

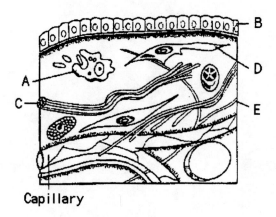

Capillary

Figure 4.2

Using Figure 4.2, identify the following:

6) Epithelium.

Answer: B
Diff: 2   Page Ref: 103

7) Collagen fiber.

Answer: C
Diff: 2   Page Ref: 110

8) Elastic fiber(s).

Answer: E
Diff: 2   Page Ref: 110

9) Fibroblast.

Answer: D
Diff: 2   Page Ref: 110

10) Macrophage.

Answer: A
Diff: 2   Page Ref: 110

Fill in the blank or provide a short answer:

11) _____ tissue forms the framework for the lamina propria of mucous membranes.

Answer: Areolar or loose connective
Diff: 1   Page Ref: 121

12) Osteocytes exist in a tiny void called a _____.

Answer: lacuna
Diff: 1   *Page Ref: 119*

13) Cardiac muscle tissue is single nucleated, has intercalated discs, and is _____.

Answer: branched
Diff: 2   *Page Ref: 122*

14) _____ muscle cells are multinucleated.

Answer: Skeletal
Diff: 1   *Page Ref: 122*

15) _____ live in the lacuna of cartilage.

Answer: Chondrocytes
Diff: 1   *Page Ref: 118*

16) The uppermost layer of skin is composed of _____.

Answer: keratinized stratified squamous epithelium
Diff: 1   *Page Ref: 105*

17) Kidney tubules are composed of _____ epithelium.

Answer: simple cuboidal
Diff: 1   *Page Ref: 102*

18) Multiple rows of epithelia in which the cells are about the same size from the basement membrane to the lumen would be _____ epithelia.

Answer: transitional
Diff: 1   *Page Ref: 105*

19) All epithelial tissue rests upon a _____.

Answer: basement membrane
Diff: 1   *Page Ref: 100*

20) The salivary glands are a good example of a _____ exocrine gland.

Answer: compound tubuloalveolar
Diff: 2   *Page Ref: 107*

21) Macrophage–like cells are found in many different tissues, and may have specific names that reflect their location or specializations. What is the one functional characteristic common to all macrophage–like cells?

Answer: phagocytosis
Diff: 1   *Page Ref: 111*

22) All of the following statements refer to events of tissue repair. Put the events in proper numbered order according to the sequence of occurrence. The initial event, the injury, is already indicated as number one.

1. The skin receives a cut that penetrates into the dermis and bleeding begins.
2. Epithelial regeneration is nearly complete.
3. Granulation tissue is formed.
4. Blood clotting occurs and stops the blood flow.
5. The scar retracts.
6. Macrophages engulf and clean away cellular debris.
7. Fibroblasts elaborate connective tissue fibers to span the break.

Answer: 1-4-3-7-6-5-2
Diff: 2   Page Ref: 124-125

23) Tendon tears or breaks are difficult to repair both physiologically and surgically. Why?

Answer: Tendons are composed of dense regular connective tissue, which consists of densely packed, parallel connective tissue fibers. This type of tissue has relatively few cells and vascular supply is poor; consequently, repair is slow. Because of the structure of the tissue, surgical repair can be compared to attempting to suture two bristle brushes together.
Diff: 4   Page Ref: 114-116

Matching Questions

Match the following:

1) Column 1: The epithelial membrane that lines the closed ventral cavities of the body.

Column 2: Serous membrane

Answer: Serous membrane
Diff: 1   Page Ref: 121

2) Column 1: The epithelial membrane that lines body cavities open to the exterior.

Column 2: Mucous membrane

Answer: Mucous membrane
Diff: 1   Page Ref: 121

3) Column 1: Consists of keratinized stratified squamous epithelium.

Column 2: Cutaneous membrane

Answer: Cutaneous membrane
Diff: 2   Page Ref: 120

4) Column 1: Found lining the digestive
            and respiratory tracts.

   Column 2: Mucous membrane

   Answer: Mucous membrane
   Diff: 2   *Page Ref: 121*

5) Column 1: Makes up the pleura and
            pericardium.

   Column 2: Serous membrane

   Answer: Serous membrane
   Diff: 2   *Page Ref: 121*

6) Column 1: Lines blood vessels and the
            heart.

   Column 2: Endothelium

   Answer: Endothelium
   Diff: 1   *Page Ref: 101*

Match the following:

7) Column 1: Voluntary, striations.

   Column 2: Skeletal

   Answer: Skeletal
   Diff: 2   *Page Ref: 122*

8) Column 1: Involuntary, striations and
            branching cells.

   Column 2: Cardiac

   Answer: Cardiac
   Diff: 2   *Page Ref: 122*

9) Column 1: Spindle–shaped uninucleate
            cells.

   Column 2: Smooth

   Answer: Smooth
   Diff: 2   *Page Ref: 122*

10) Column 1: Involved in peristalsis,
             emptying of the bladder, and
             the birth process.

    Column 2: Smooth

    Answer: Smooth
    Diff: 2   *Page Ref: 122*

11) Column 1: Large multinucleate cells with striations.

Column 2: Skeletal

Answer: Skeletal
Diff: 2   *Page Ref: 122*

12) Column 1: Has close junctions called intercalated discs.

Column 2: Cardiac

Answer: Cardiac
Diff: 1   *Page Ref: 122-123*

13) Column 1: Forms the walls of the heart.

Column 2: Cardiac

Answer: Cardiac
Diff: 1   *Page Ref: 122*

14) Column 1: Found in the walls of hollow organs.

Column 2: Smooth

Answer: Smooth
Diff: 1   *Page Ref: 122*

Match the following:

15) Column 1: Tissue is stressed in many directions.

Column 2: Dense irregular connective tissue

Answer: Dense irregular connective tissue
Diff: 1   *Page Ref: 114-116*

16) Column 1: Contains large amounts of neutral fat.

Column 2: Adipose

Answer: Adipose
Diff: 2   *Page Ref: 113-114*

17) Column 1: Major component of tendons and aponeuroses.

Column 2: Dense regular connective tissue

Answer: Dense regular connective tissue
Diff: 2   *Page Ref: 114-116*

18) Column 1: Transport vehicle for the
        cardiovascular system.

    Column 2: Blood

    Answer: Blood
    Diff: 1   *Page Ref: 118*

19) Column 1: Provides insulation for the
        body.

    Column 2: Adipose

    Answer: Adipose
    Diff: 1   *Page Ref: 113–114*

20) Column 1: Protects and supports soft
        tissues.

    Column 2: Areolar connective tissue

    Answer: Areolar connective tissue
    Diff: 1   *Page Ref: 111–113*

Match the following:

21) Column 1: Structural support of the
        external ear and other
        structures that need support
        with flexibility.

    Column 2: Elastic cartilage

    Answer: Elastic cartilage
    Diff: 1   *Page Ref: 116*

22) Column 1: Forms the embryonic skeleton
        and covers the articular
        surfaces of long bones.

    Column 2: Hyaline cartilage

    Answer: Hyaline cartilage
    Diff: 1   *Page Ref: 116*

23) Column 1: Embryonic connective tissue
        that arises from mesoderm
        and produces all types of
        connective tissues.

    Column 2: Mesenchyme

    Answer: Mesenchyme
    Diff: 2   *Page Ref: 111*

24) Column 1: Wharton's jelly; fetal
              connective tissue.

Column 2: Mucous connective tissue

Answer: Mucous connective tissue
Diff: 2   Page Ref: 111

25) Column 1: Forms internal supporting
              framework of soft organs such
              as the spleen.

Column 2: Reticular tissue

Answer: Reticular tissue
Diff: 2   Page Ref: 114

True/False Questions

1) The shock–absorbing pads between the vertebrae are formed of fibrocartilage.

Answer: TRUE
Diff: 1   Page Ref: 116–118

2) Brown fat is frequently deposited between the shoulder blades of infants.

Answer: TRUE
Diff: 1   Page Ref: 114

3) Achilles was wounded by damage to the tendon connecting his calf muscles to his heel. This and all tendons are composed mainly of dense irregular connective tissue.

Answer: FALSE
Diff: 2   Page Ref: 115

4) Macrophages are found in areolar and lymphatic tissues.

Answer: TRUE
Diff: 1   Page Ref: 111

5) Goblet cells are found with pseudostratified ciliated columnar epithelium.

Answer: TRUE
Diff: 2   Page Ref: 106

6) Epithelial tissues always exhibit polarity; that is, they have a free surface and a basal surface.

Answer: TRUE
Diff: 1   Page Ref: 99

7) Simple cuboidal epithelia are usually associated with secretion and absorption.

Answer: TRUE
Diff: 1   Page Ref: 103

8) Depending on the functional state of the bladder, transitional epithelium may resemble stratified squamous or stratified cuboidal epithelium.

Answer: TRUE
Diff: 1   *Page Ref: 105*

9) Endothelium covers and lines internal cavities such as the pleural and peritoneal cavities.

Answer: FALSE
Diff: 1   *Page Ref: 101*

10) Merocrine glands produce their secretions by accumulating their secretions internally and then rupturing the cell.

Answer: FALSE
Diff: 1   *Page Ref: 107*

11) Salivary glands exhibit simple tubuloalveolar glandular arrangement.

Answer: FALSE
Diff: 2   *Page Ref: 107*

12) Connective tissues that possess a large quantity of collagen fibers often provide the framework for organs such as the spleen and lymph nodes.

Answer: FALSE
Diff: 1   *Page Ref: 114*

13) The basic difference between dense irregular and dense regular connective tissues is in the amount of elastic fibers and adipose cells present.

Answer: FALSE
Diff: 1   *Page Ref: 114–116*

14) A major characteristic of fibrocartilage is its unique amount of flexibility and elasticity.

Answer: FALSE
Diff: 2   *Page Ref: 116*

15) Cartilage tissue tends to heal less rapidly than bone tissue.

Answer: TRUE
Diff: 1   *Page Ref: 116*

16) Intercalated discs and striations suggest the presence of skeletal muscle.

Answer: FALSE
Diff: 1   *Page Ref: 122*

17) Smooth muscle cells possess central nuclei but lack striations.

Answer: TRUE
Diff: 1   *Page Ref: 122–123*

18) Neurons have branched cytoplasmic extensions that may extend only short distances.

Answer: FALSE
Diff: 1   Page Ref: 121

19) Most connective tissues have regenerative capacity, while most epithelial tissues do not.

Answer: FALSE
Diff: 2   Page Ref: 99

20) Squamous cells are flattened and scalelike when mature.

Answer: TRUE
Diff: 1   Page Ref: 101

21) All connective tissues arise from mesenchyme.

Answer: TRUE
Diff: 1   Page Ref: 111

22) Functions of connective tissues include binding, support, insulation, and protection.

Answer: TRUE
Diff: 1   Page Ref: 109

23) Wharton's jelly is the best representative of embryonic epithelial tissue.

Answer: FALSE
Diff: 2   Page Ref: 111

24) Muscle and connective tissues develop from endoderm.

Answer: FALSE
Diff: 2   Page Ref: 111

25) Sweat glands are apocrine glands.

Answer: FALSE
Diff: 2   Page Ref: 108

26) Endocrine glands are often called ducted glands.

Answer: FALSE
Diff: 1   Page Ref: 106

27) Blood is considered a type of connective tissue.

Answer: TRUE
Diff: 1   Page Ref: 118

28) Nervous tissue consists mainly of neurons and collagen fibers.

Answer: FALSE
Diff: 1   Page Ref: 121

Multiple-Choice Questions

1) Which of the following is not found in the matrix of cartilage but is in bone?

   A) live cells   B) lacunae   C) blood vessels   D) organic fibers

   Answer: C
   Diff: 2   Page Ref: 108

2) The reason that intervertebral discs exhibit a large amount of tensile strength to absorb shock is because they possess:

   A) hydroxyapatite crystals.   B) collagen fibers.

   C) reticular fibers.   D) elastic fibers.

   Answer: B
   Diff: 2   Page Ref: 110

3) The presence of lacunae, calcium salts, and blood vessels would indicate:

   A) cartilage tissue.   B) fibrocartilaginous tissue.

   C) osseous tissue.   D) areolar tissue.

   Answer: C
   Diff: 2   Page Ref: 118

4) Hyaline cartilage is different from elastic or fibrocartilage because:

   A) it is stronger.   B) it contains more nuclei.

   C) fibers are not visible with normal stains.   D) it has more densely packed fibers.

   Answer: C
   Diff: 1   Page Ref: 116

5) Epithelial tissue:

   A) is highly vascularized.   B) has a basement membrane.

   C) is usually acellular.   D) contains a number of neuron types.

   Answer: B
   Diff: 2   Page Ref: 99

6) Which of the following would be of most importance to goblet cells and other glandular epithelium?

   A) microvilli   B) Golgi bodies   C) lysosomes   D) multiple nuclei

   Answer: B
   Diff: 2   Page Ref: 106

7) Simple columnar epithelium of the digestive tract is characterized by:

   A) dense microvilli.   B) a rich vascular supply.

   C) fibroblasts.   D) cilia.

   Answer: A
   Diff: 1   Page Ref: 103

8) Pseudostratified cuboidal epithelium:

   A) lines the respiratory tract.   B) aids in digestion.

   C) possesses numerous goblet cells.   D) is not an epithelial classification.

   Answer: D
   Diff: 2   Page Ref: 103

9) A single-celled layer of epithelium that forms the lining of serous membranes is:

   A) simple transitional.   B) simple columnar.

   C) simple squamous.   D) simple cuboidal.

   Answer: C
   Diff: 1   Page Ref: 121

10) Which statement best describes connective tissue?

   A) usually contains a large amount of matrix

   B) always arranged in a single layer of cells

   C) primarily concerned with secretion

   D) usually lines a body cavity

   Answer: A
   Diff: 1   Page Ref: 108

11) Matrix is:

   A) cells and fibers.   B) fibers and ground substance.

   C) ground substance and cells.   D) composed of all organic compounds.

   Answer: B
   Diff: 1   Page Ref: 108-109

12) Cell types likely to be seen in areolar connective tissue include all except:

   A) chondrocytes.   B) fibroblasts.   C) macrophages.   D) mast cells.

   Answer: A
   Diff: 1   Page Ref: 110

13) The tissue type that arises from all three embryonic germ layers is:

   A) epithelial tissue.   B) connective tissue.

   C) nervous tissue.   D) muscle tissue.

   Answer: A
   Diff: 2   Page Ref: 100

14) The fiber type that gives connective tissue great tensile strength is:

   A) elastic fiber.   B) collagen fiber.   C) reticular fiber.   D) muscle fiber.

   Answer: B
   Diff: 1   Page Ref: 110

15) Organized groups of cells (plus their intercellular substances) that have a common purpose form a(n):

A) organ.   B) tissue.   C) organism.   D) organ system.

Answer: B
Diff: 1   *Page Ref: 99*

16) The shape of the external ear is maintained by:

A) adipose tissue.   B) elastic cartilage.
C) hyaline cartilage.   D) fibrocartilage.

Answer: B
Diff: 1   *Page Ref: 117*

17) Inability to absorb digested nutrients and secrete mucous might indicate a disorder in which tissue?

A) simple squamous   B) transitional
C) simple columnar   D) stratified squamous

Answer: C
Diff: 3   *Page Ref: 103*

18) Glands, such as the thyroid, that secrete their products directly into the blood rather than through ducts are classified as:

A) exocrine.   B) endocrine.   C) sebaceous.   D) ceruminous.

Answer: B
Diff: 1   *Page Ref: 106*

19) Which of the following is true about epithelia?

A) Simple epithelia are commonly found in areas of high abrasion.

B) Stratified epithelia are associated with filtration.

C) Endothelium provides a slick surface lining all hollow cardiovascular organs.

D) Pseudostratified epithelia are commonly keratinized.

Answer: C
Diff: 2   *Page Ref: 100–106*

20) Chondroblasts:

A) are mature cartilage cells located in spaces called lacunae.

B) within the cartilage divide and secrete new matrix.

C) located deep to the perichondrium divide and secrete new matrix on the internal portions of the cartilage.

D) never lose their ability to divide.

Answer: B
Diff: 2   *Page Ref: 116*

21) _____ epithelium appears to have two or three layers of cells, but all the cells are in contact with the basement membrane.

A) Stratified cuboidal

B) Stratified columnar

C) Transitional

D) Pseudostratified columnar

Answer: D
Diff: 1   Page Ref: 103

22) A multilayered epithelium with cuboidal basal cells and flat cells at its surface would be classified as:

A) simple cuboidal.

B) simple squamous.

C) transitional.

D) stratified squamous.

Answer: D
Diff: 2   Page Ref: 104

23) An epithelial membrane:

A) usually involves transitional epithelium.

B) is formed of epithelium and smooth muscle.

C) contains simple or stratified epithelia and a basement membrane.

D) never contains mucus–forming cells.

Answer: C
Diff: 2   Page Ref: 118

24) Multicellular exocrine glands can be classified:

A) structurally into alveolar and acinar types.

B) structurally into ductless and ducted types.

C) functionally into merocrine, holocrine, and apocrine divisions.

D) functionally into secreting or nonsecreting types.

Answer: C
Diff: 2   Page Ref: 107

25) Which of the following is true about the mode of secretion of exocrine glands?

A) Merocrine glands are not altered by the secretory process.

B) Apocrine cells are destroyed, then replaced after secretion.

C) Holocrine cells are slightly damaged by the secretory process, but repair themselves.

D) These glands are ductless.

Answer: A
Diff: 2   Page Ref: 107–108

26) Which of these is not considered connective tissue?

A) cartilage   B) adipose   C) muscle   D) blood

Answer: C
Diff: 1   Page Ref: 122

27) What are glycosaminoglycans?

   A) Positively charged proteins.
   B) Negatively charged proteins.
   C) Positively charged polysaccharides.
   D) Negatively charged polysaccharides.

   Answer: D
   Diff: 1   Page Ref: 109

28) Which is true concerning muscle tissue?

   A) highly cellular and well vascularized
   B) cuboidal shape enhances function
   C) contains contractile units made of collagen
   D) is a single-celled tissue

   Answer: A
   Diff: 1   Page Ref: 122

29) The first step in tissue repair involves:

   A) replacement of destroyed tissue by the same kind of cells.
   B) proliferation of fibrous connective tissue.
   C) formation of granulation tissue.
   D) formation of scar tissue.

   Answer: C
   Diff: 2   Page Ref: 124

30) Select the correct statement regarding multicellular exocrine glands.

   A) Compound glands are so called because they are constructed from more than one cell type.
   B) The secretory cells of holocrine glands release their product by rupturing.
   C) Exocrine glands lack ducts.
   D) Merocrine glands release their secretion by pinching off part of the cell.

   Answer: B
   Diff: 2   Page Ref: 107

31) The three main components of connective tissue are:

   A) ground substance, fibers, and cells.
   B) alveoli, fibrous capsule, and secretory cells.
   C) collagen, elastin, and reticular fibers.
   D) fibroblasts, chondroblasts, and osteoblasts.

   Answer: A
   Diff: 1   Page Ref: 108

32) Which of the following statements is true of connective tissue?
   A) Elastin fibers are sometimes called white fibers.
   B) When connective tissue is stretched, collagen gives it the ability to snap back.
   C) Collagen fibers provide high tensile strength.
   D) Reticular fibers form thick, ropelike structures.

   Answer: C
   Diff: 1   Page Ref: 110

33) Select the correct statement regarding the cells of connective tissue.
   A) Connective tissue does not contain cells.
   B) Connective tissue cells are nondividing.
   C) Chondroblasts are the main cell type of connective tissue proper.
   D) "Blast" cells are undifferentiated, actively dividing cells.

   Answer: D
   Diff: 2   Page Ref: 111

34) Select the correct statement regarding tissue repair.
   A) Granulation tissue is highly susceptible to infection.
   B) Inflammation causes capillaries to dilate and become permeable.
   C) Granulation tissue is another name for a blood clot.
   D) The clot is formed from dried blood and transposed collagen fibers.

   Answer: B
   Diff: 2   Page Ref: 124

35) Select the correct statement regarding epithelia.
   A) Simple epithelia form impermeable barriers.
   B) Stratified epithelia are tall, narrow cells.
   C) Stratified epithelia are present where protection from abrasion is important.
   D) Pseudostratified epithelia consist of at least two layers of cells stacked on top of one another.

   Answer: C
   Diff: 2   Page Ref: 100–105

36) Select the correct statement regarding adipose tissue.
   A) It is composed mostly of extracellular matrix.
   B) Its primary function is nutrient storage.
   C) Mature adipose cells are highly mitotic.
   D) Most of the cell volume is occupied by the nucleus.

   Answer: B
   Diff: 1   Page Ref: 113

37) _____ are commonly found wedged between simple columnar epithelial cells.

A) Goblet cells   B) Mast cells   C) Macrophages   D) Cilia

Answer: A
Diff: 1   Page Ref: 106

38) Select the correct statement regarding factors that affect the repair process.

A) The type of tissue injured is not an important factor.

B) Nutrition does not seem to influence tissue repair.

C) The age of the person is a factor in the repair process.

D) The health of an individual does not seem to make any difference in the speed of repair.

Answer: C
Diff: 2   Page Ref: 124

39) A large round cell with a peripheral nucleus describes a(n):

A) nerve.   B) fibroblast.   C) adipocyte.   D) cuboidal cell.

Answer: C
Diff: 1   Page Ref: 113

Clinical Questions

1) A 45-year-old woman is admitted to the hospital for surgical removal of a tumor on her thyroid gland. The surgeon informs her that she will have only a very small scar. How could this be possible?

Answer: By making a thin incision, the amount of granulation (scar-forming) tissue will be minimal. As the scar tissue beneath matures and contracts, the layer of epithelium thickens and resembles the adjacent tissue. The final result may be only a fine white line.
Diff: 4   Page Ref: 124-125

2) John, a 72-year-old grandfather, had been smoking heavily for 24 years and had a persistent cough. A biopsy of his lung tissue revealed considerable amounts of carbon particles. How could this happen considering the natural cleaning mechanism of the respiratory system?

Answer: The sweeping action of the ciliated epithelium is essential in order to propel inhaled dust and other debris out of the respiratory tract. Anything that inhibits this mechanism would allow foreign substances to remain in the tract, which may cause damage. Chemicals such as nicotine may inhibit the action of the cilia, allowing carbon particles found in smoke to remain in the lungs.
Diff: 5   Page Ref: 103

3) Aunt Jessie woke up one morning with excruciating pain in her chest. She had trouble breathing for several weeks. Following a visit to the doctor, she was told she had pleurisy. What is this condition and what did it affect?

Answer: Pleurisy is an inflammation of the pleura, the serosal membranes covering the lungs and lining the thoracic wall. Pain is caused by the irritation and friction as the lungs rub against the walls of the cavity.
Diff: 4   Page Ref: 121

4) In adult humans, most cancers are carcinomas or adenocarcinomas. These include cancers of the skin, lung, colon, breast, and prostate. Which of the four basic tissue types is involved? Why do you think this is so?

Answer: Epithelium gives rise to most cancers. This is probably because epithelial cells divide more, leading to more opportunity for damage to growth control mechanisms, and because epithelia are more often in contact with environmental insults such as ultraviolet radiation and carcinogens.

Diff: 3   *Page Ref: 99–100*

5) Since mature adipocytes do not divide, how can adults gain weight?

Answer: Adipocytes contain a fat–filled vacuole that can fill or empty, causing the cell to gain or lose volume.

Diff: 2   *Page Ref: 113–114*

6) What is a scar, and what is the clinical term for it?

Answer: Scars are called keloids and occur when wounds cannot close, or when the wound is very deep. Connective tissue fills in the space before epithelial tissue can cover it.

Diff: 3   *Page Ref: 124*

CHAPTER 5   The Integumentary System

Fill–in–the–Blank/Short Answer Questions

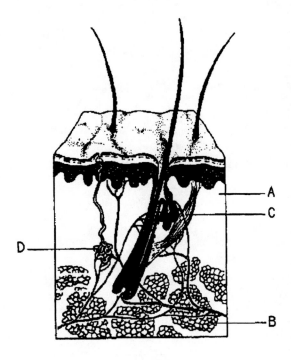

Figure 5.1

Using Figure 5.1, identify the following:

1) Responsible for the dermal ridges that produce whorled ridges on the epidermal surfaces.

   Answer: A
   Diff: 1   Page Ref: 131

2) Responsible for shock absorption and located in the hypodermis.

   Answer: B
   Diff: 1   Page Ref: 131

3) Pulls the hair follicle into an upright position.

   Answer: C
   Diff: 1   Page Ref: 131

4) Sudoriferous gland.

   Answer: D
   Diff: 1   Page Ref: 131

Fill in the blank or provide a short answer:

5) Cradle cap in infants is called _____.

Answer: seborrhea
Diff: 2   Page Ref: 135

6) The white crescent portion of the nail is called the _____.

Answer: lunula
Diff: 1   Page Ref: 139

7) The layer of the epidermis immediately under the stratum lucidum is the stratum _____.

Answer: granulosum
Diff: 1   Page Ref: 130

8) The _____ is a small muscle located in the dermis that causes goose bumps.

Answer: arrector pili
Diff: 1   Page Ref: 136

9) A summertime golden bronze tan may not be a tan at all; especially if the skin appears almost metallic bronze, it may be the result of _____ disease.

Answer: Addison's
Diff: 2   Page Ref: 133

10) The coarse hair of the eyebrows and scalp is called _____ hair.

Answer: terminal
Diff: 1   Page Ref: 136

11) _____ burns injure the epidermis and the upper regions of the dermis.

Answer: Second-degree
Diff: 1   Page Ref: 141

12) _____ are pigment-producing cells in the epidermis.

Answer: Melanocytes
Diff: 1   Page Ref: 128

13) The only place you will find stratum _____ is in the skin that covers the palms, fingertips, and soles of the feet.

Answer: lucidum
Diff: 1   Page Ref: 130

14) The dermis is composed of the reticular and _____ layers.

Answer: papillary
Diff: 1   Page Ref: 132

15) There are several reasons other than genetics for hair loss. Identify some of these other factors.

   Answer: Stressors such as acutely high fever, surgery, severe emotional trauma; drugs such as antidepressants and chemotherapy drugs; and a protein–deficient diet can cause hair loss or thinning.
   Diff: 3   *Page Ref: 136*

16) In addition to the synthesis of vitamin D, keratinocytes are able to carry out some other biologically important functions. Name at least two of these other functions.

   Answer: Keratinocyte enzymes can neutralize carcinogens that penetrate the epidermis. Keratinocytes are also able to convert topical steroid hormones to a powerful anti–inflammatory drug.
   Diff: 3   *Page Ref: 140*

17) How are burns classified? Give an example.

   Answer: Burns are classified according to their severity or depth. For example, in first–degree burns, only the epidermis is damaged.
   Diff: 2   *Page Ref: 141*

18) What are vellus hairs?

   Answer: Pale, fine body hair associated with newborn children, women, and bald men.
   Diff: 2   *Page Ref: 136*

19) Balding men have tried all kinds of remedies, including hair transplants, to restore their lost locks. Explain the cause of male pattern baldness.

   Answer: It appears to be genetically determined and sex linked, and is possibly caused by a delayed–action gene that alters normal metabolism.
   Diff: 3   *Page Ref: 138*

20) Billions of consumer dollars are spent for deodorants and antiperspirants each year. Explain the production of body odors frequently associated with axillary skin.

   Answer: Sweat is mostly an odorless watery secretion produced by eccrine and apocrine glands. The odor usually arises due to the metabolic activities of bacteria on the surface of the skin.
   Diff: 3   *Page Ref: 134*

21) What complications might be anticipated from loss of large areas of skin surfaces?

   Answer: Large losses of skin, as with severe burn injuries, allow excessive fluid loss and infection. Skin grafting is necessary.
   Diff: 3   *Page Ref: 141*

Matching Questions

Match the following:

1) Column 1: The cells found in skin that function in immunity.

   Column 2: Langerhans'

   Answer: Langerhans'
   Diff: 1   Page Ref: 128

2) Column 1: Characteristic redness caused by a sunburn.

   Column 2: Erythema

   Answer: Erythema
   Diff: 2   Page Ref: 133

Match the following:

3) Column 1: The most abundant cells of the epidermis.

   Column 2: Keratinocytes

   Answer: Keratinocytes
   Diff: 1   Page Ref: 128

4) Column 1: Must be activated in the skin in order to enhance calcium metabolism.

   Column 2: Vitamin D

   Answer: Vitamin D
   Diff: 1   Page Ref: 140

5) Column 1: The protein found in the epidermis that is responsible for waterproofing and toughening the skin.

   Column 2: Keratin

   Answer: Keratin
   Diff: 1   Page Ref: 130

Match the following:

6) Column 1: The layer of the epidermis where the cells are considered protective but nonviable.

   Column 2: Stratum corneum

   Answer: Stratum corneum
   Diff: 1   Page Ref: 130–131

7) Column 1: The glands that serve an important function in thermoregulation.

   Column 2: Sudoriferous glands

   Answer: Sudoriferous glands
   Diff: 1   *Page Ref: 133–134*

8) Column 1: The layer that contains the mitotic viable cells of the epidermis.

   Column 2: Stratum germinativum

   Answer: Stratum germinativum
   Diff: 2   *Page Ref: 130*

9) Column 1: Hair that lacks pigment and is often called "immature hair."

   Column 2: Vellus hairs
        Foil: Dermal papillae

   Answer: Vellus hairs
   Diff: 1   *Page Ref: 136*

True/False Questions

1) The apocrine sweat glands are fairly unimportant in thermoregulation.

   Answer: TRUE
   Diff: 1   *Page Ref: 134*

2) Arrector pili muscles are associated with each hair follicle.

   Answer: FALSE
   Diff: 1   *Page Ref: 136*

3) Skin surface markings that reflect points of tight dermal attachment to underlying tissues are called epidermal ridges.

   Answer: FALSE
   Diff: 1   *Page Ref: 132*

4) The dense fibrous connective tissue portion of the skin is located in the reticular region of the dermis.

   Answer: TRUE
   Diff: 1   *Page Ref: 132*

5) The outermost sheath of a hair follicle is the connective tissue root sheath.

   Answer: TRUE
   Diff: 1   *Page Ref: 136*

6) The protein found in large amounts in the outermost layer of epidermal cells is collagen.

Answer: FALSE
Diff: 1   Page Ref: 130

7) Joe just burned himself on a hot pot. A blister forms and the burn in painful. Joe's burn would best be described as a third–degree burn.

Answer: FALSE
Diff: 2   Page Ref: 141

8) Destruction of the matrix of the hair bulb would result in its inability to produce oil.

Answer: FALSE
Diff: 2   Page Ref: 136

9) The outer protective layer of the skin is composed of stratified squamous epithelium.

Answer: TRUE
Diff: 1   Page Ref: 130

10) The hyponychium is commonly called the cuticle.

Answer: FALSE
Diff: 1   Page Ref: 139

11) The nail is actually a modification of the skin and corresponds to the hooves of animals.

Answer: TRUE
Diff: 1   Page Ref: 138

12) The reason that the nail bed appears pink is the presence of a large number of melanocytes in the underlying dermis.

Answer: FALSE
Diff: 2   Page Ref: 138

13) During the resting phase of hair growth, the matrix is inactive and the follicle atrophies.

Answer: TRUE
Diff: 1   Page Ref: 136

14) The most dangerous skin cancer is cancer of the melanocytes.

Answer: TRUE
Diff: 1   Page Ref: 140

15) The skin is not able to receive stimuli because the cells of the epidermis are not living and therefore there are no sensory receptors in the skin.

Answer: FALSE
Diff: 1   Page Ref: 129, 132

16) The dermis composes the major portion of the skin.

Answer: TRUE
Diff: 1   *Page Ref: 129*

17) The dermis is highly vascularized, accounting for the often pink color in the cheeks of babies.

Answer: TRUE
Diff: 2   *Page Ref: 132*

18) The hypodermis is composed of adipose and dense connective tissue.

Answer: FALSE
Diff: 1   *Page Ref: 128*

19) Melanocytes are found in the deepest layer of the dermis.

Answer: FALSE
Diff: 1   *Page Ref: 128*

20) A physician is often able to detect homeostatic imbalances in the body by observing changes in the skin color.

Answer: TRUE
Diff: 3   *Page Ref: 133*

21) When an individual is exposed to extremely low air temperatures, the vasculature of the skin will dilate so that blood and heat will be dissipated.

Answer: FALSE
Diff: 3   *Page Ref: 139*

22) Regardless of race, all human beings have about the same number of melanocytes.

Answer: TRUE
Diff: 1   *Page Ref: 132*

23) Langerhans' (star-shaped cells) arise from the dermis and work together with melanocytes to protect the skin from UV rays.

Answer: FALSE
Diff: 1   *Page Ref: 128*

24) Merkel cells are associated with a disclike sensory nerve ending, and together they are called "Merkel discs," which function as pain sensory receptors.

Answer: FALSE
Diff: 2   *Page Ref: 128*

25) The stratum corneum (outermost layer of skin) is a zone of approximately four layers of viable cells that are able to synthesize proteins that keep the outer layer of skin smooth and soft.

Answer: FALSE
Diff: 2   *Page Ref: 129*

26) The dermis has a connective tissue and adipose layer that loosely binds the body together.

Answer: FALSE
Diff: 1   Page Ref: 131

27) Because the dermis is deeper than the epidermis, it is rarely subject to damage because the cornified layers of the epidermis protect it.

Answer: FALSE
Diff: 2   Page Ref: 132

28) Keratinocytes produce melanin, the polymer responsible for protecting the skin from damaging UV light.

Answer: FALSE
Diff: 2   Page Ref: 128

29) The pinkish hue of individuals with fair skin is the result of the crimson color of oxygenated hemoglobin (contained in red blood cells) circulating in the dermal capillaries and reflecting through the epidermis.

Answer: TRUE
Diff: 2   Page Ref: 133

30) Body hair on humans serves to keep the epidermis protected from harm and is located at strategic points on the body. Removal or loss of body hair could be dangerous.

Answer: FALSE
Diff: 1   Page Ref: 135

31) The pigment we observe in our hair is produced by the same cells that produce the pigment in our skin.

Answer: FALSE
Diff: 1   Page Ref: 135

32) Because body hair seems to serve no important function, there are no nerve endings associated with it and therefore no sensation from any stimulation is felt.

Answer: FALSE
Diff: 2   Page Ref: 136

33) Hair growth and density are influenced by hormones, nutrition, and, in some cases, lifestyle.

Answer: TRUE
Diff: 2   Page Ref: 136

34) When a patient is said to have "third-degree burns," this indicates that the epidermis and dermis have been destroyed.

Answer: TRUE
Diff: 1   Page Ref: 141-142

35) Sudoriferous (sweat) glands are scattered over the entire body, and the product of these glands contributes to temperature control in humans.

Answer: TRUE
Diff: 2   Page Ref: 133–134

36) Because the process of sweating is regulated by the sympathetic division of the autonomic nervous system, humans have little control over the mechanism of sweating.

Answer: TRUE
Diff: 1   Page Ref: 134

37) The organ known as skin has metabolic functions.

Answer: TRUE
Diff: 2   Page Ref: 140

Multiple-Choice Questions

1) Select the most correct statement concerning skin cancer.
   A) Most tumors that arise on the skin are malignant.
   B) Squamous cell carcinomas arise from the stratum corneum.
   C) Basal cell carcinomas are the least common but most malignant.
   D) Melanomas are rare but must be removed quickly to prevent them from metastasizing.

Answer: D
Diff: 1   Page Ref: 140–141

2) A needle would pierce the epidermal layers of the forearm in which order?
   A) basale, spinosum, granulosum, corneum
   B) basale, spinosum, granulosum, lucidum, corneum
   C) granulosum, basale, spinosum, corneum
   D) corneum, granulosum, spinosum, basale

Answer: D
Diff: 2   Page Ref: 129–130

3) The major regions of a hair shaft include all of the following except:
   A) medulla.   B) cortex.
   C) external root sheath.   D) cuticle.

Answer: C
Diff: 2   Page Ref: 135

4) Acne is a disorder associated with:
   A) sweat glands.   B) sebaceous glands.
   C) Meibomian glands.   D) ceruminous glands.

Answer: B
Diff: 1   Page Ref: 135

5) The dermis:

    A) is an avascular connective tissue layer.   B) has two distinct layers.

    C) lacks sensory corpuscles and glands.   D) is where melanocytes are found.

Answer: B
Diff: 1   *Page Ref: 131*

6) Which muscles attached to the hair follicles cause goose bumps?

    A) arrector integument   B) arrector pili

    C) levator folliculi   D) arrector folliculi

Answer: B
Diff: 1   *Page Ref: 136*

7) If a splinter penetrated the skin in to the third epidermal layer of the sole of the foot, which cells would be damaged?

    A) granulosum   B) basale   C) lucidum   D) spinosum

Answer: A
Diff: 2   *Page Ref: 130*

8) Which of the following cutaneous receptors is specialized for the reception of touch or light pressure?

    A) Meissner's corpuscles   B) Pacinian corpuscles

    C) free nerve endings   D) Krause's end bulbs

Answer: A
Diff: 2   *Page Ref: 140*

9) Melanocytes:

    A) are spidery–shaped cells in contact with cells in the stratum basale.

    B) are involved in the immune system.

    C) are involved with the nervous system.

    D) work their way up to the surface just like the keratinocytes.

Answer: A
Diff: 1   *Page Ref: 128*

10) Which statement correctly explains why hair appears the way it does?

    A) Kinky hair has flat, ribbonlike hair shafts.

    B) Perfectly round hair shafts result in wavy hair.

    C) Air bubbles in the hair shaft cause straight hair.

    D) Gray hair is the result of hormonal action altering the chemical composition of melanin.

Answer: A
Diff: 2   *Page Ref: 135*

11) Sudoriferous glands vary in distribution over the surface of the body. Which of the following is correct?

   A) Eccrine are the most numerous, being found primarily in the axillary regions.

   B) Apocrine glands are larger than eccrine, and empty secretions directly to the surface of the skin.

   C) Ceruminous glands secrete cerumen, which is thought to repel insects.

   D) Mammary glands are not considered a modified sweat gland.

   Answer: C
   Diff: 2   *Page Ref: 134*

12) Although the integument is a covering, it is by no means simple, and some of its functions include:

   A) the dermis providing the major mechanical barrier to chemicals, water, and other external substances.

   B) resident macrophage–like cells whose function is to ingest antigenic invaders and present them to the immune system.

   C) cooling the body by increasing the action of sebaceous glands during high–temperature conditions.

   D) epidermal blood vessels serving as a blood reservoir.

   Answer: B
   Diff: 3   *Page Ref: 139–140*

13) The function of the root hair plexus is to:

   A) serve as a source for new epidermal cells for hair growth after the resting stage has passed.

   B) bind the hair root to the dermis.

   C) cause apocrine gland secretion into the hair follicle.

   D) allow the hair to assist in touch sensation.

   Answer: D
   Diff: 2   *Page Ref: 136*

14) The _____ gland is a modified sudoriferous gland that secretes wax.

   A) eccrine   B) apocrine   C) ceruminous   D) mammary

   Answer: C
   Diff: 1   *Page Ref: 134*

15) Nutrients reach the surface of the skin (epidermis) through the process of:

   A) absorbing materials applied to the surface layer of the skin.

   B) utilizing the products of merocrine glands to nourish the epidermis.

   C) filtration.

   D) diffusing through the tissue fluid from blood vessels in the dermis.

   Answer: D
   Diff: 1   *Page Ref: 128*

16) The reason the hypodermis acts as a shock absorber is that:

   A) it is located just below the epidermis and protects the dermis from shock.

   B) it has no delicate nerve endings and can therefore absorb more shock.

   C) the major part of its makeup is adipose, which serves as an effective shock absorber.

   D) the cells that make up the hypodermis secrete a protective mucus.

   Answer: C
   Diff: 1   Page Ref: 128

17) The epidermis is responsible for protecting the body against invasion of bacteria and other foreign agents primarily because it is composed of:

   A) stratified columnar epithelium.

   B) three layers of keratinized cells only.

   C) four different cell shapes found in five distinct layers, each cell shape with a special function.

   D) a tough layer of connective tissue.

   Answer: C
   Diff: 2   Page Ref: 128–129

18) Keratinocytes are the most important of the epidermal cells because:

   A) they produce a fibrous protein that gives the skin its protective properties.

   B) they are able to transform from living cells to plasma membranes and still function.

   C) they are able to reproduce rapidly.

   D) they are a powerful defense against damaging UV rays.

   Answer: A
   Diff: 1   Page Ref: 128

19) Melanocytes and keratinocytes work together in protecting the skin from UV damage because the role of the keratinocytes is to:

   A) provide the melanocyte with a protective shield against abrasion.

   B) accumulate the melanin granules on their superficial portion, forming a pigment that protects DNA from UV radiation.

   C) maintain the appropriate pH in order for the melanocyte to synthesize melanin granules.

   D) maintain the appropriate temperature so the product of the melanocyte will not denature.

   Answer: B
   Diff: 1   Page Ref: 128

20) The epidermis consists of five layers of cells, each layer with a distinct role to play in the health, well–being, and functioning of the skin. Which of the following layers is responsible for cell division and replacement?

   A) stratum corneum   B) stratum granulosum

   C) stratum germinativum   D) stratum lucidum

   Answer: C
   Diff: 2   Page Ref: 129–130

21) The integumentary system is protected by our immune system through the action of cells that arise from bone marrow and migrate to the epidermis. Which of the following cells serve this immune function?

   A) cells found in the stratum spinosum

   B) macrophages called Langerhans' cells

   C) keratinocytes, because they are so versatile

   D) Merkel cells

   Answer: B
   Diff: 2   Page Ref: 128

22) Water loss through the epidermis could cause a serious threat to health and well–being. Which of the following protects us against excessive water loss through the skin?

   A) Lamellated granules of the cells of the stratum granulosum, a glycolipid that is secreted into extracellular spaces.

   B) The size and shape of the cells that make up the stratum spinosum, as well as the thick bundles of intermediate filaments.

   C) The dermis is the thickest portion of the skin and water cannot pass through it.

   D) Fat associated with skin prevents water loss.

   Answer: A
   Diff: 2   Page Ref: 130

23) The dermis is a strong, flexible connective tissue layer. Which of the following cell types are likely to be found in the dermis?

   A) goblet cells, parietal cells, and Kupffer cells

   B) monocytes, reticulocytes, and osteocytes

   C) fibroblasts, macrophages, and mast cells

   D) osteoblasts, osteoclasts, and epithelial cells

   Answer: C
   Diff: 1   Page Ref: 131

24) The dermis has two major layers; which of the following constitutes 80% of the dermis and is responsible for the tension lines in the skin?

   A) the reticular layer   B) the subcutaneous layer

   C) the hypodermal layer   D) the papillary layer

   Answer: A
   Diff: 2   Page Ref: 132

25) Despite its apparent durability, the dermis is subject to tearing. How might a person know that the dermis has been stretched and/or torn?

   A) Because the pain is acute due to the large number of Meissner's corpuscles.

   B) The appearance of visible, silvery-white scars is an indication of stretching of the dermis.

   C) The blood vessels in the dermis rupture and the blood passes through the tissue, causing "black and blue marks."

   D) The stretching causes the tension lines to disappear.

   Answer: B
   Diff: 2   *Page Ref: 132*

26) The papillary layer of the dermis is connective tissue heavily invested with blood vessels. The superior surface has structures called:

   A) dermal papillae.   B) hair follicles.
   C) ceruminous glands.   D) reticular papillae.

   Answer: A
   Diff: 1   *Page Ref: 132*

27) The design of a person's epidermal ridges is determined by the manner in which the papillae rest upon the dermal ridges to produce the specific pattern known as handprints, footprints, and fingerprints. Which of the following statements is true regarding these prints or ridges?

   A) Every human being has the same pattern of ridges.

   B) They are genetically determined, therefore unique to each person.

   C) Because we are constantly shedding epithelial cells, these ridges are changing daily.

   D) Identical twins do not have the same pattern of ridges.

   Answer: B
   Diff: 1   *Page Ref: 132*

28) Which of the following statements indicates the way in which the body's natural defenses protect the skin from the effects of UV damage?

   A) The skin is protected by the synthesis of three pigments that contribute to the skin's color.

   B) Carotene, which accumulates in the stratum corneum and hypodermal adipose tissue, is synthesized in large amounts in the presence of sunlight.

   C) The skin is protected by increasing the number of Langerhans' cells, which help to activate the immune system.

   D) Prolonged exposure to the sun induces melanin dispersion, which in turn acts as a natural sunscreen.

   Answer: D
   Diff: 2   *Page Ref: 132*

29) Changes in the color of skin are often an indication of a homeostatic imbalance. Which of the following changes would suggest that a patient is suffering from Addison's disease?

   A) The skin takes on a bronze or metallic appearance.

   B) Black–and–blue marks become evident for no apparent cause.

   C) The skin appears to have an abnormal, yellowish tint.

   D) It is impossible to suggest Addison's disease from an inspection of a person's skin.

   Answer: A
   Diff: 2   *Page Ref: 133*

30) A Langerhans' cell is a:

   A) specialized squamous epithelial cell.   B) specialized leukocyte.

   C) specialized nerve cell.   D) specialized melanocyte.

   Answer: B
   Diff: 1   *Page Ref: 128*

31) The most important factor influencing hair growth is:

   A) sex and hormones.   B) age and glandular products.

   C) the size and number of hair follicles.   D) nutrition and hormones.

   Answer: D
   Diff: 1   *Page Ref: 136*

32) Which of the following statements best describes what fingernails actually are?

   A) Fingernails are a modification of the epidermis.

   B) Fingernails are derived from osseous tissue.

   C) Fingernails are extensions of the carpal bones.

   D) Fingernails are a separate tissue from the skin, formed from a different embryonic layer.

   Answer: A
   Diff: 1   *Page Ref: 138*

33) Sudoriferous (sweat) glands are categorized as two distinct types. Which of the following are the two types of sweat glands?

   A) sebaceous and merocrine   B) mammary and ceruminous

   C) eccrine and apocrine   D) holocrine and mammary

   Answer: C
   Diff: 1   *Page Ref: 134*

34) The composition of the secretions of the eccrine glands is:

   A) primarily uric acid.

   B) 99% water, sodium chloride, and trace amounts of wastes, lactic acid, and vitamin C.

   C) fatty substances, proteins, antibodies, and trace amounts of minerals and vitamins.

   D) The major portion of the materials secreted by the eccrine glands is metabolic wastes.

   Answer: B
   Diff: 1   *Page Ref: 133*

35) Apocrine glands, which begin to function at puberty under hormonal influence, seem not to be useful in thermoregulation. Where would we find these glands in the human body?

   A) in all body regions and buried deep in the dermis

   B) beneath the flexure lines in the body

   C) in the axillary and anogenital area

   D) in the palms of the hands and soles of the feet

Answer: C
Diff: 1   Page Ref: 134

36) The sebaceous glands are simple alveolar glands that secrete a substance known as sebum. The secretion of sebum is stimulated:

   A) by high temperatures.

   B) when the air temperature drops.

   C) by hormones, especially androgens.

   D) as a protective coating when one is swimming.

Answer: C
Diff: 1   Page Ref: 134

37) In addition to protection (physical and chemical barrier), the skin serves other functions. Which of the following is another vital function of the skin?

   A) It converts modified epidermal cholesterol to a vitamin D precursor necessary in calcium metabolism.

   B) It aids in the transport of materials throughout the body.

   C) The cells of the epidermis store glucose as glycogen for energy.

   D) It absorbs vitamin C so that the skin will not be subject to diseases.

Answer: A
Diff: 1   Page Ref: 140

38) Burns are devastating and debilitating because of loss of fluids and electrolytes from the body. How would a physician estimate the volume of fluid lost in a severely burned patient?

   A) by measuring urinary output and fluid intake

   B) by observing the tissues that are usually moist

   C) through blood analysis

   D) by using the "rule of nines"

Answer: D
Diff: 1   Page Ref: 142

39) What is the first threat to life from a massive third–degree burn?

   A) infection   B) dehydration

   C) unbearable pain   D) loss of immune function

Answer: B
Diff: 2   Page Ref: 141

40) Male pattern baldness has a genetic switch that turns on in response to:

   A) age.   B) size.   C) weight.   D) male hormones.

   Answer: D
   Diff: 1   Page Ref: 138

41) Eyebrow hairs are always shorter than hairs on your head because:

   A) they grow much slower.

   B) eyebrow follicles are only active for a few months of the year.

   C) the vascular supply of the eyebrow follicle is one-tenth that of the head hair follicle.

   D) hormones in the eyebrow follicle switch the growth off after it has reached a predetermined length.

   Answer: B
   Diff: 2   Page Ref: 136

Clinical Questions

1) We are told that every surface we touch is teeming with bacterial cells, and bacteria are found in the pools we swim in, the water we wash with, and on the hands of friends. Why are we not inundated with bacterial infections on our skin?

   Answer: The low pH of the skin secretions otherwise known as the acid mantle retards the multiplication of bacteria on the skin. Also, in areas where sufficient sebum is produced regularly, many species of bacteria cannot exist.
   Diff: 4   Page Ref: 134

2) The temperature yesterday was an uncomfortable 98° F. You unwisely chose to play tennis at noon, counting on your body's internal defenses to protect you against heat exhaustion. How did your body respond to this distress?

   Answer: The thermoreceptors in the skin relayed a message to the brain; the hypothalamus responded by sending impulses to sweat glands, which released their watery products, which in turn evaporated and cooled the body. Blood vessels in the dermis also responded to neural stimulation by dilating and releasing heat to the exterior.
   Diff: 3   Page Ref: 139

3) Mary noticed a large, brown spot on her skin. She has been playing tennis in the sun for several years without sun protection. She reported the discovery to a friend, who told her to apply the ABCD rule to determine whether or not she had malignant melanoma. Her friend told her that if her answer was "no" to the questions that were asked by the ABCD rule, she had nothing to worry about. What is the ABCD rule and should she ignore the spot if her answers are negative?

   Answer: The ABCD rule refers to the following: asymmetry—where the two sides of the spot do not match; border irregularity—the borders are not round and smooth; color—the pigmented spot contains shades of black, brown, tan, and sometimes blues and reds; and diameter—the spot is larger than 6 mm in diameter. It is imperative that Mary have a physician examine the spot immediately. Any unusual lesion on the skin of a sun worshipper should be examined.
   Diff: 3   Page Ref: 141

4) The Waldorf family was caught in a fire but escaped. Unfortunately, the father and daughter suffered burns. The father had second–degree burns on his chest, abdomen, and both arms, and third–degree burns on his entire left lower extremity. The daughter suffered first–degree burns on her head and neck and second–degree burns on both lower extremities.

a. What percentage of the father's body was covered by burns?
b. What percentage of the daughter's body received first–degree burns?
c. What part of the daughter's body has both the dermis and epidermis involved?
d. The father experiences a good deal of pain in the area of the chest and abdomen, but little pain in the leg. Why?

Answer: a. 48%, b. 9%, c. 36%, d. Normally, third–degree burns sear nerve endings off. When the tissue regenerates, pain will return. Second–degree burns are usually very painful because of the irritation to the nerve endings.
Diff: 4   *Page Ref: 141–142*

5) John, a younger teenager, notices that he is experiencing a lot of pimples and blackheads, which frequently become infected. What is causing this problem?

Answer: Because of hormonal changes, teenagers frequently have overactive sebaceous (oil) glands, which can clog. Scratching, squeezing, or irritating the tissue can lead to infection.
Diff: 1   *Page Ref: 135*

CHAPTER 6   Bones and Skeletal Tissue

Fill-in-the-Blank/Short Answer Questions

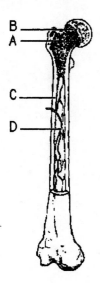

Figure 6.1

Using Figure 6.1, identify the following:

1) Compact bone.

Answer: C
Diff: 1   Page Ref: 149

2) Location of the epiphyseal plate.

Answer: B
Diff: 1   Page Ref: 149

3) Area where yellow marrow is found.

Answer: D
Diff: 1   Page Ref: 149

4) Area where red marrow is found.

Answer: A
Diff: 2   Page Ref: 149

Fill in the blank or provide a short answer:

5) A fracture in which a bone is broken into many pieces would be classified as a _____ fracture.

Answer: comminuted
Diff: 1   Page Ref: 160

6) Blood cell formation is called _____.

Answer: hematopoiesis
Diff: 1   Page Ref: 148

7) A bone embedded in a tendon is called a _____ bone.

Answer: sesamoid
Diff: 1   Page Ref: 148

8) A Haversian canal may contain arteries, veins, capillaries, lymph vessels, and _____ fibers.

Answer: nerve
Diff: 1   Page Ref: 150

9) A narrow slitlike opening generally between two bones is called a _____ .

Answer: fissure
Diff: 1   Page Ref: 152

10) A long bone forms by a process known as _____ ossification.

Answer: endochondral
Diff: 1   Page Ref: 154

11) _____ growth is growth in the diameter of long bones.

Answer: Appositional
Diff: 1   Page Ref: 145

12) _____ are multinucleated cells that destroy bone.

Answer: Osteoclasts
Diff: 1   Page Ref: 157

13) _____ is a disease of the bone in which bone reabsorption outpaces bone deposit, leaving the person with thin and often very fragile bones.

Answer: Osteoporosis
Diff: 1   Page Ref: 162

14) A round or oval hole through a bone that contains blood vessels and/or nerves is called a _____ .

Answer: foramen
Diff: 1   Page Ref: 152

15) List the steps in the repair process of a simple fracture.

Answer: Hematoma formation, fibrocartilaginous callus formation, bony callus formation, and remodeling.
Diff: 1   Page Ref: 161

16) What is found in a Haversian canal?

Answer: Blood vessels, lymphatic vessels, and nerves.
Diff: 1   Page Ref: 150

17) Several hormones control the remodeling of bones. Which two respond to changing blood calcium levels?

Answer: To keep bones in proper dimensions, PTH and calcitonin are the major determinants of whether and when remodeling will occur in response to changing blood calcium.
Diff: 2   Page Ref: 157

18) Bones appear to be lifeless structures. Does bone material renew itself?

Answer: Approximately 5-7% of our bone mass is recycled each week. Up to 0.5 g of calcium may enter or leave the bones each day, depending on the negative feedback hormonal mechanism and gravitational forces.
Diff: 3   Page Ref: 156

19) Compare the function of the organic materials in the bone matrix with the function of the inorganic materials in the matrix.

Answer: The organic matrix contributes to the bone structure and its tensile strength, while the inorganic matrix contributes to hardness and resistance to compression.
Diff: 3   Page Ref: 152

20) Growth hormones act indirectly to make the epiphyseal plate cartilage grow. What then acts directly to make it grow?

Answer: The growth hormone stimulates the liver to release a growth factor called somatomedin, which in turn controls the epiphyseal plate cartilage.
Diff: 3   Page Ref: 156

21) How can a tooth be moved in a bony socket?

Answer: Since bone deposition and reabsorption can occur, and since bone responds to mechanical stress (Wolff's law), a tooth can be moved. By applying slight pressure to a tooth, the bone on the forward side will reabsorb, while the bone on the reverse side will be reformed. The mediating force is from the periodontal ligaments that support the tooth.
Diff: 4   Page Ref: 158-159

22) Archeologists are always excited to find skeletons in "lost civilizations" because the bones can tell them so much about daily life. Give a couple of examples of how bones might help the archeologist find out about a past way of life.

Answer: Because stress models bones, any thickened or misshapen bones might tell if the individual was working with his or her hands or feet. Possibly flattening of the skull from carrying heavy objects on the head. Odd-shaped toes from using them to hold things like nets. Recent discoveries in South America revealed an odd way of sitting on crossed legs from the deformities in the toes. A number of skeletons with epiphyseal plates would indicate that young people were either being sacrificed or were working in hazardous conditions such as mercury mines.

Diff: 5   Page Ref: 152

Matching Questions

Match the following:

1) Column 1: Bones are porous and thin but bone composition is normal.

Column 2: Osteoporosis

Answer: Osteoporosis
Diff: 2   Page Ref: 162

2) Column 1: Bone formed is poorly mineralized and soft. Deforms on weight-bearing.

Column 2: Osteomalacia

Answer: Osteomalacia
Diff: 2   Page Ref: 161

3) Column 1: Abnormal bone formation and reabsorption.

Column 2: Paget's disease

Answer: Paget's disease
Diff: 1   Page Ref: 162

Match the following:

4) Column 1: An incomplete fracture or cracking of the bone without actual separation of the parts. Common in children.

Column 2: Greenstick
        Foil: Compound

Answer: Greenstick
Diff: 1   Page Ref: 160

5) Column 1: Bone fragments into many
pieces.

Column 2: Comminuted

Answer: Comminuted
Diff: 1   *Page Ref: 160*

Match the following:

6) Column 1: The lining of the marrow
cavity.

Column 2: Endosteum

Answer: Endosteum
Diff: 1   *Page Ref: 149*

7) Column 1: Cells that can dissolve the
bony matrix.

Column 2: Osteoclasts

Answer: Osteoclasts
Diff: 1   *Page Ref: 149*

8) Column 1: Layers of calcification that are
found in bone.

Column 2: Lamellae

Answer: Lamellae
Diff: 1   *Page Ref: 150*

9) Column 1: Small channels that radiate
through the matrix of bone.

Column 2: Canaliculi

Answer: Canaliculi
Diff: 1   *Page Ref: 150*

10) Column 1: Cells that can build bony
matrix.

Column 2: Osteoblasts

Answer: Osteoblasts
Diff: 1   *Page Ref: 149*

Match the following:

11) Column 1: The cells responsible for
endochondral ossification.

Column 2: Chondrocytes

Answer: Chondrocytes
Diff: 2   *Page Ref: 145*

12) Column 1: The growth pattern of bone in which matrix is laid down on the surface.

   Column 2: Appositional growth

   Answer: Appositional growth
   Diff: 2   Page Ref: 145

13) Column 1: The area of long bones where cartilage cells are replaced by bone cells.

   Column 2: Diaphyseal

   Answer: Diaphyseal
   Diff: 2   Page Ref: 156

14) Column 1: Area where bone growth takes place.

   Column 2: Epiphyseal plate

   Answer: Epiphyseal plate
   Diff: 2   Page Ref: 155–156

True/False Questions

1) Hematopoiesis refers to the formation of blood cells within the red marrow cavities of certain bones.

   Answer: TRUE
   Diff: 1   Page Ref: 149–150

2) Bones are classified by whether they are weight-bearing or protective in function.

   Answer: FALSE
   Diff: 1   Page Ref: 146–148

3) The periosteum is a tissue that serves only to protect the bone because it is not supplied with nerves or blood vessels.

   Answer: TRUE
   Diff: 1   Page Ref: 148

4) Short, irregular, and flat bones have large marrow cavities in order to keep the weight of the bones light.

   Answer: FALSE
   Diff: 1   Page Ref: 147–148

5) In newborn infants, the medullary cavity and all areas of spongy bone contain yellow bone marrow.

   Answer: FALSE
   Diff: 1   Page Ref: 149

6) The structural unit of compact bone (osteon) resembles the growth rings of a tree trunk.

Answer: TRUE
Diff: 1   Page Ref: 150

7) The term *osteoid* refers to the organic part of the matrix of compact bones.

Answer: TRUE
Diff: 1   Page Ref: 152

8) Sixty–five percent of the mass of bone is an organic compound called *hydroxyapatite*.

Answer: TRUE
Diff: 1   Page Ref: 152

9) All bones formed by intramembranous ossification are irregular bones.

Answer: FALSE
Diff: 1   Page Ref: 153

10) An osteon contains osteocytes, lamellae, and a central canal, and is found in compact bone only.

Answer: TRUE
Diff: 1   Page Ref: 150

11) The trabeculae of spongy bone are oriented toward lines of stress.

Answer: TRUE
Diff: 2   Page Ref: 151

12) Each bone lamella has collagen fibers that wrap in opposite directions.

Answer: TRUE
Diff: 2   Page Ref: 150

Multiple-Choice Questions

1) The structure of bones suits the function. Which of the following bones is adapted to withstand stress?

A) spongy bone   B) irregular bone   C) compact bone   D) trabecular bone

Answer: A
Diff: 1   Page Ref: 151

2) Yellow bone marrow contains a large percentage of:

A) fat.   B) blood-forming cells.

C) elastic tissue.   D) Sharpey's fibers.

Answer: A
Diff: 1   Page Ref: 150

3) The cell responsible for secreting the matrix of bone is the:

A) osteocyte.   B) osteoblast.   C) osteoclast.   D) chondrocyte.

Answer: B
Diff: 1   Page Ref: 149

4) What kind of tissue is the forerunner of long bones in the embryo?

A) elastic connective tissue   B) dense fibrous connective tissue

C) fibrocartilage   D) hyaline cartilage

Answer: D
Diff: 1   Page Ref: 154

5) In bone formation, a deficiency of growth hormone will cause:

A) inadequate calcification of bone.

B) decreased osteoclast activity.

C) decreased proliferation of the epiphyseal plate cartilage.

D) increased osteoclast activity.

Answer: C
Diff: 1   Page Ref: 156

6) A fracture in the shaft of a bone would be a break in the:

A) epiphysis.   B) metaphysis.

C) diaphysis.   D) articular cartilage.

Answer: C
Diff: 1   Page Ref: 148

7) The term *diploe* refers to:

A) the double-layered nature of the connective tissue covering the bone.

B) the fact that most bones are formed of two types of bone tissue.

C) the internal layer of spongy bone in flat bones.

D) the two types of marrow found within most bones.

Answer: C
Diff: 1   Page Ref: 150

8) Select the correct statement concerning the location of blood–forming tissue.

A) There is blood-forming marrow in most long bones of an adult.

B) The sternum (breastbone) is a good source of blood-forming tissue.

C) There is blood-forming marrow in most short bones of an adult.

D) Blood–forming tissue is found in the skull and pelvic bones only.

Answer: C
Diff: 1   Page Ref: 150

9) Factors in preventing (or delaying) osteoporosis include:

A) drinking fluoridated water.

B) decreasing weight–bearing exercise.

C) increasing dietary vitamin C.

D) decreasing exposure to the sun.

Answer: A
Diff: 1   Page Ref: 162

10) Ossification of the ends of long bones:

A) is a characteristic of intramembranous bone formation.

B) involves medullary cavity formation.

C) is characterized by secondary ossification.

D) takes twice as long as diaphysis.

Answer: C
Diff: 1   Page Ref: 155

11) Cartilage is found in strategic places in the human skeleton. What is responsible for the resilience of cartilage?

A) water   B) hydroxyapatite   C) calcium influx   D) phosphate

Answer: A
Diff: 1   Page Ref: 145

12) The most abundant skeletal cartilage type is:

A) hyaline.   B) elastic.   C) fibrocartilage.   D) epiphyseal.

Answer: A
Diff: 1   Page Ref: 145

13) Which of the following is (are) not the function(s) of the skeletal system?

A) support

B) storage of minerals

C) production of blood cells (hematopoiesis)

D) strength

Answer: D
Diff: 1   Page Ref: 148

14) The functional unit of compact bone is:

A) osseous matrix.   B) spongy bone.   C) lamellar bone.   D) the osteon.

Answer: D
Diff: 1   Page Ref: 150

15) Bones are covered and lined by a protective tissue called periosteum. The inner (osteogenic) layer consists primarily of:

A) cartilage and compact bone.

B) marrow and osteons.

C) osteoblasts and osteoclasts.

D) chondrocytes and osteocytes.

Answer: C
Diff: 1   Page Ref: 149

16) The periosteum is secured to the underlying bone by dense connective tissue called:
   A) Volkmann's canals.   B) a bony matrix with hyaline cartilage.
   C) Sharpey's fibers.   D) the struts of bone known as spicules.

   Answer: C
   Diff: 1   Page Ref: 149

17) The canal that runs through the core of each osteon (the Haversian canal) is the site of:
   A) cartilage and interstitial lamellae.   B) osteoclasts and osteoblasts.
   C) yellow marrow and spicules.   D) blood vessels and nerve fibers.

   Answer: D
   Diff: 1   Page Ref: 150

18) The small spaces in bone tissue that are holes in which osteocytes live are called:
   A) lacunae.   B) Volkmann's canals.
   C) Haversian canals.   D) trabeculae.

   Answer: A
   Diff: 1   Page Ref: 150

19) For intramembranous ossification to take place, which of the following is necessary?
   A) A bone collar forms around the cartilage model.
   B) An ossification center forms in the fibrous connective tissue.
   C) The cartilage matrix begins to deteriorate.
   D) A medullary cavity forms.

   Answer: B
   Diff: 1   Page Ref: 153

20) The process of bones increasing in width is known as:
   A) closing of the epiphyseal plate.
   B) long bones reaching adult length and width.
   C) appositional growth.
   D) concentric growth.

   Answer: C
   Diff: 1   Page Ref: 155

21) Bones are constantly undergoing resorption for various reasons. Which of the following cells accomplishes this process?
   A) osteoclast   B) osteocyte   C) chondrocyte   D) stem cell

   Answer: A
   Diff: 1   Page Ref: 157

22) Which hormone increases osteoclast activity to release more calcium ions into the bloodstream?

A) calcitonin   B) thyroxine

C) parathyroid hormone   D) estrogen

Answer: C
Diff: 1   Page Ref: 157

23) Vertebrae are considered _____ bones.

A) long   B) flat   C) short   D) irregular

Answer: D
Diff: 1   Page Ref: 148

24) A bone fracture perpendicular to the bone's axis is called a(n) _____ fracture.

A) nondisplaced   B) linear   C) transverse   D) incomplete

Answer: C
Diff: 2   Page Ref: 159

25) Wolff's law is concerned with:

A) vertical growth of bones being dependent on age.

B) the thickness and shape of a bone being dependent on stresses placed upon it.

C) the function of bone being dependent on shape.

D) the diameter of the bone being dependent on the ratio of osteoblasts to osteoclasts.

Answer: B
Diff: 2   Page Ref: 158

26) Cranial bones develop:

A) from cartilage models.   B) within fibrous membranes.

C) from a tendon.   D) within osseous membranes.

Answer: B
Diff: 2   Page Ref: 153

27) Which of the following glands or organs produces hormones that tend to decrease blood calcium levels?

A) pineal gland   B) thyroid   C) parathyroid   D) spleen

Answer: B
Diff: 2   Page Ref: 157

28) Cartilage grows in two ways, appositional and interstitial. Appositional growth is:

   A) growth at the epiphyseal plate.

   B) the secretion of new matrix against existing cartilage.

   C) along the edges only.

   D) the lengthening of hyaline cartilage.

   Answer: B
   Diff: 2   *Page Ref: 145*

29) Which of the following statements best describes interstitial growth?

   A) Growth occurs in the lining of the long bones.

   B) Fibroblasts give rise to chondrocytes that differentiate and form cartilage.

   C) Unspecialized cells from mesenchyme develop into chondrocytes, which divide and form cartilage.

   D) Chondrocytes in the lacunae divide and secrete matrix, allowing the cartilage to grow from within.

   Answer: D
   Diff: 2   *Page Ref: 145*

30) In the epiphyseal plate, cartilage grows:

   A) from the diaphysis to the epiphysis.   B) from the epiphysis to the diaphysis.

   C) from the edges inward.   D) in a circular fashion.

   Answer: B
   Diff: 2   *Page Ref: 155*

31) Spongy bones are made up of a framework called:

   A) osteons.   B) lamellar bone.

   C) trabeculae.   D) osseous lamellae.

   Answer: C
   Diff: 2   *Page Ref: 151*

32) Osteogenesis is the process of:

   A) bone healing.   B) bone remodeling.

   C) bone formation.   D) Both B and C are correct.

   Answer: D
   Diff: 2   *Page Ref: 153*

33) Bone growth (lengthwise) during infancy and youth is exclusively through:

   A) interstitial growth of the epiphyseal plates.

   B) the secretion of bone matrix into the medullary cavity.

   C) differentiation of osteoclasts.

   D) calcification of the matrix.

   Answer: A
   Diff: 2   *Page Ref: 155-156*

34) Growth of bones is controlled by a symphony of hormones. Which hormone is important for bone growth during infancy and childhood?

    A) thyroid hormone   B) somatomedins

    C) growth hormone   D) prolactin

Answer: C
Diff: 2   *Page Ref: 156*

35) In some cases the epiphyseal plate of the long bones of youngsters closes too early. What might be the cause?

    A) overproduction of thyroid hormone

    B) elevated levels of sex hormones

    C) too much vitamin D in the diet

    D) osteoblast activity exceeds osteoclast activity

Answer: B
Diff: 2   *Page Ref: 156*

36) It is thought that remodeling or bone growth is in response to the forces placed on it. Which of the following hypotheses may explain how mechanical forces communicate with cells responsible for bone remodeling?

    A) Increase in the synthesis of growth hormone directs the remodeling process.

    B) Vitamin D enhances the remodeling process.

    C) Bone deposition by osteoclasts is responsible for remodeling.

    D) Electrical signals direct the remodeling process.

Answer: D
Diff: 2   *Page Ref: 159*

Clinical Questions

1) Alice and James recently adopted a 3-year-old child. They noticed that her legs were bowed and there were some deformities in her cranial and pelvic bones. They brought her to a physician for a diagnosis. What was the diagnosis, and what was the treatment for the disorder?

    Answer: The child most likely has rickets, a condition caused by poor diet, especially one deficient in vitamin D. The parents were told to increase her intake of calcium and vitamin D and to see to it that she gets some sunshine every day.

    Diff: 3   *Page Ref: 161*

2) Joseph, a severe asthmatic, has been complaining of pain in both his arms. He has been increasing his "load" for his weight–lifting workouts, and thought perhaps this was the reason. However, he decided to have his arms X–rayed, and it was discovered that he had "hairline fractures" in the radius and ulna of both arms. His physician told him that the medication he was taking for asthma was a steroid and this was the reason his bones were so vulnerable to damage. What was the drug and why did it affect his bones?

Answer: Joseph has been taking corticosteroid drugs to relieve his asthma. This has probably caused an early onset of osteoporosis and the weight lifting imposed stress on his porous bones, causing the fractures.

Diff: 4   *Page Ref: 162*

3) A 75–year–old woman and her 9–year–old granddaughter were victims of a train crash. In both cases, trauma to the chest was sustained. X rays of the grandmother revealed several fractured ribs, but her granddaughter had none. Explain these different findings.

Answer: The youngster had more organic material in her bones, which allows them to bend, while her grandmother's bones are extensively calcified, with little organic material, and are probably thin due to osteoporosis.

Diff: 4   *Page Ref: 162*

4) Johnny fractured the lower third of his right tibia in a skiing accident. The soft tissues in the area were severely damaged and their surgical removal was necessary. After prolonged immobilization, it was found that Johnny was healing very poorly. The explanation offered by the orthopedic surgeon was that vascularization of the fracture site was still inadequate and good healing was absolutely dependent upon an adequate blood supply. Describe how a long bone receives its blood supply and trace the path of nutrient delivery to the osteocytes.

Answer: Long bones are nourished by nutrient arteries that frequently enter the shaft. Removal of the soft tissues probably reduced the flow of blood to the affected area. The pathway would include diffusion of nutrients from blood vessels to periosteum to Volkmann's canals to Haversian canals to canaliculi to lacunae.

Diff: 5   *Page Ref: 150*

CHAPTER 7   The Skeleton

Fill–in–the–Blank/Short Answer Questions

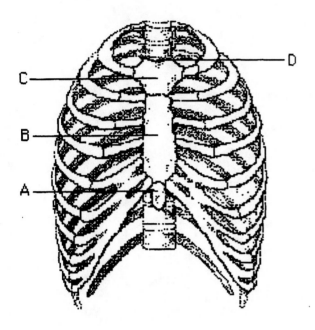

Figure 7.1

Using Figure 7.1, identify the following:

1) Xiphoid process.

> Answer: A
> *Diff: 1   Page Ref: 188*

2) Body.

> Answer: B
> *Diff: 1   Page Ref: 188*

3) Jugular notch.

> Answer: D
> *Diff: 1   Page Ref: 188*

4) Manubrium.

> Answer: C
> *Diff: 1   Page Ref: 188*

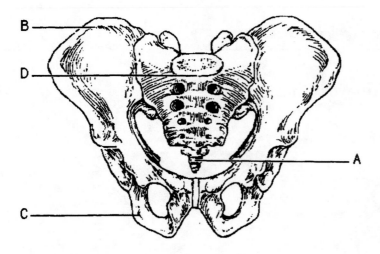

Figure 7.2

Using Figure 7.2, identify the following:

5) Iliac crest.

Answer: B
Diff: 1   Page Ref: 200

6) Sacral promontory.

Answer: D
Diff: 1   Page Ref: 200

7) Coccyx.

Answer: A
Diff: 1   Page Ref: 200

8) Ischium.

Answer: C
Diff: 2   Page Ref: 200

Fill in the blank or provide a short answer:

9) The heel bone is called the _____.

Answer: calcaneus
Diff: 1   Page Ref: 205

10) The lateral condyle of the femur articulates with the lateral condyle of the _____.

Answer: tibia
Diff: 1   Page Ref: 204–205

11) The medial condyle of the femur articulates with the medial condyle of the _____.

Answer: tibia
Diff: 1   Page Ref: 204–205

12) The largest foramen in the body is the _____ foramen.

Answer: obturator
Diff: 1   Page Ref: 201

13) The smallest short bone in the hand is the _____.

Answer: pisiform
Diff: 1   Page Ref: 198

14) The styloid process of the _____ points to the thumb.

Answer: radius
Diff: 1   Page Ref: 196

15) The large fossa on the anterior aspect of the scapula is the _____.

Answer: subscapular fossa
Diff: 1   Page Ref: 194

16) Only the _____ vertebrae have transverse foramina.

Answer: cervical
Diff: 1   Page Ref: 185

17) The _____ is the primary bone in the septum of the nose.

Answer: vomer
Diff: 1   Page Ref: 175

18) Why is the area just distal to the tubercles of the humerus called the surgical neck?

Answer: This area is called the surgical neck because it is the most frequently fractured part of the humerus.
Diff: 2   Page Ref: 195

19) Describe the composition of the intervertebral discs.

Answer: Intervertebral discs are composed of an inner semifluid nucleus pulposus, which gives the discs elasticity and compressibility, and a covering of fibrocartilage, the annulus fibrosus, which limits expansion and holds successive vertebrae together.
Diff: 3   Page Ref: 182

20) Describe the differences between the bones of the lower and upper limb and briefly state why these differences exist.

Answer: The lower limbs carry the weight of the body and are subjected to exceptional forces. These bones are thicker and stronger. The upper limb bones are adapted for flexibility and mobility and are therefore smaller and lighter.
Diff: 3   Page Ref: 195, 203

21) How are the pectoral and pelvic girdles structurally different? How is this difference reflected in their functions?

Answer: The pectoral girdle moves freely across the thorax and allows the upper limb a high degree of mobility, while the pelvic girdle is secured to the axial skeleton to provide strength and support.

Diff: 3   *Page Ref: 190–191, 199–201*

22) How do the first two cervical vertebrae differ from other cervical vertebrae? What are their functions?

Answer: The atlas or C_1 vertebra has no body. It articulates with the skull with large curved articular surfaces to allow the skull to rock in a "yes" motion. The axis or C_2 vertebra has a dens that allows the axis to pivot, giving the head the "no" motion. The vertebral foramen of the atlas is enlarged so that when the head is pivoted in the "no" motion, the spinal cord can move.

Diff: 3   *Page Ref: 185*

23) Describe how the arches of the foot are maintained.

Answer: There are three arches: the medial and lateral longitudinal arches, and the transverse arch. Together they form a half–cone that distributes the weight of the body. They are maintained by the shape of the foot bones, strong ligaments, and by the pull of some tendons.

Diff: 4   *Page Ref: 207*

Matching Questions

Match the following:

1) Column 1: These very small bones are at the medial border of each eye.

   Column 2: Lacrimal bones

   Answer: Lacrimal bones
   Diff: 1   *Page Ref: 175*

2) Column 1: Failure of these anterior bones to fuse causes a condition known as cleft palate.

   Column 2: Maxilla

   Answer: Maxilla
   Diff: 1   *Page Ref: 175*

3) Column 1: This bone houses the apparatus of the inner and middle ear.

   Column 2: Temporal bones

   Answer: Temporal bones
   Diff: 1   *Page Ref: 169*

4) Column 1: This bone is wing-shaped and
extends behind the eyes and
forms part of the floor of the
cranial vault.

Column 2: Sphenoid

Answer: Sphenoid
Diff: 2   *Page Ref: 171–172*

Match the following:

5) Column 1: The fingers have three of these
bones and the thumb has only
two.

Column 2: Phalanges

Answer: Phalanges
Diff: 1   *Page Ref: 199*

6) Column 1: This bone articulates with the
glenoid fossa.

Column 2: Humerus

Answer: Humerus
Diff: 1   *Page Ref: 195*

7) Column 1: Forearm bone that articulates
with most of the carpals.

Column 2: Radius

Foil: Ulna

Answer: Radius
Diff: 1   *Page Ref: 196*

Match the following:

8) Column 1: Thickest centrum with short
blunt spinous processes.

Column 2: Lumbar vertebrae

Answer: Lumbar vertebrae
Diff: 1   *Page Ref: 187*

9) Column 1: Fused rudimentary tailbone.

Column 2: Coccyx

Answer: Coccyx
Diff: 1   *Page Ref: 188*

10) Column 1: A circle of bone that articulates superiorly with the occipital condyles.

Column 2: Atlas

Answer: Atlas
Diff: 1   Page Ref: 185

11) Column 1: These bones have articular facets for the ribs.

Column 2: Thoracic vertebrae

Answer: Thoracic vertebrae
Diff: 1   Page Ref: 186

12) Column 1: Allows the head to nod "yes."

Column 2: Atlas

Answer: Atlas
Diff: 1   Page Ref: 185

Match the following:

13) Column 1: Lambdoid.

Column 2: Occipital and parietal

Answer: Occipital and parietal
Diff: 1   Page Ref: 167

14) Column 1: Sagittal.

Column 2: Right and left parietal

Answer: Right and left parietal
Diff: 1   Page Ref: 167

15) Column 1: Squamosal.

Column 2: Temporal and parietal

Answer: Temporal and parietal
Diff: 1   Page Ref: 167

16) Column 1: Coronal.

Column 2: Parietal and frontal

Answer: Parietal and frontal
Diff: 1   Page Ref: 167

True/False Questions

1) The cranial cavity is a fluid-filled chamber that cushions and supports the brain.

Answer: TRUE
Diff: 1   Page Ref: 165

2) Colle's fracture is a break in the distal end of the radius.

Answer: TRUE
Diff: 1   Page Ref: 198

3) All of the bones of the skull, except the mandible, are united by sutures and are therefore immovable.

Answer: TRUE
Diff: 1   Page Ref: 165

4) Your cheek is composed primarily of the zygomatic bone.

Answer: TRUE
Diff: 1   Page Ref: 175

5) The occipital bone forms the superior and lateral portion of the skull.

Answer: FALSE
Diff: 1   Page Ref: 169

6) The foramen magnum is the occipital bone.

Answer: TRUE
Diff: 1   Page Ref: 169

7) The zygomatic bones are the cheekbones of the face.

Answer: TRUE
Diff: 1   Page Ref: 175

8) The mastoid sinuses are located at a position in the skull where they are usually free from infections.

Answer: FALSE
Diff: 1   Page Ref: 169

9) The vertebral column is held in place solely by the posterior longitudinal ligament.

Answer: FALSE
Diff: 1   Page Ref: 183

10) Ribs numbered 11 and 12 are true ribs because they have no anterior attachments.

Answer: FALSE
Diff: 1   Page Ref: 189

11) The most common site of fracture in the humerus is the anatomical neck.

Answer: FALSE
Diff: 1   Page Ref: 195

12) The bones that form the fingers are called the phalanges.

Answer: TRUE
Diff: 1   Page Ref: 199

13) The tarsus contains seven bones.

Answer: TRUE
Diff: 1   Page Ref: 205

14) The layman's name for the scapula is the collarbone.

Answer: FALSE
Diff: 1   Page Ref: 191

15) The most frequently fractured part of the humerus is called the surgical neck.

Answer: TRUE
Diff: 1   Page Ref: 195

16) A temporal bone protrusion riddled with sinuses is the styloid process.

Answer: FALSE
Diff: 1   Page Ref: 169

17) Costal cartilages join ribs to the sternum.

Answer: TRUE
Diff: 1   Page Ref: 188

18) The tubercle of a rib articulates with the transverse process of a vertebra.

Answer: TRUE
Diff: 1   Page Ref: 187

19) The "point of the shoulder" is formed by the coracoid process of the scapula.

Answer: FALSE
Diff: 1   Page Ref: 194

20) In women of childbearing age, the dimensions of the true pelvis are of utmost importance.

Answer: TRUE
Diff: 1   Page Ref: 201

21) The term *vertebrochondral ribs* refers to ribs that attach to each other before they attach to the sternum.

Answer: TRUE
Diff: 1   Page Ref: 189

22) The skull, the body's most complicated bony structure, contains a total of 14 bones.

Answer: FALSE
Diff: 1   Page Ref: 165

23) In anatomical position, the lateral forearm bone is the radius.

Answer: TRUE
Diff: 1   Page Ref: 195

24) The vomer forms part of the nasal septum.

Answer: TRUE
Diff: 1   Page Ref: 175

25) The cranial vault of the skull is also called the calvaria.

Answer: TRUE
Diff: 1   Page Ref: 165

26) The lacrimal bones contain openings that allow the tear ducts to pass.

Answer: TRUE
Diff: 1   Page Ref: 175

27) The largest and strongest bone of the face is the maxilla.

Answer: FALSE
Diff: 1   Page Ref: 173

28) The true name for cheekbones is zygomatic bones.

Answer: TRUE
Diff: 1   Page Ref: 175

29) Each intervertebral disc possesses a nucleus pulposus and an annulus fibrosus.

Answer: TRUE
Diff: 1   Page Ref: 182

30) There are seven cervical, twelve thoracic, and five lumbar vertebrae.

Answer: TRUE
Diff: 1   Page Ref: 181

31) Lordosis affects the thoracic vertebrae.

Answer: FALSE
Diff: 1   Page Ref: 182

32) All vertebrae possess a body, a spine, and transverse foramina.

Answer: FALSE
Diff: 1   Page Ref: 183

33) The dens articulates with the axis.

Answer: FALSE
Diff: 1   Page Ref: 185

34) If you broke a bone in your left index finger, you would have broken a phalanx.

Answer: TRUE
Diff: 1   Page Ref: 199

35) The tibia is also known as the shinbone.

Answer: TRUE
Diff: 1   Page Ref: 205

36) The master gland of the body (pituitary gland) is housed in a saddlelike depression in the temporal bone called the sella turcica.

Answer: FALSE
Diff: 2   Page Ref: 171

37) The hyoid bone is the only bone that does not articulate with another bone.

Answer: TRUE
Diff: 2   Page Ref: 178

38) The vertebral column articulates with the pectoral girdle.

Answer: FALSE
Diff: 2   Page Ref: 181

39) The ischium articulates with both the ilium and the pubis.

Answer: TRUE
Diff: 2   Page Ref: 201

Multiple-Choice Questions

1) A structure found on the femur is the:
   A) anterior crest.   B) malleolus.   C) linea aspera.   D) apex.

   Answer: C
   Diff: 1   Page Ref: 204

2) Which forms the major portion of the coxal bone?
   A) ischium   B) pubis   C) ilium   D) pelvic

   Answer: C
   Diff: 1   Page Ref: 199

3) The inferiormost part of the sternum is the:
   A) xiphoid process.   B) body.   C) manubrium.   D) ala.

   Answer: A
   Diff: 1   Page Ref: 189

4) The axial skeleton contains:
    A) the skull, vertebral column, and pelvis.   B) arms, legs, hands, and feet.
    C) the skull, vertebral column, and rib cage.   D) shoulder and pelvic girdles.

Answer: C
Diff: 1   Page Ref: 165

5) The ethmoid bone is composed of all of the following except the:
    A) superior nasal concha.   B) crista galli.
    C) cribriform plate.   D) inferior nasal concha.

Answer: D
Diff: 1   Page Ref: 172-173

6) Only the _____ vertebra does not have a body.
    A) last lumbar   B) axis   C) atlas   D) last cervical

Answer: C
Diff: 1   Page Ref: 185

7) The suture that connects the two parietal bones together is the:
    A) coronal.   B) sagittal.   C) lambdoid.   D) squamosal.

Answer: B
Diff: 1   Page Ref: 167

8) The pituitary gland is housed in the:
    A) vomer bone.   B) sinuses of the ethmoid.
    C) sella turcica of the sphenoid.   D) foramen lacerum.

Answer: C
Diff: 1   Page Ref: 171

9) The hyoid bone is unique because:
    A) it is the only bone of the body that does not articulate with any other bone.
    B) it is shaped like a plow.
    C) it is covered with mucosa.
    D) it has no specific function.

Answer: A
Diff: 1   Page Ref: 178

10) Along with support, the broad anterior ligament of the vertebral column also acts to:
    A) hold the discs in place.   B) prevent hyperextension of the spine.
    C) hold the spine erect.   D) protect the spinal cord.

Answer: B
Diff: 1   Page Ref: 182

11) The major function of the intervertebral discs is to:

A) absorb shock.   B) string the vertebrae together.

C) prevent injuries.   D) prevent hyperextension.

Answer: A
Diff: 1   Page Ref: 182–183

12) All of the following facial bones are paired except one. Which of the following is the unpaired facial bone?

A) palatine   B) lacrimal   C) vomer   D) maxillae

Answer: C
Diff: 1   Page Ref: 180

13) Paranasal sinuses are found in which of these facial bones?

A) zygomatic   B) nasal conchae   C) vomer   D) maxillae

Answer: D
Diff: 1   Page Ref: 178

14) Which of the following is an abnormal lateral curvature of the vertebral column often seen in the thoracic region?

A) kyphosis   B) scoliosis   C) lordosis   D) swayback

Answer: B
Diff: 1   Page Ref: 181–182

15) Which of the following phrases best describes the function of the vertebral curves?

A) to provide resilience and flexibility

B) to accommodate muscle attachment

C) to absorb shock and trauma

D) to accommodate the weight of the pelvic girdle

Answer: A
Diff: 1   Page Ref: 181

16) The body or centrum of the thoracic vertebrae are:

A) triangular.   B) oval.   C) heart-shaped.   D) round.

Answer: C
Diff: 1   Page Ref: 184

17) Which part of the vertebral column receives the most stress by bearing most of the weight of the body?

A) the sacrum   B) the cervical region

C) the lumbar region   D) the sacral promontory

Answer: C
Diff: 1   Page Ref: 187

18) The major function of the axial skeleton is to:

    A) give the body resilience.

    B) provide an attachment point for muscles that allow movement.

    C) provide central support for the body and protect internal organs.

    D) provide a space for the heart and lungs.

Answer: C
Diff: 1   *Page Ref: 165*

19) The antebrachium is composed of which of the following two bones?

A) the radius and the ulna	B) the humerus and the clavicle
C) the scapula and the clavicle	D) the humerus and the radius

Answer: A
Diff: 1   *Page Ref: 195*

20) The "true wrist" or carpus consists of:

    A) a group of eight short bones united by ligaments.

    B) the phalanges.

    C) the styloid processes of the radius and ulna.

    D) the metacarpals.

Answer: A
Diff: 1   *Page Ref: 198*

21) The short bone that attaches to the third metacarpal is the:

    A) trapezoid.   B) hamate.   C) capitate.   D) triquetral.

Answer: C
Diff: 1   *Page Ref: 198*

22) The bone in direct contact with the first metatarsal (big toe) is the:

A) medial cuneiform.	B) lateral cuneiform.
C) cuboid.	D) calcaneus.

Answer: A
Diff: 1   *Page Ref: 205*

23) The skull bone that the foramen magnum passes through is the:

    A) atlas.   B) axis.   C) occipital.   D) parietal.

Answer: C
Diff: 2   *Page Ref: 169*

24) Choose the statement that is most correct about orbits.

A) The orbits are formed of both facial and cranial bones.

B) The orbits contain only facial bones.

C) The orbits contain only cranial bones.

D) The orbits are made entirely of cartilage.

Answer: A
Diff: 2   *Page Ref: 176*

25) Which of the following is true about paranasal sinuses?

A) Paranasal sinuses lighten the skull.

B) Paranasal sinuses enhance the resonance of the voice.

C) Paranasal sinuses contain passages acting as one–way valves.

D) Paranasal sinuses are found in maxillary, ethmoid, and lacrimal bones.

Answer: B
Diff: 2   *Page Ref: 178*

26) The middle nasal concha is part of which bone?

A) maxilla   B) zygomatic   C) nasal   D) ethmoid

Answer: D
Diff: 2   *Page Ref: 177*

27) The superior orbital fissure is formed in the sphenoid bone, whereas the inferior orbital is formed between the _____ and _____.

A) sphenoid/maxilla   B) sphenoid/zygomatic
C) sphenoid/ethmoid   D) sphenoid/lacrimal

Answer: A
Diff: 2   *Page Ref: 176*

28) Thoracic vertebrae 11 and 12 are different from the others in which of the following characteristics?

A) The orientation of the articular processes is different from all the other thoracic vertebrae.

B) The transverse processes do not have facets that articulate with the tubercles of the ribs.

C) There are two foramina on vertebrae 11 and 12.

D) The spinous processes are directed parallel with the centrum.

Answer: B
Diff: 2   *Page Ref: 187*

29) A bone that contains diaphysis and epiphysis areas, a curvature for strength, and is proportionally more compact than spongy bone is the:

A) parietal bone.   B) talus.

C) humerus.   D) cervical vertebra.

Answer: C
Diff: 3   *Page Ref: 195*

Clinical Questions

1) Paul Jones fell off of the staging while painting his house. His left arm and side struck the ground with a good deal of force. When he managed to pick himself up, he had sharp pains in his left shoulder and was unable to move that arm. During the examination by the physician, it was recorded that the normal roundness of the left shoulder was absent, the humerus was abnormally slanted medially in the shoulder region, and there was a swelling below the lateral end of the clavicle. What is your diagnosis?

   Answer: Dislocated shoulder
   Diff: 3   *Page Ref: 190*

2) After having a severe cold accompanied by nasal congestion, Jamila complained that she had a frontal headache and that the right side of her face ached. What specific bony structures probably became infected by the bacteria or viruses causing the cold?

   Answer: The paranasal sinuses—specifically the frontal sinus located in the frontal bone and the right maxillary sinus located in the right maxilla.
   Diff: 3   *Page Ref: 178*

3) A group of students suffered a serious traffic accident on the way to the prom: John suffered multiple injuries to his lower left extremity. Protruding through the skin was a splintered portion of the longest bone in the body. This bone was the: a. _____. Sasha didn't consider her injuries serious so she walked several blocks to find help. Then she noticed that her right knee was not functioning normally. Examination revealed a fractured kneecap. Another name for the kneecap is: b. _____. The bones of the toes or digits are the: c. _____. Greg fractured his heelbone, more correctly called the: d. _____.

   Answer: a. femur
            b. patella
            c. phalanges
            d. calcaneus
   Diff: 3   *Page Ref: 203–208*

4) Mr. Patel, a heavy beer drinker with a large pot belly, complained of severe lower back pains; X rays disclosed displacement of the lumbar vertebrae. What would this condition be called and what could cause this?

   Answer: Lordosis—the extra weight of the belly causes the vertebrae to compensate and bend anteriorly. The pain is probably caused by pressure on the spinal nerves and cord.
   Diff: 3   *Page Ref: 182*

5) A skeleton was found in a wooded area. It was brought to a forensic medicine laboratory for identification. The first thing the coroner did was determine the age, sex, and possible size of the person. What was examined in order to get this information?

Answer: By examining the shape of the pelvic inlet, the depth of the iliac fossa, the characteristics of the ilium, and the angle inferior to the pubic symphysis, one could determine the sex. Also significant for determining the sex of the skeleton are the position of the acetabulum, the shape of the obturator foramen, and the general design of the ischium. To determine the age of the individual, bone density and markings are important. The markings where muscles were attached will reveal information about the mass and the general shape of the person.

Diff: 5   *Page Ref: 202*

CHAPTER 8   Joints

Fill–in–the–Blank/Short Answer Questions

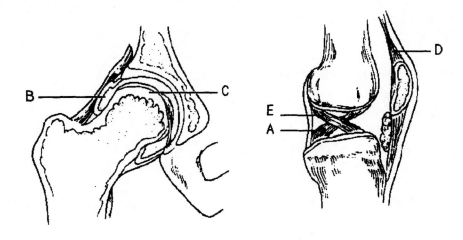

Figure 8.1

Using Figure 8.1, identify the following:

1) A circular rim of fibrocartilage that enhances the depth of the hip joint.

   Answer: B
   Diff: 1   Page Ref: 226

2) Protective covering at the bone ends.

   Answer: C
   Diff: 1   Page Ref: 226

3) The ligament that prevents forward sliding of the femur or backward displacement of the tibia.

   Answer: A
   Diff: 1   Page Ref: 229

4) The tendon of the quadriceps muscle.

   Answer: D
   Diff: 1   Page Ref: 229

5) The ligament that prevents backward sliding of the femur on the tibia when the knee is flexed.

   Answer: E
   Diff: 1   Page Ref: 229

Fill in the blank or provide a short answer:

6) Turning the foot medially at the ankle would be called _____.

Answer: inversion
Diff: 1   Page Ref: 219

7) Moving your jaw forward, causing an underbite, is called _____.

Answer: protraction
Diff: 1   Page Ref: 220

8) A _____ is a fluid-filled cavity a tendon slides over.

Answer: bursa
Diff: 1   Page Ref: 215

9) The joint between the frontal and parietal bones is called a _____ joint.

Answer: suture
Diff: 1   Page Ref: 211

10) A synchondrosis joint is a _____ structural class of joint.

Answer: cartilaginous
Diff: 1   Page Ref: 213

11) Using the functional classification, a freely movable joint would be called a _____ joint.

Answer: diarthrosis
Diff: 1   Page Ref: 211

12) The hip joint, like the shoulder joint, is a _____ joint.

Answer: ball-and-socket
Diff: 1   Page Ref: 222

13) Partial dislocation of a joint is called a _____.

Answer: subluxation
Diff: 2   Page Ref: 231

14) The joint between the carpal and the first metacarpal is called a _____ joint.

Answer: saddle
Diff: 2   Page Ref: 222

15) Synovial joints have five major features. What are they?

Answer: Articular cartilage, a joint cavity, an articular capsule, synovial fluid, and reinforcing ligaments.
Diff: 2   Page Ref: 213-214

16) Often people who exercise prudently seem to have fewer bouts with osteoarthritis. Will exercise prevent arthritis? If so, how?

Answer: Exercise does not prevent arthritis, but it strengthens muscles that in turn support and stabilize joints.
Diff: 3   Page Ref: 231–232

17) For each of the following movements, indicate the specific kind of joint involved (i.e., hinge, etc.) and the movement performed (i.e., extension, etc.). a. Bending the elbow: _____, _____. b. Turning head side to side (NO): _____, _____. c. Lowering your arm to your side: _____, _____. d. Turning the sole of foot medially: _____, _____.

Answer: a. hinge, flexion b. pivot, rotation c. ball and socket, adduction d. plane, inversion
Diff: 3   Page Ref: 220–224

18) While the fingers can exhibit flexion and extension and other angular motions, the thumb has much greater freedom. Why?

Answer: The thumb possesses a saddle joint where each articular surface has both a concave and a convex surface.
Diff: 3   Page Ref: 223

19) Describe a typical synovial joint.

Answer: The ends of each bone are covered with hyaline cartilage that is continuous with the synovial membrane enclosing the joint. Synovial fluid fills the space between the articular cartilage. Outside the synovial membrane there is a very tough, fibrous capsule that prevents the synovial membrane from bulging out as pressure is applied to the ends of the bones.
Diff: 3   Page Ref: 213–214

20) Since uric acid is a normal waste product of nucleic acid metabolism, why are so many men suffering from a condition known as gouty arthritis? How does this product that should be eliminated in the urine cause so much pain when things go wrong?

Answer: Males have higher blood levels of uric acid than females. When blood levels of uric acid rise excessively, it is deposited as urate crystals in the soft tissues of joints. Sometimes gout sufferers have an excessive rate of uric acid production; or it is possible that some are unable to flush uric acid in the urine fast enough.
Diff: 4   Page Ref: 233

21) Many inflammations of joint areas can be treated by injections of cortisone into the area. Why don't we continually get injections rather than surgeries?

Answer: A joint inflammation is always a symptom of an underlying problem such as cartilage or ligament damage, arthritis, etc. Continued injection might cause the patient to reinjure the area, or it might mask a more severe injury that may appear later.
Diff: 4   Page Ref: 231

Matching Questions

Match the following:

1) Column 1: Flexion, extension, and
            abduction.

   Column 2: Angular movements

   Answer: Angular movements
   Diff: 1   *Page Ref: 217*

2) Column 1: Partially torn ligament.

   Column 2: A sprain

   Answer: A sprain
   Diff: 1   *Page Ref: 230*

3) Column 1: Pointing toes upward.

   Column 2: Dorsiflexion

   Answer: Dorsiflexion
   Diff: 1   *Page Ref: 218*

4) Column 1: The primary movement
            permitted in a pivot joint.

   Column 2: Rotation

   Answer: Rotation
   Diff: 1   *Page Ref: 219*

True/False Questions

1) The amount of movement permitted by a particular joint is the basis for the functional classification of joints.

   Answer: TRUE
   Diff: 1   *Page Ref: 211*

2) If the body is to move, movement must occur at the joints.

   Answer: TRUE
   Diff: 1   *Page Ref: 211*

3) The nature of sutures is such that protection is one of the functions.

   Answer: TRUE
   Diff: 1   *Page Ref: 211*

4) The ligament that unites the tibia and fibula is an example of a syndesmosis.

   Answer: TRUE
   Diff: 1   *Page Ref: 212*

5) Hinge joints permit movement in only one plane.

Answer: TRUE
Diff: 1   *Page Ref: 220*

6) All synovial joints are freely movable diarthrotic joints.

Answer: TRUE
Diff: 1   *Page Ref: 213*

7) Symphyses are synarthrodial joints that are strong and allow flexibility.

Answer: FALSE
Diff: 1   *Page Ref: 213*

8) Synovial fluid is a viscous material that is derived by filtration from blood.

Answer: TRUE
Diff: 1   *Page Ref: 214*

9) The major function of tendon sheaths and bursae is to reduce friction between adjacent structures during activity that stresses the joint.

Answer: TRUE
Diff: 1   *Page Ref: 215–216*

10) The articular surfaces of synovial joints play a minimal role in joint stability.

Answer: TRUE
Diff: 1   *Page Ref: 213*

11) The major role of ligaments at synovial joints is to help direct movement and prevent undesirable movement.

Answer: TRUE
Diff: 1   *Page Ref: 214*

12) Three types of movement known as angular movements are flexion, hyperextension, and extension.

Answer: TRUE
Diff: 1   *Page Ref: 217*

13) The only movement allowed between the first two cervical vertebrae is flexion.

Answer: FALSE
Diff: 1   *Page Ref: 233*

14) Movement at the hip joint does not have as wide a range of motion as at the shoulder joint.

Answer: TRUE
Diff: 1   *Page Ref: 225*

15) A frontal blow to an extended knee is the most dangerous type of injury to that joint.

Answer: FALSE
Diff: 1   Page Ref: 230

16) A person who has been diagnosed with a sprained ankle has an injury without a dislocation.

Answer: FALSE
Diff: 1   Page Ref: 230

17) Uric acid crystals are typical findings in gouty arthritis.

Answer: TRUE
Diff: 1   Page Ref: 233

18) Moving the leg away from the midline would be adduction.

Answer: FALSE
Diff: 1   Page Ref: 219

19) The knee joint can exhibit multiaxial movements.

Answer: FALSE
Diff: 1   Page Ref: 224

20) A movement of the forearm in which the palm of the hand is turned from posterior to anterior is supination.

Answer: TRUE
Diff: 1   Page Ref: 219

21) A pivot joint will exhibit gliding movement.

Answer: FALSE
Diff: 1   Page Ref: 221

22) The wrist joint can exhibit adduction and eversion movements.

Answer: FALSE
Diff: 1   Page Ref: 223

23) Cruciate ligaments are important ligaments that stabilize ball-and-socket joints.

Answer: FALSE
Diff: 1   Page Ref: 228

24) Although cartilage is avascular, it generally repairs itself rapidly.

Answer: FALSE
Diff: 1   Page Ref: 231

25) Moving the arm in a full circle is an example of circumduction.

Answer: TRUE
Diff: 1   Page Ref: 219

26) A disorder of joints with the symptoms of chronic inflammation of articular cartilage, degeneration of the articular cartilage, and spur formation is known as osteoarthritis.

Answer: TRUE
Diff: 1   Page Ref: 231

27) A gomphosis is considered a cartilaginous joint.

Answer: FALSE
Diff: 1   Page Ref: 213

28) Synarthrotic joints do not exhibit movement.

Answer: TRUE
Diff: 1   Page Ref: 211

29) Flexion of the ankle so that the superior aspect of the foot approaches the shin is called dorsiflexion.

Answer: TRUE
Diff: 1   Page Ref: 218

30) Elevation of the mandible results in a movement called protraction.

Answer: FALSE
Diff: 1   Page Ref: 220

31) The gripping of the trochlea by the trochlear notch constitutes the "hinge" for the elbow joint.

Answer: TRUE
Diff: 1   Page Ref: 227

32) The ligamentum teres represents a very important stabilizing ligament for the hip joint.

Answer: FALSE
Diff: 1   Page Ref: 226

33) The structural classification of joints is based on the composition of the binding material and the presence or absence of a joint cavity.

Answer: TRUE
Diff: 2   Page Ref: 211

34) Synovial fluid contains phagocytic cells that protect the cavity from invasion by microbes or other debris.

Answer: TRUE
Diff: 2   Page Ref: 214

35) A person who has been diagnosed with rheumatoid arthritis would be suffering loss of the synovial fluids.

Answer: FALSE
Diff: 2   Page Ref: 232

36) A ball–and–socket joint will exhibit several movements.

Answer: TRUE
Diff: 2   Page Ref: 222

37) Bending of the tips of the finger exhibits flexion.

Answer: TRUE
Diff: 2   Page Ref: 217

38) A nonaxial movement is usually seen at a joint such as a hinge.

Answer: FALSE
Diff: 2   Page Ref: 220

Multiple–Choice Questions

1) A fibrous joint that is a peg–in–socket is called a _____ joint.
    A) syndesmosis   B) suture   C) synchondrosis   D) gomphosis

Answer: D
Diff: 1   Page Ref: 212

2) The cruciate ligaments of the knee:
    A) tend to run parallel to one another.
    B) are also called collateral ligaments.
    C) prevent hyperextension of the knee.
    D) assist in defining the range of motion of the leg.

Answer: C
Diff: 1   Page Ref: 228

3) If a patient was suffering from bursitis, this condition would be designated as inflammation of a(n):
    A) sesamoid bone found at a joint.   B) cavity within a long bone.
    C) small sac containing fluid.   D) articular cartilage.

Answer: C
Diff: 1   Page Ref: 231

4) An immovable joint found only between skull bones is called a:
    A) suture.   B) condyle.
    C) cartilaginous joint.   D) synovial joint.

Answer: A
Diff: 1   Page Ref: 211

5) Articular cartilage found at the ends of the long bones serves to:
   A) attach tendons.
   B) produce red blood cells (hemopoiesis).
   C) provide a smooth surface at the ends of synovial joints.
   D) form the synovial membrane.

   Answer: C
   Diff: 1   Page Ref: 213

6) A joint united by dense fibrocartilaginous tissue that permits a slight degree of movement is a:
   A) suture.   B) syndesmosis.   C) symphysis.   D) gomphosis.

   Answer: C
   Diff: 1   Page Ref: 213

7) On the basis of structural classification, which joint is fibrous connective tissue?
   A) symphysis   B) synchondrosis   C) pivot   D) syndesmosis

   Answer: D
   Diff: 1   Page Ref: 212

8) Connective tissue sacs lined with synovial membranes that act as cushions in places where friction develops are called:
   A) menisci.   B) bursae.   C) ligaments.   D) tendons.

   Answer: B
   Diff: 1   Page Ref: 215

9) Articulations permitting only slight degrees of movement are:
   A) amphiarthroses.   B) synarthroses.   C) diarthroses.   D) synovial joints.

   Answer: A
   Diff: 1   Page Ref: 211

10) Which of these joint types affords multiaxial movement?
    A) gliding   B) hinge   C) ball and socket   D) pivot

    Answer: C
    Diff: 1   Page Ref: 222

11) _____ are cartilaginous joints.
    A) Syndesmoses   B) Sutures   C) Synchondroses   D) Gomphoses

    Answer: C
    Diff: 1   Page Ref: 213

12) The gliding motion of the wrist is accomplished because of the _____ joint.
    A) hinge   B) plane   C) pivot   D) condyloid

    Answer: B
    Diff: 1   Page Ref: 220

13) The ligaments that protect the alignment of the femoral and tibial condyles and limit the movement of the femur anteriorly and posteriorly are called:

    A) cruciate ligaments.   B) patellar ligaments.

    C) anterior ligaments.   D) tibial collateral ligaments.

Answer: A
Diff: 1   Page Ref: 228

14) Bending your head back until it hurts is an example of:

    A) flexion.   B) extension.   C) hyperextension.   D) circumduction.

Answer: C
Diff: 1   Page Ref: 218

15) In the classification of joints, which of the following is true?

    A) Immovable joints are called amphiarthroses.

    B) All synovial joints are freely movable.

    C) Synarthrotic joints are slightly movable.

    D) In cartilaginous joints, a joint cavity is present.

Answer: B
Diff: 1   Page Ref: 211

16) A joint that is known as a suture is found:

    A) in the skull only.   B) in areas most prone to fracture.

    C) where functionally it is amphiarthrotic.   D) in areas where bones have not yet closed.

Answer: A
Diff: 1   Page Ref: 211

17) Synarthrotic joints:

    A) are found at the junction of the epiphysis and diaphysis of growing bone.

    B) are cartilaginous joints.

    C) permit essentially no movement.

    D) have large joint cavities.

Answer: C
Diff: 1   Page Ref: 211

18) Fibrous joints are classified as:

    A) pivot, hinge, and ball and socket.   B) symphysis, sacroiliac, and articular.

    C) hinge, saddle, and ellipsoidal.   D) sutures, syndesmoses, and gomphoses.

Answer: D
Diff: 1   Page Ref: 211

19) In symphysis joints the articular surfaces of the bones are covered with:

    A) hyaline cartilage.   B) synovial membranes.

    C) fibrocartilage.   D) tendon sheaths.

Answer: A
Diff: 1   *Page Ref: 213*

20) Synovial fluid is present in joint cavities of freely movable joints. Which of the following statements is true about this fluid?

    A) It contains enzymes only.   B) It contains lactic acid.

    C) It contains hyaluronic acid.   D) It contains hydrochloric acid.

Answer: C
Diff: 1   *Page Ref: 214*

21) Which of the following statements defines synchondroses?

    A) amphiarthrotic joints designed for strength and flexibility

    B) interphalangeal joints

    C) joints that permit angular movements

    D) cartilaginous joints where hyaline cartilage unites the ends of bones

Answer: D
Diff: 1   *Page Ref: 215*

22) Menisci refers to:

    A) a cavity lined with cartilage.   B) a small sac containing synovial fluid.

    C) semilunar cartilage pads.   D) a tendon sheath.

Answer: C
Diff: 1   *Page Ref: 228*

23) Which of the following is a true statement regarding gliding movements?

    A) Gliding movements occur at the intercarpal and intertarsal joints.

    B) Gliding movements allow flexibility of the upper limbs.

    C) Gliding movements are multiaxial.

    D) An example of a gliding movement is nodding one's head.

Answer: A
Diff: 1   *Page Ref: 216-217*

24) When one is moving a limb away from the median plane of the body along the frontal plane, it is called:

    A) abduction.   B) adduction.   C) inversion.   D) dorsiflexion.

Answer: A
Diff: 1   *Page Ref: 219*

25) The terms inversion and eversion pertain only to:

   A) the hands.

   B) the feet.

   C) the arms.

   D) Both A and B are correct.

   Answer: B
   Diff: 1   *Page Ref: 219*

26) The shoulder joint is a good example of a _____ synovial joint.

   A) nonaxial   B) uniaxial   C) biaxial   D) multiaxial

   Answer: D
   Diff: 1   *Page Ref: 223*

27) The only movement allowed in a pivot joint is:

   A) biaxial movement.

   B) flexion.

   C) uniaxial rotation.

   D) extension.

   Answer: C
   Diff: 1   *Page Ref: 221*

28) Compared to the shoulder, displacements of the hip joints are:

   A) common due to the weight-bearing the hip endures.

   B) rare because of the ligament reinforcement.

   C) common in all people who are overweight.

   D) rare because the rotator cuff stabilizes the hip joint.

   Answer: B
   Diff: 1   *Page Ref: 226*

29) The _____ ligament holds the radius to the ulna at the proximal end.

   A) annular   B) ulnar collateral   C) radial collateral   D) iliofemoral

   Answer: A
   Diff: 1   *Page Ref: 227*

30) Which ligament of the knee initiates the knee–jerk reflex when tapped?

   A) the patellar ligament

   B) the medial patellar retinacula

   C) the lateral patellar retinacula

   D) the extracapsular ligament

   Answer: A
   Diff: 1   *Page Ref: 228*

31) Football players often sustain lateral blows to the extended knee. Which of the ligaments is/are damaged as a result?

A) oblique popliteal and extracapsular ligament

B) suprapatellar

C) arcuate popliteal and the posterior cruciate

D) medial collateral, medial meniscus, and anterior cruciate

Answer: D
Diff: 1   Page Ref: 230

32) Which of the following conditions is generally considered a noninflammatory type of arthritis?

A) bursitis   B) tendonitis

C) osteoarthritis   D) rheumatoid arthritis

Answer: C
Diff: 1   Page Ref: 232

33) Gouty arthritis is a painful condition caused by:

A) excessive blood levels of uric acid deposited as crystals in the soft tissue joints.

B) a disorder in the body's immune system resulting in destruction of joints.

C) a thickening of the synovial membrane and a decrease in fluid production.

D) a bacterial infection in the bursae.

Answer: A
Diff: 1   Page Ref: 233

34) When a ballerina points the toes, it is known as:

A) circumduction.   B) plantar flexion.   C) pronation.   D) protraction.

Answer: B
Diff: 1   Page Ref: 218

35) Which of the following is a true statement?

A) The head of the humerus articulates with the acromion process.

B) The greater tubercule of the humerus articulates at the coracoid process of the scapula.

C) The "rotator cuff" is responsible for the flexible extensions at the elbow joint.

D) The annular ligament surrounds the head of the radius.

Answer: D
Diff: 2   Page Ref: 227

36) Multiaxial joints of the body include:

A) the knee and elbow.   B) the ankle and wrist.

C) the hip and shoulder.   D) intercarpal and intertarsal joints.

Answer: C
Diff: 2   Page Ref: 222–223

37) The following characteristics define what type of joint: presence of a synovial cavity, articular cartilage, synovial membrane, and ligaments?

    A) suture   B) synchondrosis   C) symphysis   D) hinge joint

Answer: D
Diff: 2   Page Ref: 213

38) Extracapsular ligaments stabilizing the knee include:

    A) the patellar ligament extending from femur to patella.

    B) lateral and medial collateral ligaments preventing lateral or medial angular movements.

    C) cruciate ligaments, which help secure the articulating bones together.

    D) the oblique popliteal crossing the knee anteriorly.

Answer: B
Diff: 2   Page Ref: 228

39) Which of the following statements best describes angular movements?

    A) They allow movement only in one plane.

    B) They allow movement in several planes.

    C) They occur only between bones with flat articular processes.

    D) They change (increase or decrease) the angle between two bones.

Answer: D
Diff: 2   Page Ref: 217

40) Saddle joints have concave and convex surfaces. Name the bones of the hand that articulate to form a saddle joint:

    A) the scaphoid of the index finger and the triquetral of the middle finger.

    B) the trapezium of the ring finger and the capitate of the fourth finger.

    C) the scaphoid of the middle finger and lunate of the index finger.

    D) the trapezium of the carpal bone and the thumb's metacarpal.

Answer: D
Diff: 2   Page Ref: 222

41) Tendon sheaths:

    A) act as friction–reducing structures.

    B) are lined with dense irregular connective tissue.

    C) form channels for tendons.

    D) help anchor the tendon to the muscle.

Answer: A
Diff: 3   Page Ref: 215

Clinical Questions

1) After reading a medical report, you learn that a 45–year–old female has the following symptoms: inflammation of synovial membranes, accumulation of synovial fluid, pain and tenderness about the joints, pannus formation, and some immobility at certain joints. On the basis of these symptoms, what would the patient probably have?

Answer: Rheumatoid arthritis.
Diff: 3   Page Ref: 232

2) Akira, a 2.5–ranked tennis player (who thought he was a 4.5 player!), experienced severe pain in his elbow joint after playing for five straight hours, well beyond his limit. He told everyone it was due to a fall while diving to retrieve a difficult shot. What do you think?

Answer: It was probably tennis elbow or inflammation of the bursa close to the olecranon process because he overextended his abilities.
Diff: 3   Page Ref: 231

3) Mary has been suffering from a "bad knee" for several months. She is a tennis player who often slides in to attack a ball; she is an aerobic devotee and a jogger. She visited an orthopedic surgeon last week who told her that he would "like to have a look at her knee joint." He also told her that her symptoms indicated damage to the meniscus, and it might have to be removed. What will the doctor do to see the joint, and if the meniscus is removed will Mary be able to play tennis again?

Answer: The doctor will perform arthroscopic surgery on Mary in order to view the interior of the joint. If she has severely damaged the meniscus, it can be removed with little impairment to the knee except some loss in stability.
Diff: 3   Page Ref: 230

4) Farhad begins inputting his term paper on his new computer early one morning. After 8 hours of typing, he notices that his wrists are stiff and very sore. The next morning, Farhad begins to finish his paper, but soon finds his wrists hurt worse than last night. What is wrong?

Answer: Farhad is suffering from tendonitis. If he continues to use the keyboard incorrectly, the tendonitis could develop into a very serious condition called carpal tunnel syndrome.
Diff: 3   Page Ref: 231

5) Greg is somewhat of a "weekend athlete" who has overextended himself by pitching baseball for a local team during the week and playing golf on the weekends for several hours. He presented himself to the emergency room last week with severe shoulder pain (at the glenohumeral joint). The physician told him that the X ray was not conclusive, but he may have damage to his "rotator cuff." What is the rotator cuff, and how might he have caused this damage? What remedies will the physician recommend?

Answer: Greg has either stretched or torn his rotator cuff. He will be told to rest for a few months, and if the pain does not subside, surgery will be necessary. The rotator cuff is four tendons that belong to the subscapularis, supraspinatus, infraspinatus, and teres minor muscles and encircle the shoulder joint. They are vunerable to damage when the arm is circumducted vigorously. Greg is obviously overdoing his activities by pitching four baseball games per week and playing golf on weekends.
Diff: 5   Page Ref: 225

Fill–in–the–Blank/Short Answer Questions

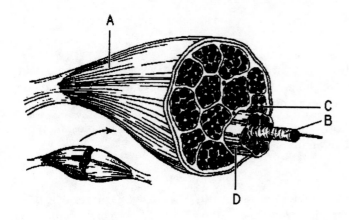

Figure 9.1

Using Figure 9.1, identify the following:

1) Endomysium.

   Answer: C
   Diff: 1   Page Ref: 237

2) Fascicle.

   Answer: D
   Diff: 1   Page Ref: 237

3) The tissue that binds muscles into functional groups.

   Answer: A
   Diff: 2   Page Ref: 237

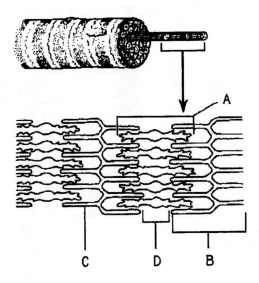

Figure 9.2

Using Figure 9.2, identify the following:

4) I band.

Answer: B
Diff: 1   Page Ref: 239

5) H zone.

Answer: D
Diff: 1   Page Ref: 239

6) A band.

Answer: A
Diff: 2   Page Ref: 239

Fill in the blank or provide a short answer:

7) Only _____ muscle cells are multinucleated.

Answer: skeletal
Diff: 1   Page Ref: 238

8) The end of the muscle that moves when a muscle contracts is called the _____.

Answer: insertion
Diff: 1   Page Ref: 237

9) The _____ zone of a sarcomere contains no actin.

Answer: H
Diff: 1   Page Ref: 238

10) In the synaptic cleft of a neuromuscular junction, _____ is always present.

Answer: acetylcholinesterase (AChE)
Diff: 1   *Page Ref: 248*

11) The time in which cross bridges are active is called the period of _____.

Answer: contraction
Diff: 1   *Page Ref: 252*

12) _____ fibers are slow (oxidative) fibers.

Answer: Red
Diff: 1   *Page Ref: 261–262*

13) The only connective tissue around a smooth muscle cell is the _____.

Answer: endomysium
Diff: 1   *Page Ref: 236*

14) Only _____ muscle cells branch.

Answer: cardiac
Diff: 1   *Page Ref: 268*

15) A smooth, sustained contraction is called _____.

Answer: tetanus
Diff: 1   *Page Ref: 253*

16) Define muscle fatigue.

Answer: Fatigue occurs when ATP production fails to keep pace with ATP use even though the muscle still receives stimuli.
Diff: 1   *Page Ref: 258*

17) When a person suffering a broken limb has been wearing a cast for several weeks, after removal what best describes the condition of the muscles in that limb?

Answer: *Atrophy* is the term that describes decreased or lost muscle tone due to immobilization.
Diff: 1   *Page Ref: 264*

18) _____ refers to a group of inherited muscle–destroying diseases that generally appear during childhood.

Answer: Muscular dystrophy
Diff: 2   *Page Ref: 264*

19) Compare red and white muscles relative to their speed of action and endurance.

Answer: Red muscles tend to have a slow (oxidative) rate and fatigue resistance, whereas white muscle cells have a fast (oxidative) rate and fatigue easily.
Diff: 2   *Page Ref: 263*

20) What is happening during the power stroke of a skeletal muscle contraction?

Answer: The myosin cross bridges swivel toward the center of the sarcomere, resembling the oars of a boat.
Diff: 2   *Page Ref: 245*

21) Briefly, what causes rigor mortis?

Answer: Following the death of an individual, ATP is rapidly consumed and cannot be replaced. Because cross bridge detachment and calcium active transport is ATP driven, calcium leakage from the sarcoplasmic reticulum causes attachment of cross bridges, and lack of ATP prevents detachments.
Diff: 3   *Page Ref: 246*

22) Long–distance runners often push their muscles to the limit. What allows them to have the energy to keep going?

Answer: Excessive activity may cause depletion of creatine phosphate, in which case glucose is catabolized to generate ATP.
Diff: 3   *Page Ref: 259*

23) What ultimately stops a muscle contraction?

Answer: The ultimate switch is the enzyme, acetylcholinesterase (AChE). When the neuron stops releasing ACh, the muscle would not stop contracting if the AChE did not split the ACh into its two components, acetyl and choline, making them release their binding sites.
Diff: 3   *Page Ref: 248*

Matching Questions

Match the following:

1) Column 1: Primary energy fuel is fat.

Column 2: Slow (oxidative), fatigue-resistant fibers

Foil: Fast (oxidative or glycolytic), fatigue–resistant fibers

Answer: Slow (oxidative), fatigue-resistant fibers
Diff: 1   *Page Ref: 263*

2) Column 1: Have very fast–acting myosin ATPases and depend upon anaerobic metabolism during contraction.

Column 2: Fast (oxidative or glycolytic), fatigable fibers

Answer: Fast (oxidative or glycolytic), fatigable fibers
Diff: 1   *Page Ref: 263*

3) Column 1: Red fibers, the smallest of the
            fiber types.

   Column 2: Slow (oxidative),
             fatigue–resistant fibers

   Answer: Slow (oxidative), fatigue–resistant fibers
   Diff: 2   Page Ref: 263

4) Column 1: Contain abundant amounts of
            glycogen.

   Column 2: Fast (oxidative or glycolytic),
             fatigable fibers

   Answer: Fast (oxidative or glycolytic), fatigable fibers
   Diff: 2   Page Ref: 263

5) Column 1: Abundant in postural
            muscles.

   Column 2: Slow (oxidative),
             fatigue–resistant fibers

   Answer: Slow (oxidative), fatigue–resistant fibers
   Diff: 2   Page Ref: 263

6) Column 1: A high percentage are found
            in marathon runners.

   Column 2: Slow (oxidative),
             fatigue–resistant fibers

   Answer: Slow (oxidative), fatigue–resistant fibers
   Diff: 2   Page Ref: 263

Match the following:

7) Column 1: The stimulus above which no
            stronger contraction can be
            elicited, because all motor
            units are firing in the muscle.

   Column 2: Maximal stimulus

   Answer: Maximal stimulus
   Diff: 1   Page Ref: 253

8) Column 1: The phenomenon in which the
            contraction strength of a
            muscle increases, due to
            increased enzyme efficiency
            during the warm-up.

   Column 2: Treppe

   Answer: Treppe
   Diff: 1   Page Ref: 253–254

9) Column 1: Continued sustained smooth
            contraction due to rapid
            stimulation.

   Column 2: Tetanus

   Answer: Tetanus
   Diff: 1   Page Ref: 253

10) Column 1: The situation in which
            contractions become stronger
            due to a rapid stimulation
            rate. Partial relaxation occurs
            between contractions.

   Column 2: Wave summation

   Answer: Wave summation
   Diff: 1   Page Ref: 252

11) Column 1: How a smooth increase in
            muscle force is produced.

   Column 2: Multiple motor unit
            summation

   Answer: Multiple motor unit summation
   Diff: 2   Page Ref: 253

Match the following:

12) Column 1: A sarcomere is the distance
            between two _____.

   Column 2: Z discs

        Foil: Actin

   Answer: Z discs
   Diff: 1   Page Ref: 238

13) Column 1: The _____ contains only
            the actin filaments.

   Column 2: I band

   Answer: I band
   Diff: 1   Page Ref: 238

14) Column 1: The thicker filaments are the
            _____ filaments.

   Column 2: Myosin

   Answer: Myosin
   Diff: 1   Page Ref: 241

15) Column 1: Both actin and myosin are found in the _____.

Column 2: A band

Answer: A band
Diff: 1   *Page Ref: 238*

16) Column 1: The myosin filaments are located in the _____.

Column 2: A band

Answer: A band
Diff: 2   *Page Ref: 238*

Match the following:

17) Column 1: Serves as the actual "trigger" for muscle contraction by removing the inhibition of the troponin molecules.

Column 2: Calcium ions

Answer: Calcium ions
Diff: 1   *Page Ref: 244*

18) Column 1: A neurotransmitter substance released at motor end plates by the axonal endings.

Column 2: Acetylcholine

Answer: Acetylcholine
Diff: 1   *Page Ref: 247*

19) Column 1: A metabolic pathway that provides for a large amount of ATP per glucose because oxygen is used. Products are water and carbon dioxide and ATP.

Column 2: Aerobic respiration

Answer: Aerobic respiration
Diff: 1   *Page Ref: 257–258*

20) Column 1: Normally stored in the terminal cisternae.

Column 2: Calcium ions

Answer: Calcium ions
Diff: 1   *Page Ref: 242*

21) Column 1: Used to convert ADP to ATP
by transfer of a high–energy
phosphate group. A reserve
high–energy compound.

   Column 2: Creatine phosphate

   Foil: Aerobic respiration

   Answer: Creatine phosphate
   Diff: 2   *Page Ref: 257*

22) Column 1: Destroys ACh.

   Column 2: Cholinesterase

   Answer: Cholinesterase
   Diff: 2   *Page Ref: 248*

True/False Questions

1) Smooth muscle fibers are the shortest of the muscle cell types.

   Answer: TRUE
   Diff: 1   *Page Ref: 265*

2) Skeletal muscle is called involuntary because it is the only type of muscle usually subject to conscious control.

   Answer: FALSE
   Diff: 1   *Page Ref: 235*

3) The oxygen–binding protein myoglobin is found stored in the T tubules of voluntary muscle.

   Answer: FALSE
   Diff: 1   *Page Ref: 262*

4) A single muscle fiber contains only a few myofibrils.

   Answer: FALSE
   Diff: 1   *Page Ref: 238*

5) The thin filaments (actin) contain a polypeptide subunit G actin that seems to have no function.

   Answer: FALSE
   Diff: 1   *Page Ref: 241*

6) The sarcoplasmic reticulum and the T tubules are vital to the integrity of muscle contraction.

   Answer: TRUE
   Diff: 1   *Page Ref: 242*

7) Rigor mortis is caused by cessation of ATP synthesis and the irreversible cross-linking of actin and myosin.

Answer: TRUE
Diff: 1   Page Ref: 246

8) Skeletal muscles need nerve stimulation for contraction to occur.

Answer: TRUE
Diff: 1   Page Ref: 246

9) The force of muscle contraction is controlled by multiple motor unit summation or recruitment.

Answer: TRUE
Diff: 1   Page Ref: 253

10) The maximal (strongest) stimulus that produces an increase in contractile force is called the threshold stimulus.

Answer: FALSE
Diff: 1   Page Ref: 253

11) The force exerted by a contracting muscle on an object is referred to as linear tension.

Answer: FALSE
Diff: 1   Page Ref: 254

12) Eccentric contractions are much more forceful than concentric contractions.

Answer: TRUE
Diff: 1   Page Ref: 254

13) A nerve cell and all the muscle cells that it stimulates are referred to as a motor end plate.

Answer: FALSE
Diff: 1   Page Ref: 251

14) Peristalsis is characteristic of smooth muscle.

Answer: TRUE
Diff: 1   Page Ref: 265

15) Myotonic dystrophy is a sex-linked form of muscular dystrophy.

Answer: FALSE
Diff: 1   Page Ref: 264

16) A contraction in which the muscle does not shorten but its tension increases is called isometric.

Answer: TRUE
Diff: 1   Page Ref: 254

17) During isotonic contraction, the heavier the load, the faster the velocity of contraction.

Answer: FALSE
Diff: 1   Page Ref: 255

18) Cardiac muscle fibers are relatively short, tapering cells within a single centrally located nucleus.

Answer: FALSE
Diff: 1   Page Ref: 268

19) The neurotransmitter used by the nervous system to activate skeletal muscle cells is acetylcholine.

Answer: TRUE
Diff: 1   Page Ref: 247

20) During isometric contraction, the energy used appears as movement.

Answer: FALSE
Diff: 1   Page Ref: 255

21) Muscle fatigue and soreness are caused by a buildup of pyruvic acid.

Answer: FALSE
Diff: 1   Page Ref: 259

22) The basis of the "warm–up" period is to increase the efficiency of muscle enzyme systems.

Answer: TRUE
Diff: 1   Page Ref: 254

23) One of the important functions of skeletal muscle is production of heat.

Answer: TRUE
Diff: 1   Page Ref: 259

24) Oxygen debt refers to the oxygen required to make creatine phosphate.

Answer: FALSE
Diff: 1   Page Ref: 259

25) A sustained partial contraction of a muscle is called muscle tone.

Answer: TRUE
Diff: 1   Page Ref: 254

26) An aponeurosis is a ropelike piece of muscle fascia that forms indirect connections to muscles of the leg.

Answer: FALSE
Diff: 1   Page Ref: 238

27) Muscle contraction will always promote movement of body parts regardless of how they are attached.

Answer: FALSE
Diff: 1   *Page Ref: 251*

28) Although there are no sarcomeres, smooth muscle still possesses thick and thin filaments.

Answer: TRUE
Diff: 1   *Page Ref: 268*

29) Whereas skeletal muscle cells are electrically coupled, smooth muscle cells appear to be chemically coupled by gap junctions.

Answer: FALSE
Diff: 1   *Page Ref: 266*

30) Smooth muscle, in contrast to skeletal muscle, is in contact with neural endings that may release acetylcholine or norepinephrine.

Answer: TRUE
Diff: 1   *Page Ref: 267*

31) Single–unit smooth muscle is found in the intestines.

Answer: TRUE
Diff: 1   *Page Ref: 270*

32) The Cori cycle involves the breakdown of muscle glycogen to lactic acid and conversion to glycogen in the liver, where it can be reconverted to muscle glycogen after being sent back to the muscles.

Answer: TRUE
Diff: 2   *Page Ref: 257*

33) A resting potential is caused by a difference in the concentration of certain ions inside and outside the cell.

Answer: TRUE
Diff: 2   *Page Ref: 247*

34) The effect of the neurotransmitter on the muscle cell membrane is to modify its permeability properties temporarily.

Answer: TRUE
Diff: 2   *Page Ref: 247*

35) When a muscle fiber contracts, the I bands diminish in size, the H zones disappear, and the A bands move closer together but do not diminish in length.

Answer: TRUE
Diff: 2   *Page Ref: 244*

36) The more slowly a muscle is stimulated, the greater its exerted force becomes.

Answer: FALSE
Diff: 2   Page Ref: 252

Multiple-Choice Questions

1) With muscular dystrophy:

   A) muscles decrease in size due to loss of fat and connective tissue.

   B) muscle fibers degenerate and atrophy.

   C) most forms do not appear to be inherited.

   D) most cases appear in young females.

   Answer: B
   Diff: 1   Page Ref: 264

2) Which of the following should affect the strength or force of skeletal muscle contraction?

   A) the number of muscle fibers contracting   B) the degree of muscle stretch

   C) the series–elastic elements   D) stronger stimuli

   Answer: D
   Diff: 1   Page Ref: 253

3) Which of the following is not a usual result of exercise?

   A) increase in the efficiency of the respiratory system

   B) increase in the efficiency of the circulatory system

   C) increase in the number of muscle cells

   D) increase in the number of myofibrils within the muscle cells

   Answer: C
   Diff: 1   Page Ref: 262–263

4) In muscle contraction, calcium apparently acts to:

   A) increase the action potential transmitted along the sarcolemma.

   B) release the inhibition on Z discs.

   C) remove the blocking action of tropomyosin.

   D) cause ATP binding to actin.

   Answer: C
   Diff: 1   Page Ref: 244

5) Calcium ions bind to the _____ molecule in skeletal muscle cells.

   A) actin   B) tropomyosin   C) troponin   D) myosin

   Answer: C
   Diff: 1   Page Ref: 244

6) Myoglobin:

A) breaks down glycogen.

B) is a protein involved in the direct phosphorylation of ADP.

C) holds a reserve supply of oxygen in muscle cells.

D) produces the end plate potential.

Answer: C
Diff: 1   Page Ref: 238, 262

7) An elaborate network of membranes in skeletal muscle cells that functions in calcium storage is the:

A) sarcoplasmic reticulum.

B) mitochondria.

C) intermediate filament network.

D) myofibrilar network.

Answer: A
Diff: 1   Page Ref: 242–243

8) A sarcomere is:

A) the nonfunctional unit of skeletal muscle.

B) the area between two Z discs.

C) the area between two intercalated discs.

D) the wavy lines on the cell seen in the microscope.

Answer: B
Diff: 1   Page Ref: 238

9) Immediately following the arrival of the stimulus at a skeletal muscle cell there is a short period called the _____ period during which the events of excitation–contraction coupling occur.

A) contraction   B) relaxation   C) latent   D) refractory

Answer: C
Diff: 1   Page Ref: 247

10) Creatine phosphate functions in the muscle cell by:

A) forming a temporary chemical compound with myosin.

B) forming a chemical compound with actin.

C) inducing a conformational change in the myofilaments.

D) storing energy that will be transferred to ADP to resynthesize ATP as needed.

Answer: D
Diff: 1   Page Ref: 257

11) After nervous stimulation of the muscle cell has ceased, the calcium:

   A) is destroyed by cholinesterase.

   B) is chemically bound to the filaments.

   C) level in the cytoplasm drops.

   D) is actively pumped into the extracellular fluid for storage until the next contraction.

   Answer: C
   Diff: 1   Page Ref: 250

12) The major function of the sarcoplasmic reticulum in muscle contraction is to:

   A) make and store phosphocreatine.

   B) synthesize actin and myosin myofilaments.

   C) provide a source of myosin for the contraction process.

   D) regulate intracellular calcium concentration.

   Answer: D
   Diff: 1   Page Ref: 242

13) The condition of muscle fatigue can be best explained by:

   A) the all–or–none law.

   B) the inability to generate sufficient quantities of ATP due to feedback regulation of synthesis.

   C) insufficient intracellular quantities of ATP due to excessive consumption.

   D) a total lack of ATP.

   Answer: C
   Diff: 1   Page Ref: 258–259

14) The striations of a skeletal muscle cell are produced, for the most part, by:

   A) a difference in the thickness of the sarcolemma.

   B) the arrangement of myofilaments.

   C) the sarcoplasmic reticulum.

   D) the T tubules.

   Answer: B
   Diff: 1   Page Ref: 238

15) Which of the following are composed of myosin?

   A) thick filaments   B) thin filaments

   C) all myofilaments   D) Z discs

   Answer: A
   Diff: 1   Page Ref: 238–241

16) During muscle contraction, myosin cross bridges attach to which active sites?

    A) myosin filaments

    B) actin filaments

    C) Z discs

    D) thick filaments

    Answer: B
    Diff: 1   Page Ref: 241

17) Which of the following surrounds the individual muscle cell?

    A) perimysium   B) endomysium   C) epimysium   D) fascicle

    Answer: B
    Diff: 1   Page Ref: 236

18) Smooth muscles that act like skeletal muscles but are controlled by autonomic nerves and hormones are:

    A) single–unit muscles

    B) multiunit muscles

    C) red muscles

    D) white muscles

    Answer: B
    Diff: 1   Page Ref: 270

19) Rigor mortis occurs because:

    A) the cells are dead.

    B) sodium ions leak out of the muscle.

    C) ATP is required to release the attached actin and myosin molecules.

    D) proteins are beginning to break down, thus preventing a flow of calcium ions.

    Answer: C
    Diff: 1   Page Ref: 246

20) Which of the following statements is true concerning motor neurons?

    A) A single motor neuron makes contact with an average of 150 muscle fibers.

    B) The number of motor neurons associated with each muscle fiber depends on the location of the muscle.

    C) There are several motor neurons for each muscle fiber.

    D) Skeletal muscle contraction is not absolutely dependent on its nerve supply.

    Answer: A
    Diff: 1   Page Ref: 251

21) The term aponeurosis refers to:

    A) the bands of myofibrils.

    B) an indirect attachment to a skeletal element.

    C) the rough endoplasmic reticulum.

    D) the tropomyosin–troponin complex.

    Answer: B
    Diff: 1   Page Ref: 238

22) The oxygen–binding protein found in muscle cells is:

   A) hemoglobin.   B) ATP.   C) myoglobin.   D) immunoglobin.

   Answer: C
   Diff: 1   *Page Ref: 238*

23) The contractile units of skeletal muscles are:

   A) microtubules.   B) mitochondria. C) T tubules.   D) myofibrils.

   Answer: D
   Diff: 1   *Page Ref: 238*

24) The site of calcium regulation in the smooth muscle cell is:

   A) actin.   B) troponin.   C) myosin.   D) calmodulin.

   Answer: D
   Diff: 1   *Page Ref: 267*

25) One functional unit of a skeletal muscle is:

   A) a sarcomere.   B) the myofilaments.
   C) the myofibrils.   D) the sarcoplasmic reticulum.

   Answer: A
   Diff: 1   *Page Ref: 238*

26) The functional role of the T tubules is to:

   A) stabilize the G and F actin.
   B) enhance cellular communication during muscle contraction.
   C) hold cross bridges in place in a resting muscle.
   D) synthesize ATP to provide energy for muscle contraction.

   Answer: B
   Diff: 1   *Page Ref: 243*

27) The role of calcium ions in muscle contraction is to:

   A) act as a third messenger.
   B) reestablish glycogen stores.
   C) bind to regulatory sites on troponin, changing the configuration.
   D) initiate the conversion of carbon dioxide to oxygen for storage.

   Answer: C
   Diff: 1   *Page Ref: 250*

28) The warm–up period required of athletes in order to bring their muscles to peak performance is called:

   A) twitch.   B) wave summation.
   C) treppe.   D) incomplete tetanus.

   Answer: C
   Diff: 1   *Page Ref: 254*

29) The main effect of the warm-up period of athletes, as the muscle contractions increase in strength, is to:

    A) increase the myoglobin content.

    B) convert glycogen to glucose.

    C) tone the muscles and stabilize the joints for the workout.

    D) enhance the availability of calcium and the efficiency of enzyme systems.

Answer: D
Diff: 1   *Page Ref: 254*

30) Athletes sometimes complain of oxygen debt, a condition that results when insufficient oxygen is available to completely break down pyruvic acid. As a result, the pyruvic acid is converted to:

    A) a strong base.   B) stearic acid.

    C) hydrochloric acid.   D) lactic acid.

Answer: D
Diff: 1   *Page Ref: 257*

31) When a muscle is unable to respond to stimuli temporarily, it is in which of the following periods?

    A) relaxation period   B) refractory period

    C) latent period   D) fatigue period

Answer: B
Diff: 1   *Page Ref: 247*

32) In an isotonic contraction, the muscle:

    A) changes in length and moves the "load."

    B) does not change in length but increases tension.

    C) never converts pyruvate to lactate.

    D) rapidly resynthesizes creatine phosphate and ATP.

Answer: A
Diff: 1   *Page Ref: 251*

33) Which of the following represents the percentage of energy released during muscle contraction?

    A) 50–65%   B) 90–100%   C) 20–25%   D) less than 10%

Answer: C
Diff: 1   *Page Ref: 259*

34) The muscle cell membrane is called a(n):

    A) endomysium.   B) sarcolemma.   C) perimysium.   D) epimysium.

Answer: B
Diff: 1   *Page Ref: 235*

35) Smooth muscle is significantly different from striated muscle in several ways. Which of the following is true?

   A) Smooth muscle has transverse tubules.

   B) Smooth muscle is larger and more powerful than striated muscle.

   C) The fibers of smooth muscle are arranged quadrangularly.

   D) Smooth muscle shortens and stretches to a greater extent than does striated muscle.

   Answer: D
   Diff: 1   Page Ref: 267

36) The mechanism of contraction in smooth muscle parallels that of skeletal muscle in the following ways except:

   A) Actin and myosin interact by the sliding filament mechanism.

   B) The trigger for contraction is a rise in intracellular calcium.

   C) The site of calcium regulation differs.

   D) ATP energizes the sliding process.

   Answer: C
   Diff: 1   Page Ref: 267

37) The cells of single-unit visceral muscle:

   A) contract all at once.

   B) are chemically coupled to one another by gap junctions.

   C) exhibit spontaneous action potentials.

   D) consist of muscle fibers that are structurally independent of each other.

   Answer: C
   Diff: 1   Page Ref: 266

38) Which of the following is true about smooth muscle contraction?

   A) Certain smooth muscle cells can actually divide to increase their numbers.

   B) Smooth muscle, in contrast to skeletal muscle, cannot synthesize or secrete any connective tissue elements.

   C) Smooth muscle cannot stretch as much as skeletal muscle.

   D) Smooth muscle has well-developed T tubules at the site of invagination.

   Answer: A
   Diff: 2   Page Ref: 265–266

39) Smooth muscle is characterized by all of the following except:

   A) it appears to lack troponin.

   B) there are more thick filaments than thin filaments.

   C) there are no sarcomeres.

   D) there are noncontractile intermediate filaments that attach to dense bodies within the cell.

   Answer: B
   Diff: 2   Page Ref: 265–266

40) Muscle tissue has all of the following properties except:

    A) transmissibility.   B) contractility.   C) extensibility.   D) excitability.

Answer: A
Diff: 2   *Page Ref: 236*

41) The giant protein titin maintains the organization of the _____ assisting in muscle stretching.

    A) A band   B) I band   C) Z disc   D) M line

Answer: A
Diff: 2   *Page Ref: 242*

42) Which of the following statements is true?

    A) Cardiac muscle cells have many nuclei.

    B) Smooth muscle cells have T tubules.

    C) Striated muscle cells are long and cylindrical with many nuclei.

    D) Cardiac muscle cells can respire in aerobic and anaerobic environments.

Answer: C
Diff: 2   *Page Ref: 268*

43) An anaerobic metabolic pathway that results in the production of two net ATP per glucose plus two pyruvic acid molecules is:

    A) the citric acid cycle.   B) glycolysis.

    C) hydrolysis.   D) the electron transport chain.

Answer: B
Diff: 2   *Page Ref: 256–257*

44) Muscle tone is:

    A) the ability of a muscle to efficiently cause skeletal movements.

    B) the feeling of well-being following exercise.

    C) a state of sustained partial contraction.

    D) the condition of athletes after intensive training.

Answer: C
Diff: 2   *Page Ref: 254*

45) The sliding filament model of contraction involves:

    A) actin and myosin sliding past each other but not shortening.

    B) the shortening of thick filaments so that thin filaments slide past.

    C) actin and myosin shortening but not sliding past each other.

    D) the Z discs sliding over the myofilaments.

Answer: A
Diff: 2   *Page Ref: 243*

46) The first thing that stops a contraction after the nerve stops sending ACh is:

   A) calcium ions return to the terminal cisternae.

   B) the tropomyosin blocks the myosin.

   C) AChE destroys the ACh, and they are removed from the membrane receptors.

   D) the action potential stops going down the T tubule.

   Answer: C
   Diff: 2   *Page Ref: 248*

47) Which of the following is most correct?

   A) Muscle tension remains constant during isotonic contraction.

   B) Myofilaments may be sliding during isotonic contraction.

   C) The I band does not shorten during isotonic contraction.

   D) Myofilaments slide during isometric contractions.

   Answer: A
   Diff: 2   *Page Ref: 251*

48) In the stress–relaxation response:

   A) a hollow organ is allowed to expand rapidly so as to expel some of its contents.

   B) the stretching of the muscle leads to contraction followed by relaxation.

   C) chemical stress causes relaxation of the muscle.

   D) one feels the "need" to go to the bathroom.

   Answer: B
   Diff: 2   *Page Ref: 270*

49) The most distinguishing characteristic of muscle tissue is:

   A) the design of the fibers.

   B) the sarcoplasmic reticulum.

   C) the diversity of activity of muscle tissue.

   D) the ability to transform chemical energy into mechanical energy.

   Answer: D
   Diff: 2   *Page Ref: 236*

50) Three discrete types of muscle fibers are identified on the basis of their size, speed, and endurance. Which of the following athletic endeavors best represents the use of red fibers?

   A) a sprint by an Olympic runner   B) a long, relaxing swim

   C) lifting weights   D) mountain climbing

   Answer: B
   Diff: 2   *Page Ref: 261–262*

51) Of the following muscle types, which has only one nucleus, no sarcomeres, and no gap junctions?

    A) visceral smooth muscle

    B) multiunit smooth muscle

    C) cardiac muscle

    D) skeletal muscle

    Answer: B
    Diff: 2   Page Ref: 268

52) Theoretically, if a muscle were stretched to the point where thick and thin filaments no longer overlapped:

    A) cross bridge attachment would be optimum because of all the free binding sites on actin.

    B) no muscle tension could be generated.

    C) maximum force production would result since the muscle has a maximum range of travel.

    D) ATP consumption would increase since the sarcomere is "trying" to contract.

    Answer: B
    Diff: 3   Page Ref: 243–246

53) An individual has just ingested a chemical that binds irreversibly to the ACh receptors in the sarcolemma. By itself it does not alter membrane potential, yet prevents normal neurotransmitter binding. Ignoring the effects on any other system, the consequence to skeletal muscle would be:

    A) irreversible contraction as soon as the first nervous stimulation reached the sarcolemma.

    B) no contraction at all by nervous mechanisms.

    C) contraction if stimulated by an external electrode.

    D) B and C are both correct.

    Answer: D
    Diff: 3   Page Ref: 247

Clinical Questions

1) Gary was injured in an automobile accident, resulting in the severing of the motor neurons innervating the quadriceps. Even though he has had extensive physical therapy, he is still suffering muscle atrophy. Why is the therapy not working?

    Answer: In denervation atrophy, muscle shrinkage results in fibrous tissue replacing muscle tissue. When atrophy is complete, fibrous tissue cannot be reversed to muscle tissue.
    Diff: 3   Page Ref: 264

2) Aaron arrived at the hospital with the following symptoms: drooping eyelids; fatigue and weakness of his muscles; and difficulty in talking, breathing, and swallowing. What was his diagnosis?

    Answer: Aaron probably has myasthenia gravis (an autoimmune disease), which involves a shortage of ACh receptors at the neuromuscular junction.
    Diff: 3   Page Ref: 247

3) Pam contracted polio before she had an opportunity to obtain the vaccine and found that the disease affected the neural innervation of her legs. She experienced significant muscle atrophy. Why did this happen?

Answer: Skeletal muscle requires continuous electrical or neural stimulation to remain viable. Without the stimulation, the myofibrils within the cell will deteriorate and much of the muscle will be replaced with connective tissue.
Diff: 3   Page Ref: 264

4) A long-distance runner is about to enter a 5-mile race. Beforehand, he spends several minutes "warming up." During the warm-up period, the phenomenon of treppe is occurring in body muscles being used. What is treppe and why does it occur?

Answer: Treppe is the staircase phenomenon in which muscles increase their strength of contraction due to increased availability of calcium. Additionally, the increased warmth due to activity causes an increase in the efficiency of muscle enzyme systems.
Diff: 3   Page Ref: 253-254

5) Robert, a chronic couch potato, decided very unexpectedly to walk his dog. The dog had other ideas and turned a slow walk into a race for over an hour, leaving Robert out of breath. The next day Robert complained of soreness and stiffness in his legs. What caused this problem?

Answer: He experienced a period of oxygen debt during his jaunt caused by his poor circulatory system. This resulted in a buildup of lactic acid, which caused the pain.
Diff: 3   Page Ref: 259

6) After removal of an elbow cast, Lauren noticed her arm was immovable. What happened to her arm?

Answer: Two things have occurred to Lauren while she was convalescing from her injury. First, the immobilizing of the arm caused atrophy of some muscle mass. Second, the loss of muscle was replaced with tough connective tissue that locked her arm in place. With therapy the tissue can be stretched or torn enough to return the full range of motion.
Diff: 5   Page Ref: 264

CHAPTER 10   The Muscular System

Fill-in-the-Blank/Short Answer Questions

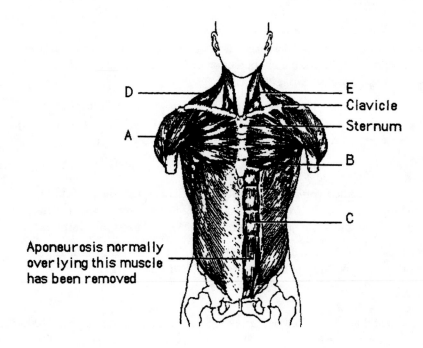

Figure 10.1

Using Figure 10.1, identify the following:

1) The trapezius muscle.

   Answer: D
   Diff: 1   Page Ref: 278

2) Flex and rotate lumbar region of vertebral column, fix and depress ribs, stabilize pelvis during walking, increase intra-abdominal pressure.

   Answer: C
   Diff: 1   Page Ref: 297

3) May extend and laterally rotate the arm.

   Answer: A
   Diff: 2   Page Ref: 304

4) Prime mover to protract and hold the scapula against the chest wall; rotates scapula so that its inferior angle moves laterally and upward.

   Answer: B
   Diff: 2   Page Ref: 301

5) A muscle that has its origin on the manubrium of the sternum and medial portion of the clavicle, and its insertion in the mastoid process of the temporal bone.

Answer: E
Diff: 2   *Page Ref: 290*

6) Can extend the head.

Answer: D
Diff: 2   *Page Ref: 291*

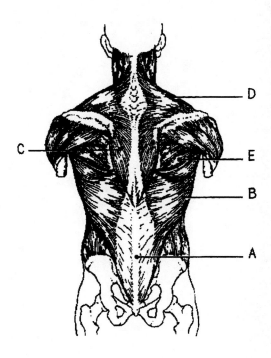

Figure 10.2
Using Figure 10.2, identify the following:

7) Trapezius muscle.

Answer: D
Diff: 1   *Page Ref: 301*

8) Teres major muscle.

Answer: E
Diff: 1   *Page Ref: 301, 303*

9) The latissimus dorsi.

Answer: B
Diff: 1   *Page Ref: 301–302*

10) Rotates scapula.

Answer: D
Diff: 2   Page Ref: 301

11) Depresses scapula.

Answer: E
Diff: 2   Page Ref: 301

Fill in the blank or provide a short answer:

12) _____ is a powerful forearm extensor.

Answer: Triceps brachii
Diff: 1   Page Ref: 305

13) The _____ runs deep to the external oblique.

Answer: internal oblique
Diff: 1   Page Ref: 296

14) The _____ helps keep food between the grinding surfaces of the teeth during chewing.

Answer: buccinator
Diff: 1   Page Ref: 286

15) _____ draws the corners of the mouth downward as in expressing horror.

Answer: Platysma
Diff: 1   Page Ref: 284

16) _____ is the main chewing muscle.

Answer: Masseter
Diff: 1   Page Ref: 286

17) The pectoralis major has a _____ arrangement of fascicles.

Answer: convergent
Diff: 1   Page Ref: 274

18) _____ fibers run at right angles to the axis of the muscle.

Answer: Transverse
Diff: 1   Page Ref: 296

19) Bodybuilders have "great quads." What are they?

Answer: These are the muscles of the front and sides of the thigh, and include the rectus femoris and the lateral, medial, and intermediate vastus muscles.
Diff: 1   Page Ref: 317

20) The quadriceps femoris is composed of three vastus muscles and the _____.

Answer: rectus femoris
Diff: 2   *Page Ref: 317–318*

21) _____ is a synergist of the latissimus dorsi; it extends, medially rotates, and adducts the humerus.

Answer: Teres major
Diff: 2   *Page Ref: 302*

22) A woman mentions to her friend that another person on the beach has "great abs." What is she talking about?

Answer: The woman is referring to well-developed rectus abdominis muscles on some individual. This is a term coined by bodybuilders and refers to the bulging muscles between the tendinous intersections.
Diff: 2   *Page Ref: 296*

23) Muscles that act as synergists seem to have valuable functions, especially in stabilizing joints. Briefly explain the function.

Answer: Synergists aid agonists by promoting the same movement or by reducing undesirable or unnecessary movements that might occur as the prime mover contracts.
Diff: 2   *Page Ref: 273*

24) How does an antagonist differ from a prime mover? How is it the same?

Answer: A prime mover is the muscle that causes the desired movement to occur. An antagonist is a muscle that opposes the action of the prime mover in a given movement. If, however, the direction of movement reverses, the former antagonist is now the prime mover and the former prime mover is now the antagonist.
Diff: 2   *Page Ref: 273*

25) _____ extends the great toe.

Answer: Extensor hallucis longus
Diff: 3   *Page Ref: 327*

26) How can a lever system work at a disadvantage but still be of use to us?

Answer: A lever that operates with the load far from the fulcrum and the effort applied near the fulcrum is operating at a disadvantage, but the advantage is that the load can move over large distances at a rapid rate.
Diff: 3   *Page Ref: 275–280*

Matching Questions

Match the following muscle actions:

1) Column 1: Flexes the wrist.

   Column 2: Flexor carpi ulnaris

   Answer: Flexor carpi ulnaris
   Diff: 1   *Page Ref: 306*

2) Column 1: Slow–acting finger flexor.

   Column 2: Flexor digitorum profundus

   Answer: Flexor digitorum profundus
   Diff: 1   *Page Ref: 307*

3) Column 1: Powerful wrist flexors that
   also stabilize the wrist during
   finger extension.

   Column 2: Flexor carpi ulnaris

   Answer: Flexor carpi ulnaris
   Diff: 1   *Page Ref: 306*

4) Column 1: Extends and abducts the
   wrist.

   Column 2: Extensor carpi radialis longus
   and brevis

   Answer: Extensor carpi radialis longus and brevis
   Diff: 1   *Page Ref: 308*

5) Column 1: Extends the thumb.

   Column 2: Extensor pollicis longus and
   brevis

   Foil: Extensor carpi ulnaris

   Answer: Extensor pollicis longus and brevis
   Diff: 1   *Page Ref: 308*

Match the following:

6) Column 1: Muscle that opposes and
   reverses the action of another
   muscle.

   Column 2: Antagonist

   Answer: Antagonist
   Diff: 1   *Page Ref: 273*

7) Column 1: Muscle that stabilizes the
   origin of another muscle.

   Column 2: Fixator

   Answer: Fixator
   Diff: 1   *Page Ref: 273*

8) Column 1: Muscle that is primarily
            responsible for bringing about
            a particular movement.

   Column 2: Agonist

   Answer: Agonist
   Diff: 1   Page Ref: 273

9) Column 1: Muscle that aids another by
            promoting the same
            movement.

   Column 2: Synergist

   Answer: Synergist
   Diff: 1   Page Ref: 273

True/False Questions

1) A pair of tweezers is a good example of a second–class lever.

   Answer: FALSE
   Diff: 1   Page Ref: 276–278

2) The "bi" in biceps refers to the number of insertions the muscle has.

   Answer: FALSE
   Diff: 1   Page Ref: 305

3) Both first- and second–class levers operate at a mechanical disadvantage.

   Answer: FALSE
   Diff: 1   Page Ref: 276–278

4) Although all skeletal muscles have different shapes, the fascicle arrangement of each muscle is exactly the same.

   Answer: FALSE
   Diff: 1   Page Ref: 274

5) Muscles are only able to pull, they never push.

   Answer: TRUE
   Diff: 1   Page Ref: 273

6) The diaphragm is the prime mover of inspiration.

   Answer: TRUE
   Diff: 1   Page Ref: 294

7) The anconeus muscle flexes the knee and stabilizes the patella.

   Answer: FALSE
   Diff: 1   Page Ref: 305

8) The extensor digitorum is a prime mover of finger extension, extends the wrist, and abducts the fingers.

Answer: TRUE
Diff: 1   Page Ref: 308

9) Movements of the thigh are accomplished by muscles anchored to the pelvic girdle.

Answer: TRUE
Diff: 1   Page Ref: 315

10) The insertion of the biceps brachii is on the radius.

Answer: TRUE
Diff: 1   Page Ref: 305

11) The mastoid process attachment of the sternocleidomastoid muscle represents its insertion.

Answer: TRUE
Diff: 1   Page Ref: 290

12) The chewing muscle covering the ramus of the mandible is the buccinator.

Answer: FALSE
Diff: 1   Page Ref: 284–286

13) In a third–class lever, the effort is applied in the middle and the fulcrum is to one end, something like tweezers.

Answer: TRUE
Diff: 1   Page Ref: 278

14) If a lever operates at a mechanical disadvantage, it is always useless.

Answer: FALSE
Diff: 1   Page Ref: 279–280

15) The coccygeus is a minor muscle of the pelvic floor.

Answer: FALSE
Diff: 1   Page Ref: 298

16) A prime mover of the arm that acts in adduction would be the deltoid.

Answer: FALSE
Diff: 1   Page Ref: 303

17) The soleus is a synergist of the gastrocnemius used in plantar flexion.

Answer: TRUE
Diff: 1   Page Ref: 321

18) Muscles that help to maintain posture are often called synergists.

Answer: FALSE
Diff: 1   *Page Ref: 273*

19) In order to propel food down to the esophagus, the pharyngeal constrictor muscles would be used.

Answer: TRUE
Diff: 1   *Page Ref: 288*

20) The largest and most superficial muscle of the abdominal wall is the rectus abdominus.

Answer: FALSE
Diff: 1   *Page Ref: 296*

21) The extensor carpi radialis longus is located on the lateral aspect of the forearm.

Answer: TRUE
Diff: 1   *Page Ref: 308*

22) Plantar flexion at the ankle joint is accomplished by the tibialis anterior muscle.

Answer: FALSE
Diff: 1   *Page Ref: 321*

23) The arrangement of a muscle's fascicles determines its range of motion and power.

Answer: TRUE
Diff: 2   *Page Ref: 274*

24) Muscle power does not depend on the direction of the fascicles.

Answer: FALSE
Diff: 2   *Page Ref: 274*

25) The calcaneal tendon (Achilles tendon) is the largest, strongest tendon in the body.

Answer: TRUE
Diff: 2   *Page Ref: 324*

26) The four muscle pairs forming the abdominal wall perform the functions of support and compression of the abdominal contents.

Answer: FALSE
Diff: 2   *Page Ref: 296*

27) The digastric muscle is so named because it consists of two bellies united by an anterior tendon.

Answer: FALSE
Diff: 2   *Page Ref: 288*

28) Severing of the patellar tendon would inactivate the hamstring group.

Answer: FALSE
Diff: 2   Page Ref: 217

29) The broadest muscle of the back is the latissimus dorsi.

Answer: TRUE
Diff: 2   Page Ref: 301–302

30) A synergistic extensor muscle of the arm is the brachialis.

Answer: FALSE
Diff: 2   Page Ref: 305

31) Muscle spasms of the back would often include the erector spinae.

Answer: TRUE
Diff: 2   Page Ref: 392

32) The serratus anterior muscle adducts the arm and lowers the point of the shoulder.

Answer: FALSE
Diff: 2   Page Ref: 300

33) Paralysis of the anterior muscle group of the leg would cause a condition called foot drop.

Answer: TRUE
Diff: 2   Page Ref: 321

34) The latissimus dorsi is considered synergistic with the rhomboid major.

Answer: FALSE
Diff: 2   Page Ref: 301–302

35) The levator scapulae retracts the scapula in order to "square the shoulders."

Answer: FALSE
Diff: 3   Page Ref: 301

36) When the extensor carpi radialis longus is contracted as the flexor digitorum superficialis is shortening (contracting), it is acting as an antagonist.

Answer: TRUE
Diff: 3   Page Ref: 307–309

37) Muscles connecting to the hyoid bone are instrumental in speech.

Answer: FALSE
Diff: 3   Page Ref: 288

Multiple-Choice Questions

1) Scissors demonstrate which type of lever?

   A) a first–class lever   B) a second–class lever
   C) a third–class lever   D) a fourth–class lever

   Answer: A
   Diff: 1   Page Ref: 276–278

2) What is the major factor controlling the manner in which levers work?

   A) the structural characteristics of the muscles of the person using the lever
   B) the weight of the load
   C) the direction the load is being moved
   D) the difference in the positioning of the effort, load, and fulcrum

   Answer: D
   Diff: 1   Page Ref: 278–279

3) With regard to muscle fiber arrangement in a pennate muscle:

   A) the fascicles are short and attach obliquely to a central tendon that runs the length of a
      muscle.
   B) the fascicular pattern is circular.
   C) the fascicles form a triangle.
   D) the fascicles are in a fusiform arrangement.

   Answer: A
   Diff: 1   Page Ref: 274

4) What primarily determines the power of a muscle?

   A) the length
   B) the shape
   C) the number of neurons innervating it
   D) the total number of muscle cells available for contraction

   Answer: D
   Diff: 1   Page Ref: 274

5) A muscle that provides the major force for producing a specific movement is called:

   A) a synergist.   B) an agonist.   C) an antagonist.   D) a fixator.

   Answer: B
   Diff: 1   Page Ref: 273

6) When the term *biceps, triceps,* or *quadriceps* forms part of a muscle's name, you can assume that:
   A) the muscle has two, three, or four origins, respectively.
   B) the muscle is able to change direction twice, three times, or four times faster than other muscles, respectively.
   C) the muscle has two, three, or four functions, respectively.
   D) the muscle has two, three, or four insertions, respectively.

   Answer: A
   Diff: 1   Page Ref: 274

7) Which of the following statements is true regarding the total number of skeletal muscles in the human body?
   A) There are approximately the same number of muscles as bones: 206.
   B) There are approximately 350 muscles in the body.
   C) There are over 600 muscles in the body.
   D) If one considers the very tiny, insignificant muscles, there are over 1000 muscles in the body.

   Answer: C
   Diff: 1   Page Ref: 280

8) The names of muscles often indicate the action of the muscle. When the term *levator* is part of the descriptive term for a muscle's action, this means that:
   A) the muscle flexes and rotates a region.
   B) the muscle is a fixator and stabilizes a bone or joint.
   C) the muscle elevates and/or adducts a region.
   D) the muscle functions as a synergist.

   Answer: C
   Diff: 1   Page Ref: 274

9) The suprahyoid muscles:
   A) depress the larynx and hyoid bone if the mandible is fixed.
   B) are a group of muscles that lie superior to the hyoid bone and help form the floor of the oral cavity.
   C) move the pharynx superiorly during swallowing.
   D) are often called strap muscles.

   Answer: B
   Diff: 1   Page Ref: 288

10) The supraspinatus is named for its location on the posterior aspect of the scapula above the spine. What is its action?

A) to help hold the head of the humerus in the glenoid cavity and rotate the humerus laterally

B) to stabilize the shoulder joint and help prevent downward location of the humerus and to assist in abduction

C) to extend and medially rotate the humerus and to act as a synergist of the latissimus dorsi

D) to flex and adduct the humerus and to act as a synergist of the pectoralis major

Answer: B
Diff: 1   Page Ref: 303

11) The extensor carpi radialis brevis:

A) extends and abducts the wrist and is short.

B) extends and adducts the wrist and has a small tendon.

C) supinates the forearm and is a superficial muscle.

D) extends the thumb and is a deep muscle.

Answer: A
Diff: 1   Page Ref: 308

12) The "tailor's muscle" is the:

A) iliacus.   B) psoas.   C) sartorius.   D) rectus femoris.

Answer: C
Diff: 1   Page Ref: 315

13) The muscles that are found at openings of the body are collectively called:

A) convergent muscles.   B) circular muscles.

C) parallel muscles.   D) divergent muscles.

Answer: B
Diff: 1   Page Ref: 274

14) To produce horizontal wrinkles in the forehead, which of the following muscles is involved?

A) the medial pterygoid   B) the zygomaticus major

C) the frontalis   D) the temporalis

Answer: C
Diff: 1   Page Ref: 283

15) A cute little curly-haired child is sitting behind you in church. You turn around for a moment and she sticks her tongue out at you. Which tongue muscle did she use?

A) obicularis oris   B) stylohyoid   C) hyoglossus   D) geniohyoid

Answer: D
Diff: 1   Page Ref: 288

16) Which group of muscles flexes and rotates the neck?

    A) the scalenes   B) the iliocostals   C) the spinalis   D) the splenius

Answer: A
Diff: 1   Page Ref: 290

17) Which of the following muscles is involved in crossing one leg over the other while in a sitting position?

    A) the gastrocnemius   B) the sartorius

    C) all of the hamstrings   D) the quadriceps femoris

Answer: B
Diff: 1   Page Ref: 315

18) Which of the following muscles inserts by the calcaneal tendon?

    A) the semitendinosus   B) the sartorius

    C) the tibialis anterior   D) the gastrocnemius

Answer: D
Diff: 1   Page Ref: 324

19) If a lever operates at a mechanical disadvantage, it means that the:

    A) load is far from the fulcrum and the effort is applied near the fulcrum.

    B) lever system is useless.

    C) effort is farther than the load from the fulcrum.

    D) load is near the fulcrum and the effort is at the distal end.

Answer: A
Diff: 1   Page Ref: 276–280

20) Which of the following does not compress the abdomen?

    A) internal oblique   B) external oblique

    C) transversus abdominis   D) coccygeus

Answer: D
Diff: 1   Page Ref: 298

21) A muscle group that works with and assists the action of a prime mover is a(n):

    A) antagonist.   B) fixator.   C) synergist.   D) protagonist.

Answer: C
Diff: 1   Page Ref: 273

22) A muscle located on the dorsal side of the body is the:

    A) pectoralis minor.   B) rectus femoris.

    C) rectus abdominis.   D) infraspinatus.

Answer: D
Diff: 1   Page Ref: 303

23) Which of the following is not a member of the hamstrings?

    A) gracilis   B) semitendinosus

    C) semimembranosus   D) biceps femoris

Answer: A
Diff: 1   Page Ref: 320

24) A nursing infant develops a powerful sucking muscle that adults also use for whistling called
    the:

    A) platysma.   B) masseter.   C) zygomaticus.   D) buccinator.

Answer: D
Diff: 1   Page Ref: 284

25) Spasms of this straplike muscle often result in wryneck or torticollis.

    A) serratus anterior   B) zygomaticus

    C) platysma   D) sternocleidomastoid

Answer: D
Diff: 1   Page Ref: 290

26) Which generalization concerning movement by skeletal muscles is not true?

    A) Muscles produce movement by pulling on bones.

    B) The bones serve as levers.

    C) During contraction the two articulating bones move equally.

    D) The movements produced may be of graded intensity.

Answer: C
Diff: 1   Page Ref: 273-280

27) Which of these is not a way of classifying muscles?

    A) muscle location   B) the type of muscle fibers

    C) the type of action they cause   D) muscle shape

Answer: B
Diff: 1   Page Ref: 273-274

28) In flexing the forearm at the elbow, the:

    A) biceps brachii acts as antagonist.   B) triceps brachii acts as antagonist.

    C) brachioradialis acts as antagonist.   D) coracobrachialis acts as antagonist.

Answer: B
Diff: 1   Page Ref: 305

29) Orbicularis oris:

   A) closes, purses, and protrudes the lips.

   B) pulls the lower lip down and back.

   C) draws the eyebrows together.

   D) allows blinking, squinting, and various other protective mechanisms for the eye.

   Answer: A
   Diff: 1   Page Ref: 284

30) In a pennate muscle pattern:

   A) muscles appear to be straplike.

   B) there is a narrow origin diverging to a broad insertion.

   C) there is a broad origin and fascicles converge toward a single tendon.

   D) muscles look like a feather.

   Answer: D
   Diff: 1   Page Ref: 274

31) The extensor digitorum longus has which type of fascicle arrangement?

   A) circular   B) convergent   C) unipennate   D) bipennate

   Answer: C
   Diff: 2   Page Ref: 274

32) Tennis players often complain about pain in the arm (forearm) that swings the racquet. What muscle is usually strained under these conditions?

   A) the triceps brachii   B) the anconeus

   C) the brachioradialis   D) the flexor digitorum profundus

   Answer: C
   Diff: 2   Page Ref: 305

33) To exhale forcibly, one would contract the:

   A) diaphragm alone.   B) internal intercostals and diaphragm.

   C) external intercostals and diaphragm. D) rectus abdominis and diaphragm.

   Answer: B
   Diff: 2   Page Ref: 294

34) Paralysis of which of the following would make an individual unable to flex the thigh?

   A) biceps   B) vastus medialis

   C) soleus   D) iliopsoas and rectus femoris

   Answer: D
   Diff: 2   Page Ref: 315, 317

35) First–class levers:

A) have load at one end of the lever, fulcrum at the other, and effort applied somewhere in the middle.

B) are typified by tweezers or forceps.

C) in the body can operate at a mechanical advantage or mechanical disadvantage, depending on specific location.

D) are the type found in the joints forming the ball of the foot as used in raising the body on the toes.

Answer: C
Diff: 2   Page Ref: 276

36) What do geniohyoid, hyoglossus, and stylohyoid have in common?

A) All names reflect direction of muscle fibers.

B) Each acts synergistically to elevate the jaw.

C) All act on the tongue.

D) All names indicate the relative size of the muscle.

Answer: C
Diff: 2   Page Ref: 287–288

37) Adductor magnus, adductor longus, and adductor brevis are parts of a large muscle mass of the:

A) lateral rotators.   B) anterior compartment of the thigh.

C) posterior muscle group of the thigh. D) medial compartment of the thigh.

Answer: D
Diff: 2   Page Ref: 317

38) Which of the following muscles is involved in abduction?

A) deltoid   B) subscapularis   C) teres major   D) latissimus dorsi

Answer: A
Diff: 2   Page Ref: 303

39) Which of the following muscles is a flexor of the thigh?

A) gracilis   B) vastus lateralis

C) adductor magnus   D) gluteus maximus

Answer: C
Diff: 2   Page Ref: 317

40) Which of the following muscles is involved in inversion at the ankle joint?

A) tibialis anterior   B) extensor digitorum longus

C) peroneus tertius   D) peroneus longus

Answer: A
Diff: 2   Page Ref: 321

41) Which of the following muscles serves as a common intramuscular injection site, particularly in infants?

A) the vastus intermedius   B) the vastus medialis

C) rectus femoris   D) the vastus lateralis

Answer: D
Diff: 3   *Page Ref: 317*

42) Paralysis of which of the following would make an individual unable to flex the knee?

A) hamstring muscles   B) gluteal muscles

C) brachioradialis   D) soleus

Answer: A
Diff: 3   *Page Ref: 320*

43) Which of the following muscles does not act in plantar flexion?

A) popliteus   B) tibialis posterior

C) flexor digitorum longus   D) gastrocnemius and soleus

Answer: A
Diff: 3   *Page Ref: 325*

Clinical Questions

1) An elderly woman, with extensive osteoarthritis of her left hip joint, entered the hospital to have a total hip joint replacement (prosthesis implantation). After surgery, her left hip had to be maintained in adduction to prevent dislocation of the prosthesis while healing was occurring. Physical therapy was prescribed to prevent atrophy of the gluteal muscles during the interval of disuse. Name the gluteal muscles and describe the action of each that was being prevented while the hip was adducted.

Answer: Gluteus maximus, gluteus medius, and gluteus minimus. The origins are on the pelvis and they act as major extensors of the thigh and act in abduction and rotation.
Diff: 2   *Page Ref: 318*

2) Donna was rushing to class and slipped on a patch of ice and fell backwards. An X ray revealed a broken coccyx. All the associated muscles were bruised. Name these muscles.

Answer: The bruised muscles were levator ani and coccygeus.
Diff: 2   *Page Ref: 298*

3) Brian decided to enter a 5–mile race designed to raise money for a class trip. He did not do any preconditioning, nor has he ever jogged before. The morning after the race, Brian had so much pain in both his shins, he was unable to go to school. Explain what condition, common to runners, caused this pain?

Answer: Brian was not conditioned for this type of run, and he now has shinsplints. This is a condition in which the anterior tibialis muscle is irritated, and as the inflamed muscle swells, its circulation is impaired by the tight fascial wrappings, causing pain and tenderness.
Diff: 3   *Page Ref: 321*

4) Hank is a quarterback for his high school team. Last week, he was tackled and brought down with force that impacted on his left thigh. He has been suffering severe and prolonged pain. The trainer told Hank that he had a "charley horse" in the quadraceps. What does this mean?

Answer: Hank is suffering from a muscle contusion caused by the impact. The muscle is probably torn, and there is bleeding into the tissues.

Diff: 3   *Page Ref: 317*

5) A wide receiver for the Dallas Cowboys pulled a hamstring muscle. What muscles could be affected and what would the effect be?

Answer: The muscles include the biceps femoris, semitendinosus, and semimembranosus. They are important flexors of the leg and extensors of the thigh. Injuries here could make it impossible to run properly or to bend the thigh.

Diff: 3   *Page Ref: 320*

6) Malcolm was bending over to pick up a heavy box when he was suddenly startled by a rat. He experienced severe pain in his back with muscle spasms and was unable to straighten up. What muscles could have been affected?

Answer: He probably affected the erector spinae muscles, since these readily go into spasms when the back is injured.

Diff: 3   *Page Ref: 292*

7) A young pregnant woman went to a childbirth class and the instructor informed them about strengthening the muscles of the pelvic floor. What are these muscles?

Answer: The levator ani and coccygeus muscles form the bulk of the pelvic diaphragm (pelvic floor). Strengthening these muscles helps in the delivery of the child by resisting downward forces when "pushing."

Diff: 4   *Page Ref: 298*

CHAPTER 11   Fundamentals of the Nervous System and Nervous Tissue

Fill–in–the–Blank/Short Answer Questions

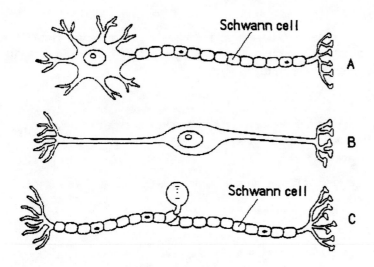

Figure 11.1

Using Figure 11.1, identify the following:

1) Which nerve would connect to a muscle?

   Answer: A
   Diff: 1   Page Ref: 338, 342

2) Which nerve would be found in the retina of the eye?

   Answer: B
   Diff: 1   Page Ref: 342

3) Which neuron is a motor neuron?

   Answer: A
   Diff: 1   Page Ref: 338, 342

4) Which neuron is a sensory neuron found in a reflex arc?

   Answer: B
   Diff: 1   Page Ref: 342

5) Which neuron is never myelinated?

   Answer: B
   Diff: 1   Page Ref: 342

6) Which neuron is rare?

   Answer: B
   Diff: 1   Page Ref: 342

7) Which neuron has its cell body inside the spinal cord?

   Answer: A
   Diff: 1   Page Ref: 338

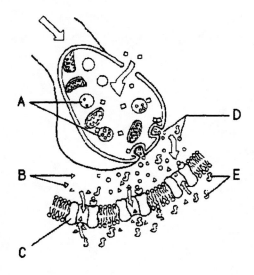

Figure 11.2

Using Figure 11.2, identify the following:

   8) Ion channel.

      Answer: C
      Diff: 1   Page Ref: 356

   9) Synaptic vesicles.

      Answer: A
      Diff: 1   Page Ref: 356

   10) Neurotransmitter molecules.

      Answer: D
      Diff: 2   Page Ref: 356

   11) Sodium ions.

      Answer: B
      Diff: 2   Page Ref: 356

12) Potassium ions.

   Answer: E
   Diff: 3   Page Ref: 356

Fill in the blank or provide a short answer:

13) That part of the nervous system that is voluntary and conducts impulses from the CNS to the skeletal muscles is the _____ nervous system.

   Answer: somatic
   Diff: 1   Page Ref: 334

14) _____ are found in the CNS and act as the glue that binds axons and blood vessels to each other.

   Answer: Astrocytes
   Diff: 1   Page Ref: 336–337

15) The gap between Schwann cells in the peripheral system is called a(n) _____.

   Answer: node of Ranvier
   Diff: 1   Page Ref: 341

16) _____ law is the relationship between voltage, current, and resistance.

   Answer: Ohm's
   Diff: 1   Page Ref: 344

17) When information is delivered within the CNS simultaneously by different parts of the neural pathway, the process is called _____ processing.

   Answer: parallel
   Diff: 1   Page Ref: 368

18) _____ potentials are short–lived, local changes in membrane potential that can be either depolarized or hyperpolarized.

   Answer: Graded
   Diff: 2   Page Ref: 347–348

19) _____ is a disease that gradually destroys the myelin sheaths of neurons in the CNS, particularly in young adults.

   Answer: Multiple sclerosis (MS)
   Diff: 2   Page Ref: 354

20) When one or more presynaptic neurons fire in rapid order it produces a much greater depolarization of the postsynaptic membrane than would result from a single EPSP; this event is called _____ summation.

   Answer: temporal
   Diff: 2   Page Ref: 359

21) _____ is a neurotransmitter of the CNS that is used by Purkinje cells of the CNS.

Answer: GABA (gamma aminobutyric acid)
Diff: 2   Page Ref: 361

22) Imagine a neuron that has several hundred axonal knobs impinging on it. The majority of these axonal knobs are shown to be "firing." However, the neuron in question does not transmit an impulse. Give a valid explanation of why this could occur.

Answer: Both excitatory and inhibitory potentials impinge on neurons. Inhibitory postsynaptic potentials (IPSPs) are "firing," but due to the neurotransmitter released and its action, the postsynaptic neuron is inhibited from "firing" (hyperpolarized).
Diff: 4   Page Ref: 357–358

Matching Questions

Match the following:

1) Column 1: Neurotransmitters are released at the _____.
   Column 2: Axonal terminal

   Answer: Axonal terminal
   Diff: 1   Page Ref: 339

2) Column 1: The rough ER of the cell.
   Column 2: Nissl bodies

   Answer: Nissl bodies
   Diff: 1   Page Ref: 337

3) Column 1: Conducts impulses toward the nerve cell body.
   Column 2: Dendrites

   Answer: Dendrites
   Diff: 1   Page Ref: 339

4) Column 1: Conducts impulses away from the nerve cell body.
   Column 2: Axon
       Foil: Cell body

   Answer: Axon
   Diff: 1   Page Ref: 339

Match the following:

5) Column 1: Period during which the neuron cannot respond to a second stimulus, no matter how strong.

    Column 2: Absolute refractory period

    Answer: Absolute refractory period
    Diff: 1   Page Ref: 352

6) Column 1: The interior of the cell becomes less negative due to an influx of sodium ions.

    Column 2: Depolarization

    Answer: Depolarization
    Diff: 1   Page Ref: 346

7) Column 1: The specific period during which potassium ions diffuse out of the neuron due to a change in membrane permeability.

    Column 2: Repolarization

    Answer: Repolarization
    Diff: 1   Page Ref: 350

8) Column 1: Called a nerve impulse when transmitted.

    Column 2: Action potential

    Answer: Action potential
    Diff: 1   Page Ref: 348

9) Column 1: An exceptionally strong stimulus can trigger a response.

    Column 2: Relative refractory period

    Answer: Relative refractory period
    Diff: 1   Page Ref: 352

Match the following:

10) Column 1: Numerous nerve impulses arriving at a synapse at closely timed intervals exert a cumulative effect.

    Column 2: Temporal summation

    Answer: Temporal summation
    Diff: 1   Page Ref: 359

11) Column 1: Stimulation of a postsynaptic
              neuron by many terminals at
              the same time.

    Column 2: Spatial summation

    Answer: Spatial summation
    Diff: 1   *Page Ref: 359*

12) Column 1: An insufficient stimulus.

    Column 2: Subthreshold stimulus

    Answer: Subthreshold stimulus
    Diff: 1   *Page Ref: 351*

13) Column 1: Any stimulus below this
              intensity will result in no
              response in a neuron.

    Column 2: Threshold stimulus

    Answer: Threshold stimulus
    Diff: 2   *Page Ref: 351*

True/False Questions

1) The all–or–none phenomenon as applied to nerve conduction states that the whole nerve cell must be stimulated for conduction to take place.

   Answer: FALSE
   Diff: 1   *Page Ref: 352*

2) Reflexes are rapid, automatic responses to stimuli.

   Answer: TRUE
   Diff: 1   *Page Ref: 368*

3) A sensory neuron carries stimuli from the central nervous system to the effector.

   Answer: FALSE
   Diff: 1   *Page Ref: 334*

4) Efferent nerve fibers may be described as motor nerve fibers.

   Answer: TRUE
   Diff: 1   *Page Ref: 334*

5) Saltatory conduction occurs because of the presence of salt (NaCl) around the neuron.

   Answer: FALSE
   Diff: 1   *Page Ref: 353*

6) Cell bodies of sensory neurons are located in ganglia lying outside the central nervous system.

   Answer: TRUE
   Diff: 1   *Page Ref: 341*

7) Myelination of the nerve fibers in the central nervous system is the job of the oligodendrocyte.

Answer: TRUE
Diff: 1   Page Ref: 341

8) During depolarization, the inside of the neuron's membrane becomes less negative.

Answer: TRUE
Diff: 1   Page Ref: 346

9) Neurons in the CNS are organized into functional groups.

Answer: TRUE
Diff: 1   Page Ref: 341-343

10) Strong stimuli cause the amplitude of action potentials generated to increase.

Answer: FALSE
Diff: 1   Page Ref: 347-348

11) The oligodendrocytes can myelinate several axons.

Answer: TRUE
Diff: 1   Page Ref: 341

12) Neurons do not undergo mitosis in adults.

Answer: TRUE
Diff: 1   Page Ref: 337

13) Enkephalins and endorphins are peptides that act like morphine.

Answer: TRUE
Diff: 1   Page Ref: 362

14) A synapse formed between the axonal ending of one neuron and the cell body of another neuron is called an axosomatic synapse.

Answer: TRUE
Diff: 1   Page Ref: 354

15) In myelinated axons the voltage-gated sodium channels are concentrated at the nodes of Ranvier.

Answer: TRUE
Diff: 1   Page Ref: 353

16) Efferent neurons transmit impulses from the periphery to the CNS.

Answer: FALSE
Diff: 1   Page Ref: 343

17) Action potentials can be generated by virtually all cells of the body because all cells possess cell membranes.

Answer: FALSE
Diff: 1   Page Ref: 348

18) In the neuron, the rough ER is also known as Nissl bodies.

Answer: TRUE
Diff: 1   Page Ref: 337

19) Voltage is always measured between two points and may be called the potential between these two points.

Answer: TRUE
Diff: 1   Page Ref: 344

20) Temporal summation occurs when the postsynaptic neuron is being stimulated by a large number of terminals from the same or different neurons at the same time.

Answer: FALSE
Diff: 1   Page Ref: 359

21) Neurons that are far away from the center of the neuron pool and that are not easily excited by an incoming stimulus are in the discharge zone.

Answer: FALSE
Diff: 1   Page Ref: 366–367

22) Both oligodendrocytes and astrocytes wrap around axons of the central nervous system.

Answer: TRUE
Diff: 1   Page Ref: 336–337

23) Acetylcholine is a biogenic amine.

Answer: FALSE
Diff: 1   Page Ref: 361

24) The two major classes of graded potential are transmitter potentials and receptor potentials.

Answer: FALSE
Diff: 2   Page Ref: 347

25) A graded potential that is the result of a neurotransmitter released into the synapse between two neurons is called a postsynaptic potential.

Answer: TRUE
Diff: 2   Page Ref: 347

26) Large–diameter nerve fibers conduct impulses much faster than do small–diameter fibers.

Answer: TRUE
Diff: 2   Page Ref: 353

27) The nodes of Ranvier are found only on myelinated, peripheral neural processes.

Answer: FALSE
Diff: 2   Page Ref: 341

28) Sensory neurons have long dendrites, while motor neurons have long axons.

Answer: TRUE
Diff: 2   Page Ref: 341-343

29) A stimulus traveling toward a synapse appears to open calcium channels at the presynaptic end, which in turn promote fusion of synaptic vesicles to the axonal membrane.

Answer: TRUE
Diff: 3   Page Ref: 356

30) A positive feedback cycle is the main force in the generation of graded potentials at receptor ends.

Answer: FALSE
Diff: 3   Page Ref: 350

31) If bacteria were to invade the CNS tissue, microglia would migrate to the area to engulf and destroy them.

Answer: TRUE
Diff: 3   Page Ref: 337

Multiple-Choice Questions

1) Direct–acting neurotransmitters:
   A) require cyclic AMP.
   B) mediate very slow responses.
   C) open ion channels to provoke rapid responses.
   D) act through second messengers.

Answer: C
Diff: 1   Page Ref: 365

2) Which of the following is correct relative to Ohm's law?
   A) $I = R \, / \, V$
   B) Current is directly proportional to the voltage.
   C) $R = V + I$
   D) The more intense the stimulus, the more voltage changes.

Answer: B
Diff: 1   Page Ref: 344

3) The nervous system exhibits all these major functions except:
   A) monitoring changes.   B) integrating impulses.
   C) storing calcium.   D) effecting responses.

   Answer: C
   Diff: 1   *Page Ref: 334*

4) Ciliated CNS neuroglia that play an active role in moving the cerebrospinal fluid are:
   A) ependymal cells.   B) Schwann cells.
   C) oligodendrocytes.   D) astrocytes.

   Answer: A
   Diff: 1   *Page Ref: 337*

5) The sheath of Schwann is also called the:
   A) myelin sheath.   B) axolemma.   C) neurilemma.   D) white matter.

   Answer: C
   Diff: 1   *Page Ref: 340*

6) Bipolar cells are commonly:
   A) motor neurons.   B) called neuroglia.
   C) found in ganglia.   D) found in the retina of the eye.

   Answer: D
   Diff: 1   *Page Ref: 341*

7) An excitatory neurotransmitter secreted by motor neurons innervating skeletal muscle is:
   A) cholinesterase.   B) norepinephrine.
   C) acetylcholine.   D) gamma aminobutyric acid.

   Answer: C
   Diff: 1   *Page Ref: 361*

8) A neural circuit in which a single impulse is transmitted over and over is a:
   A) diverging circuit.   B) converging circuit.
   C) reverberating circuit.   D) repetitive circuit.

   Answer: C
   Diff: 1   *Page Ref: 367*

9) The period after an initial stimulus when a neuron is not sensitive to another stimulus is the:
   A) resting period.   B) repolarization.
   C) depolarization.   D) refractory period.

   Answer: D
   Diff: 1   *Page Ref: 352–353*

10) A neuronal circuit that concentrates or directs a large number of incoming impulses to a rather small number of neurons is called a(n):

   A) diverging circuit.

   B) oscillating circuit.

   C) converging circuit.

   D) parallel circuit.

   Answer: C
   Diff: 1   Page Ref: 367

11) Which of the following is not a structural feature of a neuron?

   A) synaptic cleft   B) Nissl bodies   C) dendrites   D) axon

   Answer: A
   Diff: 1   Page Ref: 337–339

12) The part of a neuron that conducts impulses away from its cell body is called a(n):

   A) axon.   B) dendrite.   C) neurolemma.   D) Schwann cell.

   Answer: A
   Diff: 1   Page Ref: 339

13) If one incoming impulse causes several outgoing nerve impulses, we know that there is a:

   A) converging circuit.

   B) concentration effect.

   C) diverging circuit.

   D) reverberating circuit.

   Answer: C
   Diff: 1   Page Ref: 367

14) The point at which an impulse from one nerve cell is communicated to another nerve cell is the:

   A) cell body.   B) synapse.   C) receptor.   D) effector.

   Answer: B
   Diff: 1   Page Ref: 354

15) The role of acetylcholinesterase is to:

   A) act as a transmitting agent.

   B) amplify or enhance the effect of ACh.

   C) destroy ACh a brief period after its release by the axonal endings.

   D) stimulate the production of serotonin.

   Answer: C
   Diff: 1   Page Ref: 361

16) Which of the following is not a function of the autonomic nervous system?

A) innervation of smooth muscle of the digestive tract

B) innervation of cardiac muscle

C) innervation of glands

D) innervation of skeletal muscle

Answer: D
Diff: 1   Page Ref: 334–335

17) Collections of nerve cell bodies outside the central nervous system are called:

A) nuclei.   B) nerves.   C) ganglia.   D) tracts.

Answer: C
Diff: 1   Page Ref: 338

18) The term *central nervous system* refers to the:

A) autonomic nervous system.   B) brain, spinal cord, and peripheral nerves.

C) brain and spinal cord.   D) spinal cord and spinal nerves.

Answer: C
Diff: 1   Page Ref: 334

19) The substance released at axonal endings to propagate a nervous impulse is called a(n):

A) ion.   B) cholinesterase.

C) neurotransmitter.   D) biogenic amine.

Answer: C
Diff: 1   Page Ref: 355

20) A neuron that has as its primary function the job of connecting other neurons is called a(n):

A) efferent neuron.   B) afferent neuron.

C) association neuron.   D) glial cell.

Answer: C
Diff: 1   Page Ref: 343

21) Saltatory conduction is made possible by:

A) the myelin sheath.   B) large nerve fibers.

C) diphasic impulses.   D) erratic transmission of nerve impulses.

Answer: A
Diff: 1   Page Ref: 353

22) Which of these ions is actively transported through the cell membrane to establish a resting potential?

A) Na   B) Cl   C) Mg   D) Ca

Answer: A
Diff: 1   Page Ref: 345

23) The part of the neuron that normally receives stimuli is called:

   A) an axon.   B) a dendrite.   C) a neurolemma.   D) a Schwann cell.

   Answer: B
   Diff: 1   Page Ref: 339

24) Choose the statement that is most correct about membrane potential.

   A) Voltage is measured by placing two electrodes on the exterior of the axon.

   B) Voltage is measured by placing one electrode inside the membrane and another outside the membrane.

   C) Voltage is measured by placing one electrode on one end of the axon and another electrode on the other end.

   D) Voltage is measured by placing one electrode on the axon and grounding the other electrode.

   Answer: B
   Diff: 1   Page Ref: 345

25) The sodium pump:

   A) pumps three sodium ions outside the cell and two potassium ions inside.

   B) pumps two sodium ions outside the cell and three potassium ions inside.

   C) pumps three sodium ions inside the cell and two potassium ions outside.

   D) pumps two sodium ions inside the cell and three potassium ions outside.

   Answer: A
   Diff: 1   Page Ref: 345

26) An action potential:

   A) is essential for impulse propagation.

   B) involves the influx of negative ions to depolarize the membrane.

   C) is initiated by potassium ion movement.

   D) involves impulse propagation dependent on chemically gated ion channels.

   Answer: A
   Diff: 1   Page Ref: 350

27) Select the correct statement about synapses:

   A) Cells with interconnected cytoplasm are chemically coupled.

   B) The release of neurotransmitter molecules gives cells the property of being electrically coupled.

   C) Neurotransmitter receptors are located on the axons of cells.

   D) The synaptic cleft prevents an impulse from being transmitted directly from one neuron to another.

   Answer: D
   Diff: 1   Page Ref: 354

28) Which of the following is a good example of a neuromodulator?
   A) acetylcholine
   B) any protein
   C) any carbohydrate
   D) a hormone

Answer: D
Diff: 1   Page Ref: 360

29) Which group of fibers spreads impulses at up to 1 meter per second?
   A) group A fibers   B) group B fibers   C) group C fibers   D) group D fibers

Answer: C
Diff: 1   Page Ref: 354

30) The sympathetic and parasympathetic are subdivisions of the:
   A) central nervous system.
   B) voluntary nervous system.
   C) autonomic nervous system.
   D) somatic nervous system.

Answer: C
Diff: 1   Page Ref: 334–335

31) Ependymal cells:
   A) are a type of neuron.
   B) are a type of macrophage.
   C) are the most numerous of the neuroglia.
   D) help to circulate the cerebrospinal fluid.

Answer: D
Diff: 1   Page Ref: 337

32) Neuroglia that control the chemical environment around neurons by buffering potassium and recapturing neurotransmitters are:
   A) astrocytes.
   B) oligodendrocytes.
   C) microglia.
   D) Schwann cells.

Answer: A
Diff: 1   Page Ref: 336

33) Schwann cells are functionally similar to:
   A) ependymal cells.
   B) microglia.
   C) oligodendrocytes.
   D) astrocytes.

Answer: C
Diff: 1   Page Ref: 337

34) Immediately after an action potential has peaked, which cellular gates open?
   A) sodium   B) chloride   C) calcium   D) potassium

Answer: D
Diff: 1   Page Ref: 348–350

35) An inhibitory postsynaptic potential (IPSP) is associated with:

   A) a change in sodium ion permeability.

   B) hyperpolarization.

   C) opening of voltage-gated channels.

   D) lowering the threshold for an action potential to occur.

   Answer: B
   Diff: 1   Page Ref: 358

36) Which of the following will occur when an excitatory postsynaptic potential (EPSP) is being generated on the dendritic membrane?

   A) Specific sodium gates will open.

   B) Specific potassium gates will open.

   C) Sodium gates will open first, then close as potassium gates open.

   D) A single type of channel will open, permitting simultaneous flow of sodium and potassium.

   Answer: D
   Diff: 1   Page Ref: 357–358

37) When a sensory neuron is excited by some form of energy, resulting graded potential is called a(n):

   A) postsynaptic potential.   B) excitatory potential.

   C) action potential.   D) generator potential.

   Answer: D
   Diff: 2   Page Ref: 347

38) All of the following are true of graded potentials except that they:

   A) are short-lived.

   B) can form on receptor endings.

   C) increase amplitude as they move away from the stimulus point.

   D) can be called postsynaptic potentials.

   Answer: C
   Diff: 2   Page Ref: 347–348

39) Which of the following is true about the movement of ions across excitable living membranes?

   A) Ions always move actively across membranes through leakage channels.

   B) Some ions are prevented from moving down their concentration gradients by ATP-driven pumps.

   C) Sodium gates in the membrane can open in response to electrical potential changes.

   D) The bulk of the solutions inside a cell are negatively charged.

   Answer: B
   Diff: 2   Page Ref: 345–346

40) Select the correct statement(s) about the functional components of neurons:

   A) The conducting component usually transmits impulses toward the cell body.

   B) The secretory component causes the release of chemical substances.

   C) Axon terminals are the conducting component.

   D) Nissl bodies are found in the axons and dendrites.

   Answer: B
   Diff: 2   Page Ref: 339

41) _____ is an indolamine.

   A) Dopamine   B) Epinephrine   C) Serotonin   D) Tyrosine

   Answer: C
   Diff: 2   Page Ref: 361

42) A second nerve impulse cannot be generated until:

   A) the membrane potential has been reestablished.

   B) the Na ions have been pumped back into the cell.

   C) proteins have been resynthesized.

   D) all sodium gates are closed.

   Answer: A
   Diff: 3   Page Ref: 352–353

43) In what way does the interior surface of a cell membrane of a resting (nonconducting) neuron differ from the external environment? The interior is:

   A) positively charged and contains less sodium.

   B) negatively charged and contains less sodium.

   C) negatively charged and contains more sodium.

   D) positively charged and contains more sodium.

   Answer: B
   Diff: 3   Page Ref: 345–346

44) If a motor neuron in the body were stimulated by an electrode placed about midpoint along the length of the axon:

   A) the impulse would move to the axon terminal only.

   B) muscle contraction would occur.

   C) the impulse would spread bidirectionally.

   D) Both A and B are correct.

   Answer: C
   Diff: 3   Page Ref: 350

45) Neurons may be classified according to several characteristics. Which of the following is correct?

   A) Group A fibers are mostly somatic sensory and motor and are the smallest in diameter.

   B) Group B fibers are highly myelinated and have the highest conduction velocities.

   C) Group C fibers are not capable of saltatory conduction.

   D) A small cross-sectional area allows shorter conduction times.

   Answer: C
   Diff: 3   Page Ref: 354

46) Select the correct statement about serial processing.

   A) Spinal reflexes are an example of serial processing.

   B) Input travels along several different pathways.

   C) Smells are processed by serial pathways.

   D) Memories are triggered by serial processing.

   Answer: A
   Diff: 3   Page Ref: 368

Clinical Questions

1) Multiple sclerosis (MS) is a disease in which the myelin sheaths are destroyed. With what process does this interfere and what would be the consequence?

   Answer: Demyelination results in interference with saltatory conduction, which would result in a slowing down of nerve impulse propagation.
   Diff: 3   Page Ref: 354

2) Mr. Smith staggered home after a long night at the local pub. While attempting to navigate the stairs, he passed out cold and lay all night with his right armpit straddling the staircase banister. When he awoke the next morning, he had a severe headache, but what bothered him more was that he had no sensation in his right arm and hand. Explain what caused this symptom in his arm.

   Answer: Continuous pressure interrupts blood flow along with oxygen and nutrients to the neuronal processes. As a result, impulse transmission is inhibited temporarily.
   Diff: 4   Page Ref: 337

3) What function is served by the increased axonal diameter at the nodes of Ranvier?

   Answer: Increased diameter results in increased surface area on the membrane for sodium channels. This results in increased speed of impulse propagation.
   Diff: 2   Page Ref: 353

4) Define neurotransmitter. Name two amino acid neurotransmitters, two catecholamines, and two peptides.

   Answer: Neurotransmitters are chemical signals used as a means of communication. GABA and glycine are amino acid neurotransmitters; dopamine and norepinephrine are catecholamines; and endorphin and enkephalin are peptide transmitters.
   Diff: 3   Page Ref: 360–364

CHAPTER 12   The Central Nervous System

Fill–in–the–Blank/Short Answer Questions

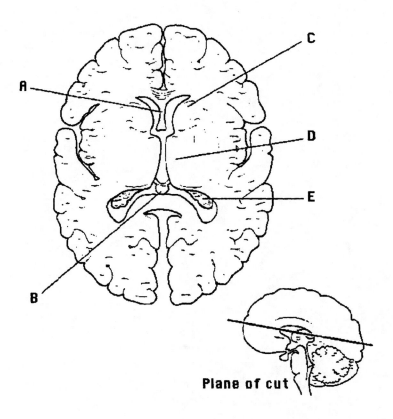

Plane of cut

Figure 12.1

Using Figure 12.1, identify the following:

1) Afferent impulses from all senses and all parts of the body converge here and synapse with at least one of its nuclei.

   Answer: D
   Diff: 1   Page Ref: 384

2) An endocrine gland.

   Answer: B
   Diff: 1   Page Ref: 384

3) A thickened portion of the septum pellucidum.

   Answer: A
   Diff: 1   Page Ref: 384

4) A capillary that secretes cerebrospinal fluid.

   Answer: E
   Diff: 1   *Page Ref: 383*

5) Part of the basal nuclei.

   Answer: C
   Diff: 1   *Page Ref: 383*

6) Thalamus.

   Answer: D
   Diff: 1   *Page Ref: 383*

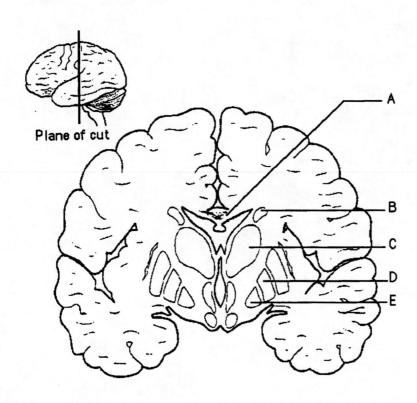

Plane of cut

Figure 12.2

Using Figure 12.2, identify the following:

7) Putamen.

   Answer: D
   Diff: 1   *Page Ref: 383*

8) Corpus callosum.

   Answer: A
   Diff: 1   *Page Ref: 383*

9) Caudate nucleus.

Answer: B
Diff: 1   Page Ref: 383

10) Globus pallidus.

Answer: E
Diff: 1   Page Ref: 383

11) Thalamus.

Answer: C
Diff: 1   Page Ref: 383

Fill in the blank or provide a short answer:

12) The fourth ventricle is continuous with the _____ of the spinal cord.

Answer: central canal
Diff: 1   Page Ref: 374

13) The large tract that connects the right and left sides of the brain is called the _____.

Answer: corpus callosum
Diff: 1   Page Ref: 382

14) The _____ is a conduction pathway between higher and lower brain centers and houses nuclei for cranial nerves V–VII.

Answer: pons
Diff: 1   Page Ref: 389–390

15) The infundibulum connects the hypothalamus to the _____.

Answer: pituitary gland
Diff: 1   Page Ref: 386

16) The _____ are sacklike and protrude externally through the dura mater to absorb cerebrospinal fluid into venous blood.

Answer: arachnoid villi
Diff: 1   Page Ref: 403

17) Sensory neurons enter the spinal cord via the _____ horn.

Answer: posterior
Diff: 1   Page Ref: 410–411

18) The _____ includes the thalamus, hypothalamus, and epithalamus.

Answer: diencephalon
Diff: 2   Page Ref: 385

19) The two longitudinal ridges on the medulla oblongata where many descending fibers cross over are called the _____.

Answer: pyramids
Diff: 2   *Page Ref: 390*

20) The _____ system is our emotional or "feelings" brain and is located on the medial aspect of each cerebral hemisphere.

Answer: limbic
Diff: 2   *Page Ref: 394*

21) The largest nuclear mass in the midbrain is the _____.

Answer: red nucleus
Diff: 3   *Page Ref: 389*

22) _____ memory requires practice, and is remembered by doing.

Answer: Skill
Diff: 1   *Page Ref: 401*

23) In stage 3 sleep, _____ and _____ waves appear.

Answer: theta; delta
Diff: 1   *Page Ref: 399*

24) _____ is a temporary cessation of breathing during sleep found most commonly in the elderly.

Answer: Sleep apnea
Diff: 2   *Page Ref: 399*

25) The _____ is the main switch station for memory; if the right and left areas are damaged, the past is lost.

Answer: amygdala
Diff: 2   *Page Ref: 402*

26) Differentiate clearly between short–term and long–term memory.

Answer: Short–term memory (STM) is a fleeting memory of events that one is continuously exposed to, and seems to be limited to 7 or 8 chunks of information at a time. Long–term memory (LTM) is semipermanent storage of information that involves the transfer of data from STM banks to LTM banks based on several factors such as rehearsal, emotional state, and association.
Diff: 3   *Page Ref: 400*

27) Describe the main ideas of the holistic processing school of thought, relative to consciousness.

Answer: Holistic processing involves many lines of reasoning that suppose that: (1) consciousness involves simultaneous activity of large areas of the cerebral cortex; (2) consciousness is superimposed on other types of neural activity; and (3) consciousness is totally interconnected.
Diff: 4   *Page Ref: 397*

28) Describe the role of the reticular activating system in cortical arousal and stimulation.

Answer: The reticular activating system (RAS) appears to mediate the alertness state of the cerebral cortex. The thalamus, hypothalamus, and other areas such as the brain stem appear to be interconnected with the RAS. The hypothalamus seems to be the structure responsible for the actual timing of the sleep–wake cycle. The primary neurotransmitter involved is serotonin.
Diff: 4   *Page Ref: 395*

29) Describe the cause of hydrocephalus and explain why this condition is much more serious in adults than in newborns.

Answer: Hydrocephaly refers to a blockage of the normal circulation and drainage of CSF throughout the meninges and ventricles. If CSF is allowed to accumulate, excessive pressure could be exerted on the brain. In newborns, the fontanels allow the skull to enlarge, while in adults, the cranial bones are fused and no expansion is possible.
Diff: 3   *Page Ref: 404*

30) Which brain areas lack a blood–brain barrier, and what purpose does this absence serve?

Answer: The blood–brain barrier is absent around the vomiting center of the brain stem, so that it can monitor the blood for poisonous substances. It is also absent around the hypothalamus, so that it can monitor the chemical composition of the blood and adjust water balance and other factors.
Diff: 3   *Page Ref: 406*

31) What is the importance of the fact that the outer portion of the cerebral hemispheres is convoluted?

Answer: The cerebral cortex is only 2–4 mm thick; however, the convolutions effectively triple the cortical surface area. As a result, the cortex accounts for 40% of the total brain mass and functions in all conscious activity, including movement, sensory perception, thinking, memory, etc.
Diff: 4   *Page Ref: 372*

32) What is the cauda equina and why is it given this name?

Answer: The cauda equina is a collection of nerve roots at the inferior end of the vertebral canal and is given this name because of its resemblance to a horse's tail. This arrangement reflects the different rates of growth between the vertebral column and spinal cord. Because the column grows more rapidly than the cord, the lower nerves must "chase" to their exit points inferiorly, thus forming the cauda equina.
Diff: 4   *Page Ref: 409*

33) How do scientists hope the discovery of drugs such as NMDA antagonists and calcium channel blockers will improve the outlook for stroke patients?

Answer: After a stroke, neurons deprived of oxygen release large amounts of glutamate. This acts as an excitotoxin on receptors, causing (among other things) calcium influx. These changes result in damage to surrounding healthy cells, which then release additional glutamate. Scientists hope that rapid administration of NMDA antagonists or calcium channel blockers will stop the chain reaction and result in the destruction of much less tissue.
Diff: 4   *Page Ref: 407*

Matching Questions

Match the following:

1) Column 1: Auditory area.

   Column 2: Temporal

   Answer: Temporal
   Diff: 1   Page Ref: 380

2) Column 1: Primary sensory cortex.

   Column 2: Parietal

   Answer: Parietal
   Diff: 1   Page Ref: 377

3) Column 1: Somatic motor cortex.

   Column 2: Frontal

   Answer: Frontal
   Diff: 1   Page Ref: 378

4) Column 1: Motor speech area.

   Column 2: Frontal

   Answer: Frontal
   Diff: 1   Page Ref: 381

5) Column 1: Premotor area.

   Column 2: Frontal

   Answer: Frontal
   Diff: 1   Page Ref: 378

6) Column 1: Visual area.

   Column 2: Occipital

   Answer: Occipital
   Diff: 1   Page Ref: 380

7) Column 1: Language/speech
   comprehension area.

   Column 2: Temporal

   Answer: Temporal
   Diff: 1   Page Ref: 381

8) Column 1: Taste (gustatory) area.

   Column 2: Parietal

   Answer: Parietal
   Diff: 1   Page Ref: 380

9) Column 1: Seat of intelligence, abstract
         reasoning.

   Column 2: Frontal

   Answer: Frontal
   Diff: 2   Page Ref: 380

Match the following stages of sleep with their descriptions:

10) Column 1: The stage when vital signs
          (blood pressure, heart rate,
          and body temperature) reach
          their lowest normal levels.

    Column 2: Stage 4

    Answer: Stage 4
    Diff: 1   Page Ref: 399

11) Column 1: Indicated by movement of the
          eyes under the lids; dreaming
          occurs.

    Column 2: REM

    Answer: REM
    Diff: 1   Page Ref: 399

12) Column 1: Theta and delta waves begin
          to appear.

    Column 2: Stage 3

    Answer: Stage 3
    Diff: 1   Page Ref: 399

13) Column 1: Very easy to awaken; EEG
          shows alpha waves; may even
          deny being asleep.

    Column 2: Stage 1

    Answer: Stage 1
    Diff: 1   Page Ref: 399

14) Column 1: Typified by sleep spindles.

    Column 2: Stage 2

    Answer: Stage 2
    Diff: 1   Page Ref: 399

15) Column 1: Begins about 90 minutes after
          the onset of sleep.

    Column 2: REM

    Answer: REM
    Diff: 1   Page Ref: 398

16) Column 1: Necessary for emotional
        health; may be neural
        "debugging."

    Column 2: REM

    Answer: REM
    Diff: 3   *Page Ref: 398*

Match the following EEG waves with their descriptions:

17) Column 1: Typical of the alert,
        wide-awake state.

    Column 2: Beta

    Answer: Beta
    Diff: 1   *Page Ref: 396*

18) Column 1: Low-frequency waves;
        uncommon in healthy awake
        adults.

    Column 2: Theta

    Answer: Theta
    Diff: 1   *Page Ref: 396*

19) Column 1: Seen in relaxed individuals
        with eyes closed.

    Column 2: Alpha

    Answer: Alpha
    Diff: 1   *Page Ref: 396*

20) Column 1: Typical of slow-wave deep
        sleep.

    Column 2: Delta

    Answer: Delta
    Diff: 1   *Page Ref: 396*

Match the following:

21) Column 1: The innermost layer of the
        meninges, delicate, contains
        many blood vessels.

    Column 2: Pia mater

    Answer: Pia mater
    Diff: 1   *Page Ref: 404*

22) Column 1: The weblike, spidery middle meningeal layer.

Column 2: Arachnoid

Foil: Ventricles

Answer: Arachnoid
Diff: 1   *Page Ref: 403*

23) Column 1: Normally, the cerebrospinal fluid flows freely from the ventricle, then into the

_____.

Column 2: Subarachnoid space

Answer: Subarachnoid space
Diff: 1   *Page Ref: 403*

Match the following:

24) Column 1: The cerebrospinal fluid helps to protect the brain and cord against shock. It is filtered into the ventricles through the

_____.

Column 2: Choroid plexus

Answer: Choroid plexus
Diff: 1   *Page Ref: 404*

25) Column 1: Any obstruction to the normal flow of cerebrospinal fluid within the brain may give rise to a condition called

_____.

Column 2: Hydrocephalus

Answer: Hydrocephalus
Diff: 1   *Page Ref: 404*

Match the following:

26) Column 1: Impulses arise in proprioceptors, ascend the cord via this tract, and terminate in the cerebellum.

Column 2: Posterior spinocerebellar tract

Answer: Posterior spinocerebellar tract
Diff: 1   *Page Ref: 414*

27) Column 1: Transmits impulses for crude
              touch and pressure to the
              opposite side of the brain.

    Column 2: Anterior spinothalamic tract

    Answer: Anterior spinothalamic tract
    Diff: 1   *Page Ref: 414*

28) Column 1: Descending (pyramidal) tract
              originating with large cells of
              the motor cortex. Major motor
              supply for musculature of the
              limbs.

    Column 2: Corticospinal tract
        Foil: Fasciculi gracilis

    Answer: Corticospinal tract
    Diff: 2   *Page Ref: 416*

29) Column 1: Important efferent pathway of
              the extrapyramidal system
              (red nucleus). Transmits
              impulses concerned with
              muscle tone to skeletal
              muscles of the opposite side of
              the body.

    Column 2: Rubrospinal tract

    Answer: Rubrospinal tract
    Diff: 3   *Page Ref: 416*

Match the following:

30) Column 1: A major relay station for
              sensory information
              ascending to primary sensory
              areas of the cerebral cortex.
              Contains many specialized
              nuclei.

    Column 2: Thalamus

    Answer: Thalamus
    Diff: 1   *Page Ref: 385*

31) Column 1: This brain area associates
              experiences necessary for the
              production of abstract ideas,
              judgment, and conscience.

    Column 2: Prefrontal area

    Answer: Prefrontal area
    Diff: 1   *Page Ref: 380–381*

32) Column 1: The axons from this area form
              the major pyramidal tracts.

    Column 2: Primary motor cortex

    Answer: Primary motor cortex
    Diff: 1   *Page Ref: 378*

33) Column 1: This area is the main visceral
              control center of the body.

    Column 2: Hypothalamus

    Answer: Hypothalamus
    Diff: 1   *Page Ref: 386*

True/False Questions

1) The visual sensory area of the cerebral cortex is located in the occipital lobe.

   Answer: TRUE
   Diff: 1   *Page Ref: 380*

2) The motor cortex is located in the postcentral gyrus of the frontal lobe.

   Answer: FALSE
   Diff: 1   *Page Ref: 378*

3) Cell bodies of the somatic motor neurons of the spinal nerves are located in the anterior horn
   of the spinal cord.

   Answer: TRUE
   Diff: 1   *Page Ref: 410–411*

4) The spinal cord ends at the level of L_1.

   Answer: TRUE
   Diff: 1   *Page Ref: 408*

5) Basal nuclei are gray matter areas buried deep within the white matter of the cerebellum.

   Answer: FALSE
   Diff: 1   *Page Ref: 382*

6) Difficulty in breathing may reflect damage to respiratory centers located in the cerebellum.

   Answer: FALSE
   Diff: 1   *Page Ref: 390*

7) Cerebrospinal fluid circulates within the ventricles of the brain and in the subarachnoid space
   outside the brain.

   Answer: TRUE
   Diff: 1   *Page Ref: 374, 404*

8) The first obvious sign that the nervous system is forming in the embryo is the thickening of the surface ectoderm to form the neural plate.

Answer: TRUE
Diff: 1   *Page Ref: 371*

9) The left cerebral hemisphere is usually dominant.

Answer: TRUE
Diff: 1   *Page Ref: 381*

10) The limbic system acts as our emotional, or affective, brain.

Answer: TRUE
Diff: 1   *Page Ref: 394*

11) A part of the diencephalon structure is formed by the hypothalamus.

Answer: TRUE
Diff: 1   *Page Ref: 386*

12) The medulla is anatomically associated with cranial nerves IX, X, XI, and XII.

Answer: FALSE
Diff: 1   *Page Ref: 390*

13) The canal connecting the third and fourth ventricles and running through the midbrain is the foramen of Monro.

Answer: FALSE
Diff: 1   *Page Ref: 374*

14) Motor impulses from the cortex always originate in the occipital lobe.

Answer: FALSE
Diff: 1   *Page Ref: 378*

15) Commissural fibers form the corpus striatum.

Answer: FALSE
Diff: 1   *Page Ref: 382*

16) The third ventricle is found in the mesencephalon.

Answer: FALSE
Diff: 1   *Page Ref: 374*

17) The cerebral hemispheres of the brain develop from the prosencephalon.

Answer: TRUE
Diff: 1   *Page Ref: 373*

18) The third and fourth ventricles of the brain are separated by the septum pellucidum.

Answer: FALSE
Diff: 1   Page Ref: 374

19) A disturbance of posture, muscle tremors at rest, and uncontrolled muscle contraction are all symptoms of damage to the basal nuclei.

Answer: TRUE
Diff: 1   Page Ref: 382

20) Projection fibers in the brain connect the right and left hemispheres.

Answer: FALSE
Diff: 1   Page Ref: 382

21) Most of the ascending and descending pathways to and from the brain cross over from one side of the body to the other.

Answer: TRUE
Diff: 1   Page Ref: 412

22) Spinocerebellar tracts convey motor information from the cerebellum to motor nerve cells in the spinal cord.

Answer: FALSE
Diff: 1   Page Ref: 414

23) The ratio of brain weight to body weight is about the same for men and women.

Answer: TRUE
Diff: 1   Page Ref: 371

24) The primary visual cortex contains a map of visual space.

Answer: TRUE
Diff: 1   Page Ref: 380

25) As with the cerebral cortex, the two sides of the cerebellum communicate with the opposite side of the body.

Answer: FALSE
Diff: 1   Page Ref: 393

26) One functional center found within the medulla oblongata is a respiratory center involved in the control of the rate and depth of breathing.

Answer: TRUE
Diff: 2   Page Ref: 391–392

27) One of the major functions of the pons is to regulate the endocrine system by producing releasing factors that control the function of the anterior pituitary.

Answer: FALSE
Diff: 2   Page Ref: 389–390

28) Sorting of sensory information and relaying it to the appropriate cerebral sensory area occurs in the hypothalamus.

Answer: FALSE
Diff: 2   *Page Ref: 386–387*

29) Sensory areas of the cortex for the genitals are located deep in the postcentral fissure.

Answer: TRUE
Diff: 2   *Page Ref: 378*

30) Embryonic damage to the mesencephalon could result in improper formation of the midbrain.

Answer: TRUE
Diff: 3   *Page Ref: 373*

31) Extrapyramidal tracts are always afferent.

Answer: FALSE
Diff: 3   *Page Ref: 416*

32) NREM sleep normally exhibits four distinct stages, which appear to alternate.

Answer: TRUE
Diff: 1   *Page Ref: 398–399*

33) Huntington's disease is probably a defect within the cerebellar cortex.

Answer: FALSE
Diff: 1   *Page Ref: 408*

34) Theta waves are a brain wave pattern that can be seen during deep sleep and during anesthesia.

Answer: FALSE
Diff: 1   *Page Ref: 396*

35) Destruction of the hippocampus and amygdala regions of the brain results in widespread amnesia, especially for recent facts and events.

Answer: TRUE
Diff: 1   *Page Ref: 382*

36) One cause of sleepiness appears to be adenosine increases in the brain following periods of high ATP usage by the brain.

Answer: TRUE
Diff: 1   *Page Ref: 398*

37) One disorder of the substantia nigra is Parkinson's disease.

Answer: TRUE
Diff: 1   *Page Ref: 408*

38) Narcolepsy is a condition characterized by involuntary lapses into sleep that occur, without warning, during waking hours.

Answer: TRUE
Diff: 1   *Page Ref: 399*

39) Skill memories preserve the context in which they are learned.

Answer: FALSE
Diff: 1   *Page Ref: 401*

40) REM sleep occurs about every 90 minutes, with each REM period getting shorter.

Answer: FALSE
Diff: 1   *Page Ref: 398*

41) During REM sleep, norepinephrine and acetylcholine levels fall in active brain areas.

Answer: FALSE
Diff: 1   *Page Ref: 398*

42) The terms *fainting* and *syncope* describe the same thing.

Answer: TRUE
Diff: 1   *Page Ref: 397*

43) The RAS is comprised of specific pathways primarily in the limbic system.

Answer: FALSE
Diff: 2   *Page Ref: 395*

44) The key center for sensorimotor integration and control and for muscle coordination is the cerebral cortex.

Answer: FALSE
Diff: 2   *Page Ref: 392*

45) In order to regulate motor activity, to start and stop movements, and to coordinate postural movements, the cerebellum and basal nuclei are involved.

Answer: TRUE
Diff: 2   *Page Ref: 392*

Multiple-Choice Questions

1) Nuclei of cranial nerves V, VI, and VII are found in the:
   A) midbrain.   B) medulla.   C) pons.   D) cerebrum.

Answer: C
Diff: 1   *Page Ref: 390*

2) The arbor vitae refers to:
   A) cerebellar gray matter.
   B) cerebellar white matter.
   C) the pleatlike convolutions of the cerebellum.
   D) flocculonodular nodes.

Answer: B
Diff: 1   Page Ref: 393

3) The brain stem consists of the:
   A) cerebrum, pons, midbrain, and medulla.   B) midbrain, medulla, and pons.
   C) pons, medulla, cerebellum, and midbrain.   D) midbrain only.

Answer: B
Diff: 1   Page Ref: 388

4) The primary auditory cortex is located in the:
   A) prefrontal lobe.   B) frontal lobe.   C) temporal lobe.   D) parietal lobe.

Answer: C
Diff: 1   Page Ref: 380

5) The spinal cord has gray matter on the:
   A) outside, white matter on the inside, and a dorsal motor root.
   B) inside, white matter on the outside, and a ventral motor root.
   C) inside, white matter on the outside, and a dorsal motor root.
   D) outside, white matter on the inside, and a ventral motor root.

Answer: B
Diff: 1   Page Ref: 410

6) The subarachnoid space lies between what two layers of meninges?
   A) arachnoid and epidura   B) arachnoid and pia
   C) arachnoid and dura   D) dura and epidura

Answer: B
Diff: 1   Page Ref: 483

7) The vital centers for the control of heart rate, respiration, and blood pressure are located in the:
   A) pons.   B) medulla.   C) midbrain.   D) cerebrum.

Answer: B
Diff: 1   Page Ref: 390–392

8) Cell bodies of the sensory neurons of the spinal nerves are located in:

   A) the dorsal root ganglia of the spinal cord.   B) the ventral root ganglia of the cord.

   C) the thalamus.   D) sympathetic ganglia.

   Answer: A
   Diff: 1   Page Ref: 411–412

9) The fissure separating the cerebral hemispheres is the:

   A) central fissure.   B) longitudinal fissure.

   C) parieto–occipital fissure.   D) lateral fissure.

   Answer: B
   Diff: 1   Page Ref: 375

10) The rough, thick, leathery meningeal layer is the:

    A) dura mater.   B) subarachnoid.   C) arachnoid.   D) pia mater.

    Answer: A
    Diff: 1   Page Ref: 402–403

11) A shallow groove on the surface of the cortex is called a:

    A) sulcus.   B) fissure.   C) gyrus.   D) furrow.

    Answer: A
    Diff: 1   Page Ref: 375

12) The cerebrospinal fluid:

    A) is secreted by the arachnoid villi.

    B) enters the four ventricles after filling and circulating through the subarachnoid space.

    C) is secreted mostly by the ependymal cells lining the brain ventricles.

    D) is formed mostly by the choroid plexuses.

    Answer: D
    Diff: 1   Page Ref: 404

13) Which of the following is true concerning the development of the nervous system after birth?

    A) The hypothalamus is one of the last CNS structures to mature.

    B) Anencephaly is normally easily corrected.

    C) Most people after age 65 are actually exhibiting signs of true senility.

    D) The hypothalamus is among the first areas of the brain to mature.

    Answer: A
    Diff: 1   Page Ref: 372

14) If the posterior portion of the neural tube failed to develop properly:

A) the spinal cord may be affected.

B) the cranial nerves would not form.

C) the hindbrain would not be present.

D) the telencephalon would cease development.

Answer: A
Diff: 1   Page Ref: 372–373

15) The central sulcus separates which lobes?

A) frontal from parietal   B) parietal from occipital

C) temporal from parietal   D) frontal from temporal

Answer: A
Diff: 1   Page Ref: 375

16) Neural tracts that convey life–saving information to the brain concerning burning pain would be:

A) anterior spinothalamic.   B) reticulospinal.

C) lateral spinothalamic.   D) posterior spinothalamic.

Answer: C
Diff: 1   Page Ref: 413

17) Which of these would you not find in the cerebral cortex?

A) cell bodies   B) dendrites

C) unmyelinated axons   D) fiber tracts

Answer: D
Diff: 1   Page Ref: 376

18) The hypothalamus:

A) is the thermostat of the body since it regulates temperature.

B) is an important auditory and visual relay center.

C) has the Pulvinar body as part of its structure.

D) mediates sensations.

Answer: A
Diff: 1   Page Ref: 386–387

19) The white matter of the spinal cord contains:

A) myelinated nerve fibers only.

B) unmyelinated nerve fibers only.

C) myelinated and unmyelinated nerve fibers.

D) soma that have both myelinated and unmyelinated nerve fibers.

Answer: C
Diff: 1   Page Ref: 412

20) A lateral tract in the spinal cord would be:

A) rubrospinal.   B) vestibulospinal.   C) tectospinal.   D) pyramidal.

Answer: A
Diff: 1   Page Ref: 413

21) An individual accidentally transected the spinal cord between T_{11} and L_1. This would result in:

A) paraplegia.   B) hemiplegia.
C) quadriplegia.   D) spinal shock only.

Answer: A
Diff: 1   Page Ref: 418

22) Spastic paralysis suggests involvement of the:

A) upper motor neurons.   B) lower motor neurons.
C) spinal nerve roots.   D) neuromotor junction.

Answer: A
Diff: 1   Page Ref: 418

23) The embryonic origin of all neural tissue is the:

A) neural plate.   B) telencephalon.
C) cerebral ventricles.   D) neural crest.

Answer: A
Diff: 1   Page Ref: 371

24) The fourth ventricle of the brain lies adjacent to the:

A) thalamus.   B) corpus callosum.
C) pons.   D) pituitary.

Answer: C
Diff: 1   Page Ref: 374

25) The ventricles that lie within the cerebral hemispheres are the:

A) third and fourth ventricles.   B) lateral apertures.
C) foramina.   D) lateral ventricles.

Answer: D
Diff: 1   Page Ref: 374

26) Ridges of tissue on the surface of the cerebral hemispheres are called:

A) gyri.   B) sulci.   C) fissures.   D) ganglia.

Answer: A
Diff: 1   Page Ref: 375

27) The frontal lobe is separated from the temporal lobe by the:

A) longitudinal fissure.   B) lateral sulcus.

C) central sulcus.   D) cranial fossa.

Answer: B
Diff: 1   Page Ref: 375

28) Brodmann's numbers refer to:

A) molecular weight of types of neurons.

B) counts of neurons per fiber bundle.

C) structurally distinct cortical areas.

D) rates of neural division in embryogenesis.

Answer: C
Diff: 1   Page Ref: 377–378

29) Two terms for the massive motor tracts serving voluntary movement are:

A) pyramidal and corticospinal.   B) extrapyramidal and rubrospinal.

C) segmental and nigrostriatal.   D) supplementary and cerebellar–pontine.

Answer: A
Diff: 1   Page Ref: 416

30) An individual who could trace a picture of a bicycle with his or her finger but could not recognize it as a bicycle is most likely to have sustained damage to the:

A) calcarine cortex.   B) primary visual area.

C) visual association area.   D) lateral geniculate body.

Answer: C
Diff: 1   Page Ref: 380

31) Broca's area:

A) corresponds to Brodmann's area 8.   B) is usually found in the right hemisphere.

C) serves the recognition of complex objects. D) is considered a motor speech area.

Answer: D
Diff: 1   Page Ref: 379

32) The function of commissures is to connect:

A) adjacent areas of gray matter within a cerebral hemisphere.

B) corresponding areas of the two hemispheres.

C) areas of cortex with lower centers.

D) pyramidal cells with corresponding cerebellar cells.

Answer: B
Diff: 1   Page Ref: 382

33) The blood–brain barrier is effective against:

A) metabolic waste such as urea.   B) nutrients such as glucose.

C) alcohol.   D) anesthetics.

Answer: A
Diff: 1   Page Ref: 406

34) Which of the following is not part of the basal nuclei?

A) putamen   B) lentiform nucleus

C) globus pallidus   D) substantia nigra

Answer: D
Diff: 2   Page Ref: 382

35) All of the following are structures of the limbic system except the:

A) hippocampus.   B) cingulate gyrus.

C) amygdaloid nucleus.   D) caudate nucleus.

Answer: D
Diff: 2   Page Ref: 394

36) Which of the following is not a midbrain structure?

A) third ventricle   B) cerebral peduncles

C) corpora quadrigemina   D) red nucleus

Answer: A
Diff: 2   Page Ref: 388–389

37) Which of the following is not a hindbrain structure?

A) fourth ventricle   B) pons   C) medulla   D) cerebral nuclei

Answer: D
Diff: 2   Page Ref: 388

38) The brain area that regulates activities that control the state of wakefulness or alertness of the cerebral cortex is the:

A) thalamus.   B) reticular formation.

C) pyramids.   D) limbic system.

Answer: B
Diff: 2   Page Ref: 395

39) Which of the following would you not find in normal cerebrospinal fluid?

A) glucose   B) red blood cells   C) potassium   D) protein

Answer: B
Diff: 2   Page Ref: 404

40) Mr. Hom was injured in an accident that completely severed his spinal cord at the level of T_{12}. You would expect to find all of the following except:

   A) paralysis of the lower extremities.

   B) loss of sensation below the level of injury.

   C) slurred speech.

   D) perspiration in the affected area.

   Answer: C
   Diff: 2   *Page Ref: 418*

41) Injury to the hypothalamus may result in all of the following except:

   A) pathologic sleep.

   B) loss of body temperature control.

   C) production of excessive quantities of urine.

   D) loss of proprioception.

   Answer: D
   Diff: 2   *Page Ref: 386*

42) The spinal cord develops from the:

   A) caudal portion of the neural tube.

   B) sulcus limitans.

   C) anterior basal plate.

   D) anterior portion of the embryonic neural tube.

   Answer: A
   Diff: 2   *Page Ref: 373*

43) White matter of the spinal cord:

   A) is composed of myelinated fibers only.

   B) ascends to higher PNS centers.

   C) has afferent fibers carrying impluses from peripheral sensory receptors.

   D) contains the anterior and posterior spinocerebral tracts.

   Answer: D
   Diff: 2   *Page Ref: 412*

44) Which of the following does not belong with the rest?

   A) rubrospinal   B) vestibulospinal   C) corticospinal   D) reticulospinal

   Answer: C
   Diff: 2   *Page Ref: 414, 416*

45) Embryonic damage to the prosencephalon could result in improper formation of the:

   A) spinal cord.   B) cerebral hemispheres.

   C) cerebellum.   D) midbrain.

   Answer: B
   Diff: 2   *Page Ref: 372*

46) Which association is most accurate?

A) sensory–anterior
B) motor–medial
C) sensory–medial
D) motor–anterior

Answer: D
Diff: 2   Page Ref: 412

47) Which is the mildest consequence of traumatic brain injury?

A) contusion
B) concussion
C) hemorrhage
D) swelling

Answer: B
Diff: 2   Page Ref: 406

48) Which of the following is/are involved with motor activity (either initiation or coordination)?

A) postcentral gyrus
B) gustatory cortex
C) red nuclei
D) Wernicke's area

Answer: C
Diff: 3   Page Ref: 389

49) White matter (myelinated fibers) is found in all of the following locations, with the exception of the:

A) corpus callosum.
B) cerebral cortex.
C) corticospinal tracts.
D) outer surface of the spinal cord.

Answer: B
Diff: 3   Page Ref: 412

50) Loss of ability to perform skilled motor activities such as piano playing, with no paralysis or weakness in specific muscles, might suggest damage to the:

A) spinal cord.
B) premotor cortex.
C) primary motor cortex.
D) rubrospinal tracts.

Answer: B
Diff: 3   Page Ref: 379

51) The functions of the vestibulocochlear nerves concern:

A) vision and hearing.
B) smell and taste.
C) hearing and balance.
D) fine and gross motor control.

Answer: C
Diff: 3   Page Ref: 391

52) Mr. Jacobowitz was injured in an accident resulting in trauma to the reticular formation. What symptom(s) would you expect to see?

A) hypervigilance and hallucinations
B) unilateral tremors
C) photic flashes
D) a state of reduced arousal

Answer: D
Diff: 3   Page Ref: 395

53) The vestibular cortex is now believed to reside in the:

    A) basal nuclei.   B) putamen.   C) globus pallidus.   D) insula.

Answer: D
Diff: 1   *Page Ref: 375*

54) The nonspecific ascending pathways:

    A) are evolutionarily newer than the specific pathways.

    B) receive inputs from a single type of sensory receptor.

    C) are involved in the emotional aspects of perception.

    D) are also called the lemniscal system.

Answer: C
Diff: 1   *Page Ref: 413*

55) The process of linking new facts with old facts already stored in the memory bank is called:

    A) consolidation.   B) automatic memory.

    C) long–term memory.   D) rehearsal.

Answer: A
Diff: 1   *Page Ref: 401*

56) REM sleep is associated with:

    A) decreased vital signs, such as heart rate and blood pressure.

    B) decreased activity of the brain, especially the cerebral cortex.

    C) temporary skeletal muscle paralysis, except for the extrinsic eye muscles.

    D) decreased oxygen use, especially in the cerebral cortex.

Answer: C
Diff: 1   *Page Ref: 398*

57) Long–term memory is facilitated by:

    A) NREM sleep immediately after the event.   B) convergent circuits.

    C) consolidation.   D) parasympathetic activation.

Answer: C
Diff: 1   *Page Ref: 401*

58) Second–order neurons of both the specific and nonspecific ascending pathways terminate in the:

    A) spinal cord.   B) medulla.

    C) thalamus.   D) somatosensory cortex.

Answer: C
Diff: 1   *Page Ref: 414*

59) All processing at the circuit level going up to the perceptual level must synapse in the:

A) pons.

B) thalamus.

C) reticular formation.

D) medulla.

Answer: B
Diff: 1   Page Ref: 414

60) Fact memory:

A) is the ability to learn specific information.

B) is best remembered in the doing.

C) is hard to unlearn when learned once.

D) usually involves motor skills.

Answer: A
Diff: 1   Page Ref: 401

61) An electroencephalogram:

A) is a record of total body electrical activity.

B) indicates a normal frequency range of 1–30 Hz.

C) indicates an average amplitude of 20–100 V.

D) can only detect abnormal electrical activity.

Answer: B
Diff: 1   Page Ref: 396

62) Brain wave amplitude:

A) reflects the number of neurons firing synchronously.

B) is an average of about 1 V.

C) results from subtraction of delta waves from theta waves.

D) is the measure of activity of specific individual neurons.

Answer: A
Diff: 1   Page Ref: 396

63) Tremor at rest, shuffling gait, stooped posture, and expressionless face are characteristic of:

A) Huntington's disease.

B) Parkinson's disease.

C) cerebellar disease.

D) spinal cord disease.

Answer: B
Diff: 1   Page Ref: 408

64) Which statement about coma is true?

A) Coma is defined as total unresponsiveness to stimuli for a long period of time.

B) During coma, brain oxygen consumption resembles that of a waking state.

C) Coma is neurologically identical to syncope.

D) Coma is rarely caused by damage to brain stem structures.

Answer: A
Diff: 1   Page Ref: 397

65) Which statement is true of short-term memory?

  A) It has a capacity of 15–20 chunks of information.

  B) It lasts from a few hours to a few weeks.

  C) Its contents are generally permanent.

  D) It lasts from a few seconds to a few hours.

  Answer: D
  Diff: 1   Page Ref: 410

66) Storing information in long-term memory:

  A) depends on the remaining capacity of long-term memory.

  B) is interfered with by emotional arousal.

  C) is facilitated by the release of norepinephrine.

  D) is always dependent on the formation of conscious impressions.

  Answer: C
  Diff: 1   Page Ref: 410

67) The hippocampus seems to play a special role in:

  A) learning spatial relations.

  B) sending impulses back to sensory cortical areas.

  C) retrieving fact learning for use in present tasks.

  D) linking memories to emotions.

  Answer: A
  Diff: 1   Page Ref: 402

68) The corpus striatum plays a special role in:

  A) face recognition.   B) fact learning.   C) spatial learning.   D) skill learning.

  Answer: D
  Diff: 1   Page Ref: 402

69) Huntington's disease:

  A) begins to appear at ages 10 to 15.

  B) has symptoms the opposite of Parkinson's disease.

  C) usually subsides by ages 35 to 40.

  D) may be a result of a defective 26th chromosome.

  Answer: B
  Diff: 1   Page Ref: 408

70) _____ always takes a nonspecific ascending pathway.

  A) Touch   B) Pain   C) Temperature   D) Arousal

  Answer: A
  Diff: 1   Page Ref: 413

71) Which of the following structures is probably not directly involved in memory?

    A) hippocampus   B) medulla

    C) amygdala   D) prefrontal cortex

Answer: B
Diff: 2   *Page Ref: 400–402*

72) Important nuclei of the indirect (multineural) system that receive impulses from the equilibrium apparatus of the inner ear and help to maintain balance by varying muscle tone of postural muscles are the:

    A) red nuclei.   B) vestibular nuclei.

    C) reticular nuclei.   D) superior colliculi.

Answer: B
Diff: 2   *Page Ref: 391*

73) Fact memory is not stored in the:

    A) hippocampus.   B) amygdala.

    C) thalamus.   D) mammillary body.

Answer: D
Diff: 2   *Page Ref: 401–402*

74) Cerebellar disorders may be indicated by all except:

    A) a drunken-sailor gait.   B) lack of check.

    C) decline in muscle tone.   D) chorea.

Answer: D
Diff: 2   *Page Ref: 393*

75) Which of the following are part of the indirect (multineural) system?

    A) brain stem motor nuclei   B) basal nuclei

    C) thalamus   D) pyramidal pathways

Answer: A
Diff: 2   *Page Ref: 418*

76) All of the following are true of skill memory except that it:

    A) is hard to unlearn.   B) is acquired through practice.

    C) must involve the midbrain.   D) is best remembered in the doing.

Answer: C
Diff: 2   *Page Ref: 401*

77) Spinocerebellar tracts:

A) terminate in the spinal cord.

B) carry proprioceptive inputs to the cerebellum.

C) give rise to conscious experience of perception.

D) are found in the dorsal columns of the spinal cord.

Answer: B
Diff: 2   Page Ref: 414

78) Which statement about epilepsy is most accurate?

A) During seizures, sensory messages are processed normally but responses are blocked.

B) Petit mal epilepsy typically begins in adolescence and is often severely disabling.

C) Epilepsy is often genetically induced but also frequently caused by head trauma, stroke, infection, and tumor.

D) The aura in grand mal epilepsy typically occurs as the patient regains consciousness.

Answer: C
Diff: 2   Page Ref: 396–397

79) Which statement is not true?

A) Sleep requirements decline from infancy to early adulthood, level off, then decline again in old age.

B) Half of infant sleep is composed of REM sleep.

C) Ten–year–olds are in REM sleep about 1.5–2 hours per night.

D) Stage 4 sleep increases in old age.

Answer: D
Diff: 2   Page Ref: 378–379

80) Which of the following is/are true about human memory?

A) Memories are stored in bits and pieces all over the cerebellum.

B) Parts of the limbic system help incorporate experiences into memory.

C) The medulla oblongata is involved in memory.

D) The corpus callosum directs some of the memory paths.

Answer: B
Diff: 3   Page Ref: 400

Clinical Questions

1) The Ectors decided to visit a hospitalized friend who was in a serious accident that caused severe head injuries. They were told she had anterograde amnesia. What do you think they could expect?

Answer: A person with this type of defect could carry on a conversation but could not remember what was previously discussed. Old memories are not lost but new sensory input can not be associated with the old. The person lives here and now.
Diff: 4   Page Ref: 402

2) Jessica noticed that a fellow office worker was acting very strangely. Every so often, the fellow would slump into his chair and casually fall asleep for about 10 to 15 minutes. Everything else seemed to be normal. What do you think the disorder could be?

Answer: The worker probably has a disease called narcolepsy, a sleep disorder in which the victim lapses involuntarily into sleep during normal waking hours. The "attacks" can occur at any time.
Diff: 5   *Page Ref: 399*

3) Mr. Faham suffers brain damage. After recovery from the acute illness, testing reveals that his ability to learn new motor skills is largely intact, but his ability to learn new facts is severely compromised. What brain regions are probably spared and which are probably injured?

Answer: Since the ability to learn new facts is impaired, there is probably bilateral damage to the amygdala and hippocampus at their connections to the diencephalon or prefrontal cortex. Since the ability to learn new motor skills is intact, the corpus striatum (basal nuclei) are probably intact.
Diff: 5   *Page Ref: 401–402*

4) Stacy was involved in a car accident that caused her head to snap forward and backward forcefully. Although no external signs of injury were seen, her blood pressure suddenly dropped and she appeared paralyzed. How could this happen?

Answer: Whiplash injuries frequently cause spinal shock, which is usually a transient period of functional loss following the injury. Symptoms include loss of all reflex activity caudal to the injury, bowel and bladder reflex loss, failing blood pressure, and cessation of muscular activity.
Diff: 4   *Page Ref: 418*

5) Mrs. Sagalov has recently been diagnosed with Alzheimer's disease. What clinical symptoms is she likely to show, and what would probably be seen if her brain were examined?

Answer: Mrs. Sagalov is likely to show increasing cognitive deficits, including difficulties with memory and attention, and personality changes such as irritability, moodiness, and confusion. Her brain, particularly in the cerebral cortex and hippocampus, is likely to show senile plaques (clumps of cells and fibers around a protein core) and neurofibrillary tangles (twisted fibers within neuron cell bodies).
Diff: 4   *Page Ref: 407*

6) Mr. Mendelsen's mother brings him to an emergency room. She relates that he fell down a flight of stairs, and complained of dizziness and seeing stars, but appeared to be all right after a few minutes. Several hours later, however, he complained of nausea, malaise, and confusion, and appeared to be deteriorating. What is/are the probable cause(s) of his condition, and what should the physician probably do?

Answer: Mr. Mendelsen probably sustained a traumatic brain injury. His initial symptoms were those of a concussion from which he probably would have recovered fully. However, he also appears to be suffering from an intracranial hemorrhage. As the blood accumulates, intracranial pressure increases and compresses brain tissue. Surgical removal of the hemorrhage and repair of the torn vessel must be undertaken immediately.
Diff: 4   *Page Ref: 406*

7) Lucy is suffering from right–sided paralysis and sensory loss. She cannot speak at all. Cerebral angiography and a CAT scan have shown no cerebral vascular defects, but the CAT scan did reveal a left–sided mass wedged between the diencephalon and the basal nuclei. Using your knowledge of anatomy, explain Lucy's symptoms in terms of the specific lesion site.

Answer: The mass, located on the left side, will affect the right side of the body due to brain lateralization. The mass is probably affecting the thalamus as well, which is the major sensory relay structure. Finally, the location of this mass would also affect the primary motor cortex in the precentral gyrus, and specifically Broca's area, which is usually located in the left hemisphere.

Diff: 5   Page Ref: 381

8) On performing an autopsy on a 60–year–old man, a medical student found that the man had no corpus callosum. Apparently the man had functioned well neurologically; his medical history reported no neural dysfunctions. Explain why this finding does or does not surprise you.

Answer: The corpus callosum is composed of commissural tracts that allow communication between the right and left hemispheres. Since one hemisphere is normally dominant, usually the left, there is no absolute requirement for communication. Projection fibers can interconnect the brain and cord and the brain pathways will adjust as necessary. If the anterior commissure is still present, it is possible that the necessary linkages could be made via this pathway.

Diff: 5   Page Ref: 381–382

CHAPTER 13   The Peripheral Nervous System and Reflex Activity

Fill-in-the-Blank/Short Answer Questions

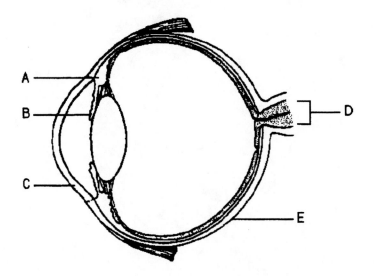

Figure 13.1

Using Figure 13.1, identify the following:

1) Cornea.

Answer: C
Diff: 1   *Page Ref: 434*

2) Optic nerve.

Answer: D
Diff: 1   *Page Ref: 434*

3) White, tough connective tissue.

Answer: E
Diff: 1   *Page Ref: 434*

4) Changes the shape of the lens.

Answer: A
Diff: 1   *Page Ref: 434*

5) Pigmented portion of the eye.

Answer: B
Diff: 1   *Page Ref: 434*

6) Oris muscle that controls the amount of light entering the eye.

Answer: B
Diff: 1   *Page Ref: 434*

7) Site of capillaries that secrete the aqueous humor.

Answer: A
Diff: 2   *Page Ref: 434*

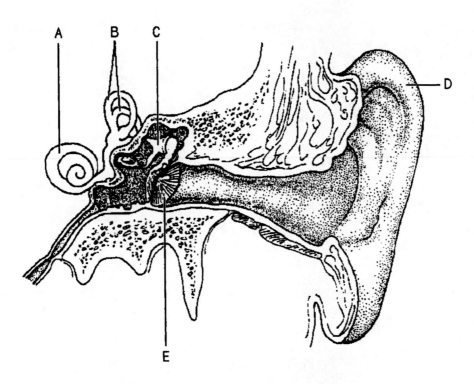

Figure 13.2

Using Figure 13.2, identify the following:

8) Pinna.

Answer: D
Diff: 1   *Page Ref: 448*

9) Tympanic membrane.

Answer: E
Diff: 1   *Page Ref: 448*

10) Incus.

> Answer: C
> *Diff: 1*   *Page Ref: 448*

11) Semicircular canals.

> Answer: B
> *Diff: 1*   *Page Ref: 448*

12) Cochlea.

> Answer: A
> *Diff: 1*   *Page Ref: 448*

13) Balance organ.

> Answer: B
> *Diff: 1*   *Page Ref: 448*

14) An ossicle.

> Answer: C
> *Diff: 1*   *Page Ref: 448*

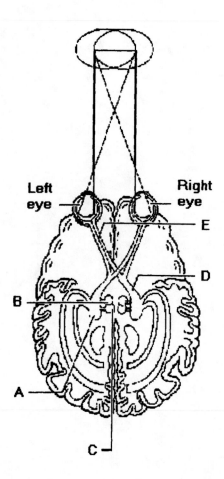

Figure 13.3

Using Figure 13.3, identify the following:

15) Optic nerve.

    Answer: E
    Diff: 1   *Page Ref: 446*

16) Lateral geniculate.

    Answer: A
    Diff: 1   *Page Ref: 446*

17) Nerve containing sensory nerves from both eyes.

    Answer: D
    Diff: 1   *Page Ref: 446*

18) Part of the thalamus.

    Answer: A
    Diff: 1   *Page Ref: 446*

19) Pretectal nucleus.

   Answer: B
   Diff: 1   *Page Ref: 446*

20) Mediate the pupillary light reflexes.

   Answer: B
   Diff: 2   *Page Ref: 446*

21) Controls the lateral rectus muscle.

   Answer: C
   Diff: 2   *Page Ref: 446*

22) Controls the medial rectus muscle.

   Answer: C
   Diff: 2   *Page Ref: 446*

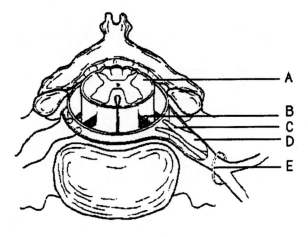

Figure 13.4

Using Figure 13.4, identify the following:

   23) Rootlets of the spinal nerve.

   Answer: B
   Diff: 2   *Page Ref: 469*

   24) Dorsal root ganglion.

   Answer: D
   Diff: 2   *Page Ref: 469*

   25) Spinal nerve.

   Answer: E
   Diff: 2   *Page Ref: 469*

26) Dorsal root.

Answer: C
Diff: 2   Page Ref: 469

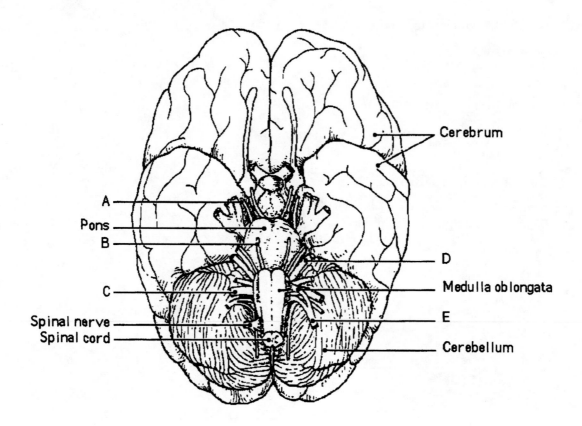

Figure 13.5

Using Figure 13.5, identify the following:

27) Innervates the superior oblique muscle.

Answer: A
Diff: 1   Page Ref: 461

28) Longest cranial nerve.

Answer: C
Diff: 2   Page Ref: 461

29) Damage to this nerve would cause dizziness, nausea, and loss of balance.

Answer: D
Diff: 2   Page Ref: 461

30) Involved in the regulation of breathing.

Answer: C
Diff: 2   *Page Ref: 461*

31) Damage to this nerve would cause difficulty in speech.

Answer: E
Diff: 2   *Page Ref: 461*

32) Damage to this nerve would keep the eye from rotating laterally.

Answer: B
Diff: 2   *Page Ref: 361*

Fill in the blank or provide a short answer:

33) The boundary of the retina is called the _____.

Answer: ora serrata retinae
Diff: 1   *Page Ref: 435*

34) The synapse of the olfactory nerves with the mitral cells is called a _____.

Answer: glomerulus
Diff: 1   *Page Ref: 430*

35) On the back of the tongue one perceives _____ tastes.

Answer: bitter
Diff: 1   *Page Ref: 427*

36) The rocks found in one's head (calcareous masses in the inner ear) are called _____.

Answer: otoliths
Diff: 1   *Page Ref: 455*

37) The middle ear ossicle is the _____.

Answer: incus
Diff: 1   *Page Ref: 449*

38) The oval window touches the stapes and the _____.

Answer: scala vestibuli
Diff: 2   *Page Ref: 449*

39) The vestibulocochlear nerve first synapses with the _____ in the medulla.

Answer: cochlear nuclei
Diff: 2   *Page Ref: 454*

40) The apex of the ear hears sounds in the range of _____ Hz.

Answer: 20
Diff: 2   *Page Ref: 453*

41) In the optic _____ the axons are all ipsilateral.

   Answer: tract
   Diff: 2   Page Ref: 445

42) Contrast light and dark adaptation and include the role of the rods and cones.

   Answer: Rods respond to low-intensity light that provides night and peripheral vision, while
           cones are bright-light, high-discrimination receptors that provide color vision. During
           light adaptation, rods are inactivated and as cones respond to the high-intensity light,
           high visual acuity results. In dark adaptation, cones do not function (visual acuity
           decreases) and rod function resumes when sufficient rhodopsin accumulates.
   Diff: 3   Page Ref: 445

43) What is the chemical composition of the rod pigment, rhodopsin, and how does it appear to
    act in the reception of light?

   Answer: Rhodopsin is a combination of retinal and scotopsin. Retinal is chemically related to
           vitamin A and is synthesized from it. Retinal can form a variety of three-dimensional
           forms called isomers. Scotopsin is a complex opsin protein that combines with the 11-*cis*
           retinal to form rhodopsin. The light-triggered changes in retinal cause
           hyperpolarization of the rods. This happens because the light turns off sodium entry,
           which then inhibits the release of neurotransmitter, thus turning off electrical signals.
   Diff: 3   Page Ref: 443

44) Explain why your nose runs during and immediately after a good cry.

   Answer: The tears flow into the lacrimal canals and then into the nasolacrimal sac. As the sac
           fills, the tears begin to run down the nasolacrimal duct and out your nose.
   Diff: 3   Page Ref: 432

45) Trace the pathway of sound as it enters the external ear until it is perceived in the brain.

   Answer: A sound wave passing through the external auditory canal causes the eardrum to
           vibrate at the same frequency as the wave. The ossicles amplify and deliver vibrations to
           the oval window. Pressure waves in the cochlear fluids cause basilar membrane
           resonance that stimulates the hair cells of the organ of Corti. Impulses are then
           generated along the cochlear nerve that travel to the cochlear nuclei of the medulla and,
           from there, through several brain stem nuclei to the auditory cortex of the brain.
   Diff: 4   Page Ref: 454

46) Explain the role of the endolymph of the semicircular canals in activating the receptors during
    angular motion.

   Answer: The crista ampullaris responds to changes in the velocity of head movement (angular
           acceleration). The crista consists of a tuft of hair cells whose microvilli are embedded in
           the gelatinous cupula. Rotational movement causes the endolymph to flow in the
           opposite direction, thus bending the cupula and exciting the hair cells.
   Diff: 4   Page Ref: 456-457

47) _____ law states that any nerve serving a muscle that produces movement at a joint also innervates the joint itself and the skin over the joint.

Answer: Hilton's
Diff: 1   Page Ref: 477

48) _____ are modified free–dendritic endings found in the stratum germinativum.

Answer: Merkel discs
Diff: 1   Page Ref: 425

49) The perineurium defines the boundary of a _____.

Answer: fascicle
Diff: 1   Page Ref: 459

50) The _____ nerve is the largest of the cranial nerves.

Answer: trigeminal
Diff: 1   Page Ref: 464

51) Ventral spinal cord roots contain _____ fibers, while the dorsal roots contain _____ fibers.

Answer: motor (efferent); sensory (afferent)
Diff: 1   Page Ref: 469

52) The facial nerve is cranial nerve number _____.

Answer: VII
Diff: 1   Page Ref: 465

53) _____ is a protective reflex that overrides the spinal pathways and prevents any other reflexes from using them at the same time.

Answer: Flexor (polysynaptic reflex)
Diff: 2   Page Ref: 485

54) _____ is the tingling sensation or numbness when blood has been cut off from an area, as when the foot "goes to sleep."

Answer: Ischemia
Diff: 2   Page Ref: 474

55) The _____, _____, _____, and _____ nerves all innervate the tongue.

Answer: trigeminal; facial; glossopharyngeal; hypoglossal
Diff: 2   Page Ref: 462–468

56) Define Golgi tendon organs and muscle spindles relative to the stretch reflex.

Answer: Golgi tendon organs work with muscle spindles to act as proprioceptors in skeletal muscles and their associated tendons. When muscles are stretched due to contraction of antagonist muscles, the sensory neurons send impulses to the spinal cord, where they synapse with motor neurons of the stretched muscle. Impulses are then sent to the stretched muscle, which then resists further stretching. This prevents muscle tissue damage.

Diff: 3   Page Ref: 426

57) Distinguish between monosynaptic and polysynaptic reflexes and between ipsilateral and contralateral reflex responses.

Answer: Monosynaptic refers to a single synapse in the reflex arc (one sensory and one motor neuron). Polysynaptic refers to more than one synapse in the arc involving sensory neurons, interneurons, and motor neurons. Ipsilateral refers to a reflex arc limited to one side of the spinal cord, while contralateral reflexes cross to the opposite side.

Diff: 3   Page Ref: 485

58) What is the normal response of the plantar reflex? What is Babinski's sign and what does it indicate?

Answer: The plantar reflex tests the integrity of the spinal cord from L_4 to S_2 and also determines if corticospinal tracts are functioning and properly myelinated. The normal plantar response is downward flexion of the toes. If there is damage, the great toe dorsiflexes and smaller toes fan laterally (Babinski's sign). Infants, who normally lack complete myelination, exhibit this sign.

Diff: 3   Page Ref: 486

59) List and describe the functions of the three cranial nerves that serve the muscles of the eye.

Answer: The three cranial nerves are: oculomotor, trochlear, and abducens. The oculomotor is mostly motor, with branches to the inferior oblique and superior, inferior, the medial rectus muscles, and to the muscles of the iris and lens. The trochlear supplies mostly motor fibers to the superior oblique muscles of the eye. The abducens supplies mostly motor fibers to the lateral rectus muscles of the eye.

Diff: 3   Page Ref: 463, 465

60) Name an exteroceptor that is not a cutaneous receptor.

Answer: Exteroceptors that are not cutaneous receptors include the chemoreceptors of the tongue and nasal mucosa, the photoreceptors of the eyes, and the mechanoreceptors of the inner ear. These all monitor changes in the external environment, so they are classified as exteroceptors.

Diff: 3   Page Ref: 424

61) What is the benefit of having the nerve supply of the diaphragm, which is located in the thoracic-lumbar area of the spinal cord, arise from cervical nerves?

Answer: The fact that the phrenic nerve originates so high in the spinal cord reduces the likelihood of spinal damage above the phrenic origin, thereby reducing the possibility that a spinal injury would stop the diaphragm from working.

Diff: 3   Page Ref: 471

62) How does accommodation of muscle spindles figure in the importance of stretch routines as a warm-up for exercise?

Answer: Initially, as muscle spindles are stretched, the reflex sends impulses back to contract the muscle. With prolonged stretching, accommodation decreases the vigor of the stretch reflex somewhat, and the muscle can relax and stretch more, reducing the risk of tearing muscle tissue during exercise.
Diff: 3   Page Ref: 482

63) The _____ nerve is the only major nerve out of the cervical plexus.

Answer: phrenic
Diff: 1   Page Ref: 471

Matching Questions

Match the following:

1) Column 1: The white, outer tough connective tissue covering of the eyeball.

Column 2: Sclera

Answer: Sclera
Diff: 1   Page Ref: 434

2) Column 1: The muscle responsible for altering the shape of the lens.

Column 2: Ciliary muscle

Answer: Ciliary muscle
Diff: 1   Page Ref: 435

3) Column 1: The vascular coat of the eyeball; deeply pigmented.

Column 2: Choroid

Answer: Choroid
Diff: 1   Page Ref: 435

4) Column 1: A muscle that moves the eyeball.

Column 2: Rectus muscle

Foil: Cornea

Answer: Rectus muscle
Diff: 1   Page Ref: 433

Match the following:

5) Column 1: The sensory layer of the eye.

   Column 2: Retina

   Foil: Suspensory ligaments

   Answer: Retina
   Diff: 1   Page Ref: 435–437

6) Column 1: The structure most
   responsible for focusing light
   rays that enter the eye.

   Column 2: Lens

   Answer: Lens
   Diff: 1   Page Ref: 438

7) Column 1: Helps maintain the
   intraocular pressure; located
   in the anterior part of the eye.

   Column 2: Aqueous humor

   Answer: Aqueous humor
   Diff: 1   Page Ref: 438

8) Column 1: Area of greatest visual acuity.

   Column 2: Fovea centralis

   Answer: Fovea centralis
   Diff: 1   Page Ref: 437

Match the following:

9) Column 1: Ear stones.

   Column 2: Otoliths

   Answer: Otoliths
   Diff: 1   Page Ref: 455

10) Column 1: Connects the middle ear with
    the nasopharynx.

    Column 2: Auditory tube

    Answer: Auditory tube
    Diff: 1   Page Ref: 448

11) Column 1: Separates external auditory
    canal from the middle ear.

    Column 2: Tympanic membrane

    Answer: Tympanic membrane
    Diff: 1   Page Ref: 448

12) Column 1: Contains utricle and saccule.

Column 2: Vestibule

Foil: Crista ampullaris

Answer: Vestibule
Diff: 1   Page Ref: 456, 457

13) Column 1: Detects acceleration.

Column 2: Vestibule

Answer: Vestibule
Diff: 1   Page Ref: 449

Match the following:

14) Column 1: A condition that often results
              from a deficiency of vitamin A.

Column 2: Night blindness

Answer: Night blindness
Diff: 1   Page Ref: 445

15) Column 1: A condition of deafness that
              may result from otosclerosis.

Column 2: Conduction deafness

Answer: Conduction deafness
Diff: 1   Page Ref: 454

16) Column 1: An inflammation of the lining
              of the middle ear.

Column 2: Otitis media

Answer: Otitis media
Diff: 1   Page Ref: 448

17) Column 1: A condition often leading to
              blindness due to increased
              intraocular pressure.

Column 2: Glaucoma

Answer: Glaucoma
Diff: 1   Page Ref: 438

Match the following:

18) Column 1: Hair cells receptive to changes
              in dynamic equilibrium are
              found in this structure.

Column 2: Crista ampullaris

Answer: Crista ampullaris
Diff: 1   Page Ref: 457

19) Column 1: Gustatory cells are found in this structure.

Column 2: Taste buds

Answer: Taste buds
Diff: 1   *Page Ref: 426*

20) Column 1: Hair cells receptive to changes in static equilibrium are found in this structure.

Column 2: Macula

Answer: Macula
Diff: 1   *Page Ref: 455*

21) Column 1: The receptors of olfaction are found in this structure.

Column 2: Superior nasal mucosa

Answer: Superior nasal mucosa
Diff: 1   *Page Ref: 429*

Match the following:

22) Column 1: Houses the spiral organ of Corti.

Column 2: Cochlear duct

Foil: Semicircular canals

Answer: Cochlear duct
Diff: 1   *Page Ref: 450*

23) Column 1: The receptor organ for hearing.

Column 2: Organ of Corti

Answer: Organ of Corti
Diff: 1   *Page Ref: 450*

24) Column 1: The central part of the bony labyrinth.

Column 2: Vestibule

Answer: Vestibule
Diff: 1   *Page Ref: 449*

25) Column 1: A membrane that transmits sound vibrations to the ossicles.

Column 2: Tympanic membrane

Answer: Tympanic membrane
Diff: 1   *Page Ref: 448*

Match the following:

26) Column 1: Can result from prolonged
exposure to very loud rock
music.

Column 2: Sensorineural deafness

Answer: Sensorineural deafness
Diff: 1   Page Ref: 454

27) Column 1: Can result from the fusion of
the ossicles.

Column 2: Conduction deafness

Answer: Conduction deafness
Diff: 1   Page Ref: 454

28) Column 1: A possible side effect of
medications such as aspirin.

Column 2: Tinnitus

Answer: Tinnitus
Diff: 1   Page Ref: 455

29) Column 1: One of the most common
results of otitis media.

Column 2: Conduction deafness

Answer: Conduction deafness
Diff: 1   Page Ref: 454

30) Column 1: Can result from impacted
cerumen.

Column 2: Conduction deafness

Answer: Conduction deafness
Diff: 3   Page Ref: 454

Match the following:

31) Column 1: Formed by the union of a
cranial and a spinal root.

Column 2: Accessory

Answer: Accessory
Diff: 1   Page Ref: 467

32) Column 1: Receptors located in
epithelium of the nasal cavity.

Column 2: Olfactory

Answer: Olfactory
Diff: 1   Page Ref: 461

33) Column 1: Serves the senses of audition and equilibrium.

   Column 2: Vestibulocochlear

   Answer: Vestibulocochlear
   Diff: 2   Page Ref: 462, 466

34) Column 1: Helps to regulate blood pressure and digestion.

   Column 2: Vagus

   Answer: Vagus
   Diff: 3   Page Ref: 467

35) Column 1: Turns the eyeball laterally.

   Column 2: Abducens

   Answer: Abducens
   Diff: 3   Page Ref: 465

Match the following cranial nerves to their function:

36) Column 1: Conveys sensory impulses from skin of anterior scalp.

   Column 2: Trigeminal

   Answer: Trigeminal
   Diff: 1   Page Ref: 464

37) Column 1: Causes lens shape changes during visual accommodation.

   Column 2: Oculomotor

   Answer: Oculomotor
   Diff: 2   Page Ref: 463

38) Column 1: Allows you to smile.

   Column 2: Facial

          Foil: Hypoglossal

   Answer: Facial
   Diff: 2   Page Ref: 465

39) Column 1: Forms a cross pattern called a chiasma.

   Column 2: Optic

   Answer: Optic
   Diff: 2   Page Ref: 465

40) Column 1: Has major sensory nerves of
            the face.

Column 2: Trigeminal

Answer: Trigeminal
Diff: 2   Page Ref: 466

Match the following reflexes to their function:

41) Column 1: Tests both upper and lower
            motor pathways. The sole of
            the foot is stimulated with a
            dull instrument extension.

Column 2: Plantar
        Foil: Crossed extensor

Answer: Plantar
Diff: 1   Page Ref: 486

42) Column 1: Checks the integrity of the
            spinal cord and dorsal rami at
            the level of T_8 to T_{12}.

Column 2: Abdominal

Answer: Abdominal
Diff: 1   Page Ref: 486

43) Column 1: Produces a rapid withdrawal
            of the body part from a painful
            stimulus; ipsilateral.

Column 2: Flexor

Answer: Flexor
Diff: 2   Page Ref: 485

Match the following:

44) Column 1: The obturator and femoral
            nerves branch from this
            plexus.

Column 2: Lumbar plexus

Answer: Lumbar plexus
Diff: 1   Page Ref: 475

45) Column 1: Striking the funny bone may
            cause injury to a nerve of this
            plexus.

Column 2: Brachial plexus

Answer: Brachial plexus
Diff: 1   Page Ref: 474

46) Column 1: Trauma to a nerve of this
        plexus may cause wristdrop.

   Column 2: Brachial plexus

        Foil: Celiac plexus

   Answer: Brachial plexus
   Diff: 2   *Page Ref: 474*

47) Column 1: Improper administration of an
        injection to the buttocks may
        injure a nerve of this plexus.

   Column 2: Sacral plexus

   Answer: Sacral plexus
   Diff: 2   *Page Ref: 476*

48) Column 1: The phrenic nerve branches
        from this plexus.

   Column 2: Cervical plexus

   Answer: Cervical plexus
   Diff: 2   *Page Ref: 471*

Match the following:

49) Column 1: Olfactory.

   Column 2: Sensory only

   Answer: Sensory only
   Diff: 1   *Page Ref: 462*

50) Column 1: Trigeminal.

   Column 2: Motor and sensory

   Answer: Motor and sensory
   Diff: 1   *Page Ref: 464*

51) Column 1: Facial.

   Column 2: Motor and sensory

   Answer: Motor and sensory
   Diff: 1   *Page Ref: 465*

52) Column 1: Glossopharyngeal.

   Column 2: Motor and sensory

   Answer: Motor and sensory
   Diff: 1   *Page Ref: 466*

53) Column 1: Vagus.

   Column 2: Motor and sensory

   Answer: Motor and sensory
   Diff: 1   *Page Ref: 467*

54) Column 1: Hypoglossal.

   Column 2: Motor only

   Answer: Motor only
   Diff: 1   *Page Ref: 468*

True/False Questions

1) The vestibule contains the saccule and utricle, which in turn house receptors for hearing.

   Answer: FALSE
   Diff: 1   *Page Ref: 449*

2) The mucous membrane that lines the eyelids and is reflected over the anterior surface of the eyeball is the conjunctiva.

   Answer: TRUE
   Diff: 1   *Page Ref: 434*

3) Vision is most acute when light rays are brought to focus on the fovea centralis.

   Answer: TRUE
   Diff: 1   *Page Ref: 437*

4) Except for the lateral rectus and superior oblique muscles, all intrinsic eye muscles are controlled by the oculomotor nerve.

   Answer: TRUE
   Diff: 1   *Page Ref: 432*

5) Like the cornea, the lens is vascular.

   Answer: FALSE
   Diff: 1   *Page Ref: 438*

6) The photoreceptor cells, rods and cones, generate action potentials rather than receptor end potentials.

   Answer: FALSE
   Diff: 1   *Page Ref: 445*

7) Taste buds are found mainly on papillae.

   Answer: TRUE
   Diff: 1   *Page Ref: 426*

8) The optic disk is the spot where the optic nerve leaves the eyeball.

Answer: TRUE
Diff: 1   Page Ref: 437

9) Taste receptors for sweet are found on the back of the tongue.

Answer: FALSE
Diff: 1   Page Ref: 427

10) Aqueous humor drains from the anterior segment of the eye directly into the scleral venous sinus.

Answer: TRUE
Diff: 1   Page Ref: 438

11) The lateral wall of the middle ear is formed primarily by the temporal bone.

Answer: TRUE
Diff: 1   Page Ref: 448

12) The fluid contained within the membranous labyrinth is called perilymph.

Answer: FALSE
Diff: 1   Page Ref: 449

13) When one has a cold, swelling of the lacrimal mucosa may result in watery eyes due to impaired drainage of tears.

Answer: TRUE
Diff: 1   Page Ref: 432

14) High-frequency sounds will stimulate the hair cells of the basilar membrane near the oval window.

Answer: TRUE
Diff: 1   Page Ref: 453

15) The structure that allows equalization of the pressure in the middle ear with that outside the body is the external auditory meatus.

Answer: FALSE
Diff: 1   Page Ref: 448

16) The bending of light rays is called reflection.

Answer: FALSE
Diff: 1   Page Ref: 439

17) The anterior chamber of the eye is filled with vitreous humor.

Answer: FALSE
Diff: 1   Page Ref: 438

18) The cortical center for olfactory sensation is located in the parietal lobe of the brain.

Answer: FALSE
Diff: 1   Page Ref: 430

19) Ageusia is the loss or impairment of smell sense.

Answer: FALSE
Diff: 1   Page Ref: 430

20) The retinal layer prevents excessive scattering of light within the eye.

Answer: FALSE
Diff: 1   Page Ref: 435

21) In order for sound to reach the organ of Corti, the stapes must vibrate the oval window and set the endolymph in motion.

Answer: TRUE
Diff: 1   Page Ref: 453

22) Sound is generally perceived in the cerebral cortex of the occipital lobe.

Answer: FALSE
Diff: 1   Page Ref: 454

23) All taste buds are found on the tongue.

Answer: FALSE
Diff: 1   Page Ref: 426

24) Visual pigments of the rod are found in the inner segment.

Answer: FALSE
Diff: 1   Page Ref: 443

25) Filaments of the olfactory nerve project through the cribriform plate of the nasal bone.

Answer: FALSE
Diff: 2   Page Ref: 428

26) Contraction of the ciliary muscle causes the lens to bend the light less.

Answer: FALSE
Diff: 3   Page Ref: 440

27) When we move from darkness to bright light, retinal sensitivity is lost, but visual acuity is gained.

Answer: TRUE
Diff: 3   Page Ref: 445

28) The function of the lens of the eye is to converge light rays.

Answer: TRUE
Diff: 3   Page Ref: 440

29) The meningeal branch of a spinal nerve actually reenters the vertebral canal to innervate the meninges and blood vessels.

Answer: TRUE
Diff: 1   Page Ref: 470

30) The cervical plexus is buried deep under the sternocleidomastoid muscle.

Answer: TRUE
Diff: 1   Page Ref: 471

31) There are 41 pairs of spinal nerves.

Answer: FALSE
Diff: 1   Page Ref: 468

32) The glossopharyngeal is the only cranial nerve that contains sensory fibers.

Answer: FALSE
Diff: 1   Page Ref: 466

33) The musculocutaneous is a major nerve of the brachial plexus.

Answer: TRUE
Diff: 1   Page Ref: 474

34) The second cranial nerve forms a chiasma at the base of the brain for partial crossover of neural fibers.

Answer: TRUE
Diff: 1   Page Ref: 463

35) The trigeminal nerve has three branches that innervate portions of the maxillary, mandibular, and ophthalmic areas.

Answer: TRUE
Diff: 1   Page Ref: 464

36) Tic douloureux is a painful condition of the facial nerve.

Answer: FALSE
Diff: 1   Page Ref: 464

37) The only cranial nerves to extend beyond the head and neck region are the vagus nerves.

Answer: TRUE
Diff: 1   Page Ref: 467

38) Cranial nerve VI is the abducens nerve.

Answer: TRUE
Diff: 1   Page Ref: 465

39) If one of the vagus nerves was severed, the effect would probably be fatal.

Answer: FALSE
Diff: 1   Page Ref: 467

40) Although spinal nerves are paired, most cranial nerves are not.

Answer: FALSE
Diff: 1   Page Ref: 461

41) The dorsal ramus consists only of motor fibers bringing information to the spinal cord.

Answer: FALSE
Diff: 1   Page Ref: 470

42) Dermatomes are skin segments that relate to sensory innervation regions of the spinal nerves.

Answer: TRUE
Diff: 1   Page Ref: 478

43) Spinal roots and rami are similar in that they both contain sensory and motor fibers.

Answer: TRUE
Diff: 1   Page Ref: 469–470

44) Irritation of the phrenic nerve may cause diaphragm spasms called hiccups.

Answer: TRUE
Diff: 1   Page Ref: 471

45) Another word for root is ramus.

Answer: FALSE
Diff: 2   Page Ref: 469–470

46) The obturator nerve branches from the sacral plexus.

Answer: FALSE
Diff: 2   Page Ref: 475

47) Reciprocal inhibition means that while one sensory nerve is stimulated another sensory neuron in the same area is inhibited and cannot respond.

Answer: FALSE
Diff: 2   Page Ref: 482

48) External strabismus and ptosis could be caused by damage to the oculomotor nerve.

Answer: TRUE
Diff: 2   Page Ref: 463

49) If the hypoglossal nerve was damaged, speech and swallowing would be impaired.

Answer: TRUE
Diff: 2   Page Ref: 468

Multiple-Choice Questions

1) What is the main function of the rods in the eye?
   A) depth perception
   C) vision in dim light
   B) color vision
   D) accommodation for near vision

Answer: C
Diff: 1   Page Ref: 445

2) What structure regulates the amount of light passing to the visual receptors of the eye?
   A) aqueous humor   B) lens   C) cornea   D) iris

Answer: D
Diff: 1   Page Ref: 441

3) Receptors for hearing are located in the:
   A) cochlea.
   C) tympanic membrane.
   B) semicircular canals.
   D) vestibule.

Answer: A
Diff: 1   Page Ref: 450

4) Astigmatism is not:
   A) the loss of elasticity of the lens.
   B) the unequal curvature of refracting surfaces.
   C) common in individuals over 50.
   D) called "old person's vision."

Answer: B
Diff: 1   Page Ref: 441

5) The oil component found in tears is produced by the:
   A) lacrimal glands.
   C) conjunctiva.
   B) ciliary gland.
   D) Meibomian glands.

Answer: D
Diff: 1   Page Ref: 431

6) The receptor for static equilibrium is the:
   A) semicircular canals.
   C) utricle.
   B) macula.
   D) cochlear duct.

Answer: B
Diff: 1   Page Ref: 455

7) The region of the tongue with the greatest sensitivity to sweet taste is the:
   A) inferior aspect.   B) lateral edges.   C) posterior aspect.   D) anterior aspect.

   Answer: D
   Diff: 1   Page Ref: 427

8) Farsightedness is more properly called:
   A) myopia.   B) hypopia.   C) hyperopia.   D) presbyopia.

   Answer: C
   Diff: 1   Page Ref: 441

9) Inhibitory cells in the olfactory bulbs are called:
   A) mitral cells.   B) granule cells.
   C) sustentacular cells.   D) basal cells.

   Answer: B
   Diff: 1   Page Ref: 430

10) Which of the following structures is not part of the external ear?
   A) pinna   B) external auditory meatus
   C) tympanic membrane   D) auditory tube

   Answer: D
   Diff: 1   Page Ref: 447–448

11) Nerve fibers from the medial aspect of each eye:
   A) go to the superior colliculus only.
   B) pass posteriorly without crossing over at the chiasma.
   C) divide at the chiasma, with some crossing and some not crossing.
   D) cross over to the opposite side at the chiasma.

   Answer: D
   Diff: 1   Page Ref: 446

12) Ordinarily, it is not possible to transplant tissues from one person to another, yet corneas can be transplanted without tissue rejection. This is because the cornea:
   A) is not a living tissue.   B) has no nerve supply.
   C) has no blood supply.   D) does not contain connective tissue.

   Answer: C
   Diff: 1   Page Ref: 435

13) The oval window is connected directly to which passageway?
   A) scala vestibuli   B) external auditory meatus
   C) pharyngotympanic tube   D) scala tympani

   Answer: A
   Diff: 1   Page Ref: 450

14) There are three layers of neurons in the retina. The axons of which of these neuron layers form the optic nerves?

    A) bipolar cells   B) ganglion cells   C) cone cells   D) rod cells

Answer: B
Diff: 1   *Page Ref: 435*

15) The first "way station" in the visual pathway from the eye, after there has been partial crossover of the fibers in the optic chiasma, is the:

    A) superior colliculi.   B) lateral geniculate nuclei of the thalamus.
    C) visual cortex.   D) temporal lobe.

Answer: B
Diff: 1   *Page Ref: 445*

16) The opsins found in rod cells are called:

    A) rhodopsins.   B) photopsins.
    C) cone opsins.   D) metarhodopsins.

Answer: A
Diff: 1   *Page Ref: 444*

17) Which of the following is true about gustatory receptors?

    A) In order for a chemical to be sensed, it must be hydrophobic.

    B) The receptors generate an action potential in response to chemical stimuli.

    C) Complete adaptation occurs in about one to five minutes.

    D) All gustatory receptors have the same threshold for activation.

Answer: C
Diff: 1   *Page Ref: 426*

18) Taste buds are not found:

    A) in fungiform papillae.   B) in filiform papillae.
    C) in circumvallate papillae.   D) lining the buccal cavity.

Answer: B
Diff: 1   *Page Ref: 426*

19) Select the correct statement about olfaction.

    A) Olfactory receptors have a high degree of specificity toward a single type of chemical.

    B) Some of the sensation of olfaction is actually one of pain.

    C) Substances must be volatile and hydrophobic in order to activate olfactory receptors.

    D) Olfactory adaptation is only due to fading of receptor cell response.

Answer: B
Diff: 1   *Page Ref: 428–430*

20) Photoreceptors:

A) replicate to replace damaged cells, in order to maintain normal vision.

B) package visual pigment in membrane-bound discs, which increases the efficiency of light trapping.

C) possess an inner segment, which is the receptor region.

D) called cones possess a short conical inner segment.

Answer: B
Diff: 1   Page Ref: 442–445

21) Olfactory glands function to:

A) produce olfactory cells.

B) assist in detection of odors.

C) produce Ca^+ ions that are taken up by the olfactory receptor cells for their use.

D) secrete mucus.

Answer: D
Diff: 1   Page Ref: 428

22) Choose the most correct statement about sound.

A) Sounds can be transmitted through a vacuum.

B) High frequency correlates with low pitch.

C) Increased amplitude corresponds to increased loudness.

D) A one-decibel increase represents a tenfold increase in sound intensity.

Answer: D
Diff: 1   Page Ref: 451–452

23) The ciliary body does not:

A) belong to the anterior chamber of the eye.   B) pull on the suspensory ligaments.

C) secrete aqueous humor.   D) attach to the iris.

Answer: A
Diff: 1   Page Ref: 435

24) What is a modiolus?

A) bone in the center of a semicircular canal

B) bone around the cochlea

C) a bone pillar in the center of the cochlea

D) a bony area around the junction of the facial, vestibular, and cochlear nerves

Answer: C
Diff: 1   Page Ref: 450

25) Which statement about night blindness is most accurate?

A) The most common cause is vitamin D deficiency.

B) Vitamin supplements will reverse degenerative changes.

C) Visual pigment content is reduced in both rods and cones.

D) The impaired vision is caused by reduced cone function.

Answer: C
Diff: 1   Page Ref: 445

26) Dark adaptation:

A) is much faster than light adaptation.

B) results in inhibition of rod function.

C) involves improvement of acuity and color vision.

D) involves accumulation of rhodopsin.

Answer: D
Diff: 1   Page Ref: 445

27) Conscious perception of vision probably reflects activity in the:

A) thalamus.

B) occipital lobe of the cortex.

C) chiasma.

D) superior colliculus.

Answer: B
Diff: 1   Page Ref: 447

28) The optic radiations project to the:

A) medial retina.

B) lateral geniculate body.

C) primary visual cortex.

D) optic chiasma.

Answer: C
Diff: 1   Page Ref: 445

29) Visual inputs to the _____ serve to synchronize biorhythms with natural light and dark.

A) pretectal nuclei

B) lateral geniculate body

C) superior colliculi

D) suprachiasmatic nucleus

Answer: D
Diff: 1   Page Ref: 446

30) The lateral geniculate nuclei:

A) receive input from the two eyes in separate layers.

B) send signals from the two eyes to the same cortical cells.

C) each receive input from only one eye.

D) dampen contrast information from the retina.

Answer: A
Diff: 1   Page Ref: 445

31) Information from balance receptors goes directly to the:

    A) motor cortex.   B) visual cortex.

    C) brain stem reflex centers.   D) back muscles.

Answer: C
Diff: 1   *Page Ref: 458*

32) Motion sickness seems to:

    A) respond best to medication taken after salivation and pallor begins.

    B) respond best to medication that "boosts" vestibular inputs.

    C) result from activation of nausea centers in the brain stem.

    D) result from mismatch between visual and vestibular inputs.

Answer: D
Diff: 1   *Page Ref: 458*

33) The blind spot of the eye is:

    A) where more rods than cones are found.   B) where the macula lutea is located.

    C) where only cones occur.   D) where the optic nerve leaves the eye.

Answer: D
Diff: 1   *Page Ref: 437*

34) Which pairing of terms is incorrectly related?

    A) frequency: loudness   B) quality: multiple frequencies

    C) frequency: pitch   D) frequency: wavelength

Answer: A
Diff: 2   *Page Ref: 452*

35) Olfactory cells and taste buds are normally stimulated by:

    A) substances in solution.   B) stretching of the receptor cells.

    C) the movement of otoliths.   D) movement of a cupula.

Answer: A
Diff: 2   *Page Ref: 428*

36) Which of the following could not be seen as one looks into the eye with an ophthalmoscope?

    A) macula lutea   B) optic chiasma   C) fovea centralis   D) optic disk

Answer: B
Diff: 2   *Page Ref: 437*

37) The cells of the retina in which action potentials are generated are the:

    A) rods and cones.   B) bipolar cells.   C) ganglion cells.   D) amacrine cells.

Answer: C
Diff: 2   *Page Ref: 445*

38) During dark adaptation:

   A) the sensitivity of the retina decreases.

   B) the rate of rhodopsin breakdown is accelerated.

   C) rhodopsin accumulates in the rods.

   D) the cones are activated.

   Answer: C
   Diff: 2   Page Ref: 445

39) Tinnitis, vertigo, and gradual hearing loss typify the disorder called:

   A) Meniere's syndrome.   B) conjunctivitis.

   C) strabismus.   D) motion sickness.

   Answer: A
   Diff: 2   Page Ref: 455

40) Which of the following is not a characteristic of olfactory receptor cells?

   A) They are ciliated.

   B) They are unipolar neurons.

   C) They are chemoreceptors.

   D) They have a short life span of about 60 days.

   Answer: B
   Diff: 2   Page Ref: 429

41) An essential part of the maculae involved in static equilibrium is the:

   A) organ of Corti.   B) cupula.   C) scala media.   D) otoliths.

   Answer: D
   Diff: 2   Page Ref: 455

42) Which of the following is true about light and vision?

   A) Human photoreceptors respond to light in the 100–300 nm range.

   B) When we see the color of an object, all light is being absorbed by that object except for the color being experienced.

   C) Light is a form of electromagnetic radiation that slows down as it enters a medium of relatively less density.

   D) The greater the incident angle of light striking a refractive surface, the less the amount of light bending.

   Answer: B
   Diff: 2   Page Ref: 439

43) The tarsal plate of the eyelid:

   A) is composed of connective tissue surrounding a thin cartilage plate.

   B) is connected to the superior rectus muscle.

   C) is connected to the levator palpebrae.

   D) assists in the act of winking.

   Answer: C
   Diff: 2   *Page Ref: 431*

44) Which of the following is true about photoreceptors?

   A) Rods absorb light throughout the visual spectrum but confer only gray tone vision.

   B) In dim light, images are focused directly on the rods in the fovea centralis.

   C) Three types of color-sensitive photoreceptors exist: red, green, and yellow.

   D) If all cones are stimulated equally, all colors are absorbed by the cones and the color perceived is black.

   Answer: A
   Diff: 2   *Page Ref: 442–443*

45) Select the correct statement about equilibrium.

   A) The weight of the endolymph contained within the semicircular canals against the maculae is responsible for static equilibrium.

   B) Cristae respond to angular acceleration.

   C) Hair cells of both types of equilibrium hyperpolarize only, resulting in an increased rate of impulse transmission.

   D) Due to dynamic equilibrium, movement can be perceived if rotation of the body continues at a constant rate.

   Answer: B
   Diff: 2   *Page Ref: 456*

46) The eye muscle that elevates and turns the eye laterally is the:

   A) lateral rectus.   B) superior oblique.
   C) inferior oblique.   D) medial rectus.

   Answer: C
   Diff: 2   *Page Ref: 432*

47) The receptor membranes of gustatory cells are:

   A) basal cells.   B) gustatory hairs.
   C) fungiform papillae.   D) taste buds.

   Answer: B
   Diff: 2   *Page Ref: 426*

48) The right optic tract:

   A) carries information about the left visual fields from both eyes.

   B) carries information about both sides of space from the left eye.

   C) carries information about the top half of space from both eyes.

   D) carries information about the right half of space from the right eye and the left half of space from the left eye.

   Answer: A
   Diff: 2   Page Ref: 448

49) Light passes through the following structures in which order?

   A) vitreous humor, lens, aqueous humor, cornea

   B) cornea, aqueous humor, lens, vitreous humor

   C) cornea, vitreous humor, lens, aqueous humor

   D) aqueous humor, cornea, lens, vitreous humor

   Answer: B
   Diff: 2   Page Ref: 440

50) Damage to the medial recti muscles would probably affect:

   A) refraction.   B) accommodation.

   C) convergence.   D) pupil constriction.

   Answer: C
   Diff: 2   Page Ref: 432

51) Pitch is to frequency of sound as loudness is to:

   A) quality.   B) overtones.   C) phase.   D) amplitude.

   Answer: D
   Diff: 2   Page Ref: 452

52) Which statement about sound localization is not true?

   A) It requires processing at the cortical level.

   B) It requires input from both ears.

   C) It uses time differences between sound reaching the two ears.

   D) It is difficult to discriminate sound sources in the midline.

   Answer: A
   Diff: 2   Page Ref: 454

53) As sound intensity increases, we hear the sound as a louder sound at the same pitch. This suggests that:

   A) 540-Hz-receptive cells are particularly refractory.

   B) cochlear cells that respond to the same pitch vary in responsiveness.

   C) the timing of the cochlear vibrations encodes the pitch.

   D) inhibitory postsynaptic potentials (IPSPs) are building up in the auditory cortex.

   Answer: B
   Diff: 2   Page Ref: 454

54) Which of the following is not a possible cause of conduction deafness?

   A) impacted cerumen   B) middle ear infection

   C) cochlear nerve degeneration   D) otosclerosis

   Answer: C
   Diff: 2   Page Ref: 454

55) Visual processing in the thalamus does not contribute significantly to:

   A) depth perception.   B) high-acuity vision.

   C) night vision.   D) movement perception.

   Answer: C
   Diff: 3   Page Ref: 447

56) An accident patient found that he could not easily detect sweet, sour, or salty substances. Which cranial nerve was probably damaged?

   A) facial   B) glossopharyngeal

   C) vagus   D) trigeminal

   Answer: A
   Diff: 3   Page Ref: 428

57) Which of the following do not appear to be especially significant in the equilibrium pathways to the brain?

   A) cerebellum   B) vestibular nuclear complex

   C) flocculonodular node   D) Wernicke's area

   Answer: D
   Diff: 3   Page Ref: 458

58) Transduction of a sound wave into electrical impulses involves:

   A) low-frequency sounds traveling a short distance into the cochlea.

   B) transmission of force through a compressible fluid.

   C) resonance of the tectorial membrane in response to specific frequencies in specific areas.

   D) the generation of receptor potentials.

   Answer: D
   Diff: 3   Page Ref: 453

59) The "knee jerk" is an example of a(n):

A) extensor thrust reflex.   B) stress reflex.

C) cross extensor reflex.   D) stretch reflex.

Answer: D
Diff: 1   Page Ref: 483

60) The _____ nerve is not a branch of the trigeminal nerve.

A) ophthalmic   B) maxillary   C) cervical   D) mandibular

Answer: C
Diff: 1   Page Ref: 464

61) Which of the following nerves does not arise from the brachial plexus?

A) median   B) phrenic   C) radial   D) ulnar

Answer: B
Diff: 1   Page Ref: 473

62) The posterior side of the thigh, leg, and foot is served by the _____ nerve.

A) obturator   B) peroneal   C) tibial   D) femoral

Answer: C
Diff: 1   Page Ref: 476

63) Starting at the spinal cord, the subdivisions of the brachial plexus are, in order:

A) rami, trunks, divisions, and cords.   B) rami, divisions, cords, and trunks.

C) divisions, rami, trunks, and cords.   D) trunks, divisions, cords, and rami.

Answer: A
Diff: 1   Page Ref: 472–473

64) The cranial nerve with a dual origin (brain and spinal cord) is the:

A) hypoglossal.   B) accessory.

C) vagus.   D) glossopharyngeal.

Answer: B
Diff: 1   Page Ref: 467

65) Which of the following is not a nerve plexus?

A) brachial   B) cervical   C) lumbar   D) thoracic

Answer: D
Diff: 1   Page Ref: 471–477

66) A major nerve of the cervical plexus is the:

A) phrenic.   B) vagus.   C) sciatic.   D) radial.

Answer: A
Diff: 1   Page Ref: 471

67) Spinal nerves exiting the cord from the level of L4 to S4 form the:

   A) lumbar plexus.   B) femoral plexus.   C) sacral plexus.   D) thoracic plexus.

   Answer: C
   Diff: 1   Page Ref: 476

68) The abducens nerve:

   A) supplies innervation to the lateral rectus muscle of the eye.

   B) relays sensory information from taste buds on the tongue.

   C) exits from the medulla.

   D) if paralyzed, exhibits Bell's palsy.

   Answer: A
   Diff: 1   Page Ref: 465

69) The neural branch that forms the plexi of the body is the:

   A) ramus communicantes.   B) meningeal branch.

   C) dorsal ramus.   D) ventral ramus.

   Answer: D
   Diff: 1   Page Ref: 470

70) Basic reflexes:

   A) are rapid, predictable, learned responses.   B) may be modified by learned behavior.

   C) are autonomic only.   D) are always mediated by the brain.

   Answer: B
   Diff: 1   Page Ref: 481

71) Which of the following is not true about the integration center of a reflex arc?

   A) The center may be a single synapse between a motor and a sensory neuron.

   B) There are always multiple synapses with chains of interneurons.

   C) It is always located in the CNS.

   D) The center is a simple reflex arc.

   Answer: B
   Diff: 1   Page Ref: 481

72) Striking the "funny bone" is actually stimulation of the:

   A) radial nerve.   B) sciatic nerve.   C) ulnar nerve.   D) median nerve.

   Answer: C
   Diff: 1   Page Ref: 474

73) Which of the following numbers of pairs of spinal nerves is correct?

   A) six cervical   B) twelve thoracic   C) six lumbar   D) eight sacral

   Answer: B
   Diff: 1   Page Ref: 468

74) Select the statement about plexuses that is most correct:

A) The dorsal rami of all spinal nerves unite to form complex networks.

B) Only ventral rami form plexuses.

C) Each branch of the plexus contains fibers from a single spinal nerve.

D) The ventral rami of thoracic spinal nerves unite to form the thoracic plexus.

Answer: B
Diff: 1   Page Ref: 470

75) A reflex that causes muscle relaxation and lengthening in response to muscle contraction is called a:

A) deep tendon reflex.   B) flexor reflex.

C) crossed extensor reflex.   D) plantar reflex.

Answer: A
Diff: 1   Page Ref: 485

76) Pressure, pain, and temperature receptors are:

A) interoceptors.   B) exteroceptors.   C) proprioceptors.   D) chemoreceptors.

Answer: B
Diff: 1   Page Ref: 424

77) Potentially damaging stimuli that result in pain are selectively detected by:

A) interoceptors.   B) photoreceptors.   C) nociceptors.   D) proprioceptors.

Answer: C
Diff: 1   Page Ref: 423

78) Meissner's corpuscles:

A) are found primarily in connective tissue.   B) are anatomically unencapsulated.

C) are interoceptors.   D) are mechanoreceptors.

Answer: D
Diff: 1   Page Ref: 425

79) Golgi tendon organs:

A) are proprioceptors.   B) are photoreceptors.

C) are found primarily in dermal papillae.   D) are exteroceptors.

Answer: A
Diff: 1   Page Ref: 425

80) The abducens nerve supplies somatic motor fibers and conveys proprioceptor impulses from the _____ to the brain.

A) medial rectus muscle   B) lateral rectus muscle

C) superior rectus muscle   D) inferior rectus muscle

Answer: B
Diff: 1   Page Ref: 455

81) Nerves that carry impulses toward the CNS only are:

    A) afferent nerves.   B) efferent nerves.   C) motor nerves.   D) mixed nerves.

Answer: A
Diff: 1   Page Ref: 459

82) After axonal injury, regeneration in peripheral nerves is guided by:

    A) Wallerian cells.   B) Schwann cells.   C) dendrites.   D) Golgi organs.

Answer: B
Diff: 1   Page Ref: 460

83) Regeneration within the CNS:

    A) is more successful than with the PNS.

    B) typically allows axonal sprouting of 20 mm.

    C) is complicated by secondary demyelination.

    D) is promoted by growth inhibitors and glial scars.

Answer: C
Diff: 1   Page Ref: 460

84) In a crossed extensor reflex, if the right arm were grabbed it would flex and the left arm would:

    A) also flex.   B) extend.   C) abduct.   D) adduct.

Answer: B
Diff: 1   Page Ref: 485

85) Axonal terminals at the neuromuscular junction:

    A) contain synaptic vesicles filled with ACh.

    B) contain one bouton for each motor end plate.

    C) release mitochondria into the synaptic cleft.

    D) are stimulated to release their neurotransmitter by inhibitory postsynaptic potentials (IPSPs).

Answer: A
Diff: 1   Page Ref: 479

86) The sciatic nerve is a combination of which two nerves?

    A) pudendal and posterior femoral cutaneous

    B) posterior femoral cutaneous and tibial

    C) pudendal and common peroneal

    D) common peroneal and tibial

Answer: D
Diff: 1   Page Ref: 477

87) The receptor surfaces of the muscle spindle:

A) are myofilaments.

B) are found in the connective tissue capsule.

C) are found on the central regions of the intrafusal fibers.

D) are found only on the nuclear chain fibers.

Answer: C
Diff: 1   Page Ref: 482

88) The largest and longest nerve of the body is found in the:

A) cervical plexus.   B) brachial plexus.   C) lumbar plexus.   D) sacral plexus.

Answer: D
Diff: 1   Page Ref: 477

89) Irritation of a major nerve of this plexus may cause hiccups.

A) cervical plexus   B) lumbar plexus   C) sacral plexus   D) thoracic plexus

Answer: A
Diff: 1   Page Ref: 471

90) Bell's palsy:

A) is characterized by partial paralysis of diaphragm muscles.

B) is characterized by loss of vision.

C) is often caused by inflammation of the trigeminal nerve.

D) is characterized by paralysis of facial muscles.

Answer: D
Diff: 1   Page Ref: 465

91) Babinski's sign is:

A) normal in an infant less than four years old.

B) a reflex whose physiological mechanism is well understood.

C) when the great toe dorsiflexes and the other toes fan laterally.

D) caused by incomplete development of the thalamus in the infant.

Answer: C
Diff: 1   Page Ref: 486

92) A simple spinal reflex goes along which of the following reflex arcs?

A) effector, afferent neuron, integration center, efferent neuron, receptor

B) receptor, afferent neuron, integration center, efferent neuron, effector

C) effector, efferent neuron, integration center, afferent neuron, receptor

D) receptor, efferent neuron, integration center, afferent neuron, effector

Answer: B
Diff: 2   Page Ref: 481

93) Mixed cranial nerves containing both motor and sensory fibers include all but which of the following?

A) oculomotor

B) vestibulocochlear

C) trigeminal

D) facial

Answer: B
Diff: 2   Page Ref: 466

94) The flexor muscles in the anterior arm (biceps brachii and brachialis) are innervated by what nerve?

A) radial

B) median

C) ulnar

D) musculocutaneous

Answer: D
Diff: 2   Page Ref: 472

95) The cranial nerves that have neural connections with the tongue include all but the:

A) trigeminal.

B) facial.

C) glossopharyngeal.

D) trochlear.

Answer: D
Diff: 2   Page Ref: 463

96) Problems in balance may follow trauma to which nerve?

A) abducens

B) vestibulocochlear

C) trigeminal

D) accessory

Answer: B
Diff: 2   Page Ref: 466

97) Which of the following regions is not innervated by nerves of the sacral plexus?

A) gluteus maximus

B) abdominal wall

C) foot

D) external genitalia

Answer: B
Diff: 2   Page Ref: 477

98) A fracture of the ethmoid bone would result in damage to which cranial nerve?

A) glossopharyngeal

B) vagus

C) olfactory

D) accessory

Answer: C
Diff: 2   Page Ref: 462

99) Select the statement that is most correct.

    A) Ganglia are collections of neuron cell bodies in the CNS that are associated with efferent fibers.

    B) Afferent nerve fibers contain cell bodies of sensory neurons.

    C) The dorsal root ganglion is a motor–only structure.

    D) The cell bodies of afferent ganglia are located in the spinal cord.

Answer: B
Diff: 2   Page Ref: 459

100) An improperly delivered gluteal injection could result in:

    A) neurofibromatosis.   B) postpoliomyelitis muscular atrophy.

    C) paresthesia.   D) sciatica.

Answer: D
Diff: 2   Page Ref: 476–477

101) Which nerve does not use the jugular foramen as a route of exit from the skull?

    A) trigeminal   B) accessory

    C) vagus   D) glossopharyngeal

Answer: A
Diff: 2   Page Ref: 464

102) The peripheral nervous system includes:

    A) sensory receptors.   B) basal nuclei.

    C) the spinal cord.   D) the corpus callosum.

Answer: A
Diff: 2   Page Ref: 422

103) Which statement is true?

    A) Stimulus strength is encoded by action potential amplitude.

    B) Stimulus strength is encoded by action potential frequency.

    C) Receptor potentials are essentially the same as inhibitory postsynaptic potentials (IPSPs).

    D) Subthreshold receptor potentials become generator potentials.

Answer: B
Diff: 2   Page Ref: 422

104) Feeling a gentle caress on your arm would likely involve all of the following except:

    A) Meissner's corpuscles.   B) Merkel discs.

    C) Pacinian corpuscles.   D) root hair plexuses.

Answer: C
Diff: 2   Page Ref: 425

105) A patient who received a blow to the side of the skull exhibits the following signs and symptoms on that side of the face: he is unable to close his eye, and the corner of his mouth droops. Which cranial nerve has been damaged?

A) facial

B) glossopharyngeal

C) hypoglossal

D) accessory

Answer: A
Diff: 3   Page Ref: 465

106) If the ventral root of a spinal nerve were cut, what would be the result in the tissue or region that nerve supplies?

A) complete loss of sensation

B) a complete loss of voluntary movement

C) loss of neither sensation nor movement but only of autonomic control

D) a complete loss of sensation and movement

Answer: B
Diff: 3   Page Ref: 469

Clinical Questions

1) Roger went for his yearly eye examination and was informed that his intraocular pressure was slightly elevated (at 22 mm Hg). The physician expressed concern over this condition and noted that if the condition got worse, eyedrops would be merited. What is wrong with Roger's eyes, and what are the possible consequences of this condition? Explain the function of eyedrops used for therapy.

Answer: If the drainage of the aqueous humor is blocked, pressure within the eye can increase, causing compression of the retina and optic nerve, resulting in a condition called glaucoma. The resulting destruction of the neural structures causes blindness unless the condition is detected early. Early glaucoma can be treated with eyedrops that increase the rate of aqueous humor drainage.
Diff: 4   Page Ref: 438

2) After head trauma from an automobile accident, a man has anosmia. Define anosmia. Why is this condition fairly common after such injuries and in cases of severe nasal cavity inflammation?

Answer: Anosmia means the loss of chemical sense of smell due to some olfactory disorder. Most anosmia results from head injuries or nasal cavity inflammations, allergies, smoking, and aging. The olfactory pathways are very sensitive to irritations or to damage, especially if the ethmoid bones have been damaged due to trauma. In many cases the problem is a lack of zinc, which appears to be a necessary growth factor for the regeneration of new olfactory receptors.
Diff: 4   Page Ref: 430

3) Baby Susie's pediatrician notices that one of her eyes rotates outward and that she does not appear to be using it for vision. What is her condition and what does the pediatrician recommend?

   Answer: Susie has strabismus, caused by congenital weakness of the external eye muscles in her affected eye. To prevent this eye from becoming functionally blind, the doctor will recommend either eye exercises or putting a patch on the unaffected eye to force her to use the affected eye. If her case is deemed severe, surgery on the eye muscles will be recommended.
   Diff: 4   Page Ref: 433

4) A 60-year-old woman is experiencing vertigo. She ignores the symptoms initially, but now her attacks are accompanied by severe nausea and vomiting, and following an attack, she hears a crackling in her ears that causes temporary deafness for some time after. What do you think her problem is, and what is its suspected cause?

   Answer: She most likely has a condition known as Meniere's syndrome. It affects both the semicircular canals and the cochlea. The cause of the syndrome is uncertain, but it may result from distortion of the membranous labyrinth by excessive endolymph accumulation. Less severe cases can usually be managed by antimotion drugs. For more debilitating attacks, salt restriction and diuretics are used to decrease overall extracellular fluid volumes.
   Diff: 5   Page Ref: 455

5) Ling, a 75-year-old grandmother, complained that her vision was becoming obscured. Upon examination by an ophthalmologist she was told she had cataracts. What are they, how do they occur, and how are they treated?

   Answer: A cataract is a clouding of the lens that causes the world to appear distorted, as if looking through frosted glass. Some cataracts are congenital, but most are related to age-related hardening and thickening of the lens, or a possible consequence of diabetes mellitus. The direct cause is probably inadequate delivery of nutrients to the deeper lens fibers. The metabolic changes that result are thought to promote unfolding of the lens proteins. Unprotected exposure to the UV rays of sunlight over time is also associated with cataract formation. The lens can be removed and replaced with an artificial lens.
   Diff: 5   Page Ref: 439

6) Ralph sustained a leg injury in a bowling accident and had to use crutches. Unfortunately, he never took the time to learn how to use them properly. After two weeks of use, he noticed his fingers were becoming numb. Shortly, his arms were getting weaker and tingling. What could be his problem?

   Answer: Compression of the radial nerve (in the region of the armpit) may cause temporary cessation of nervous transmission, often called Saturday night paralysis. Continued pressure could cause permanent damage.
   Diff: 3   Page Ref: 472

7) A patient suffers nerve damage to the sciatic nerve, requiring surgery to suture the nerve back together. After surgery, the patient reports that sensation from the lateral and medial sides of the knee seem to be reversed. How could this happen?

Answer: In suturing the nerve back together, there is no guide to ensure that each nerve fiber continues across the transection into the same neurilemma in which it started. Nerve fibers can grow into pathways different from their original ones and establish new synapses. The brain cannot keep track of which nerve fibers have grown into different pathways, and projects sensations back to the point of origin.

Diff: 3   *Page Ref: 460*

8) George, a 20–year old man, injured his jaw and lost several teeth in a barroom brawl. Several weeks later he began to experience sharp stabbing pain in his lower jaw. After visiting the dentist, he was told that he had trigeminal neuralgia. What is this condition and how is it treated?

Answer: Trigeminal neuralgia, or tic douloureux, is an inflammation of the trigeminal nerve, probably caused by the fight and subsequent damage to the jaw.

Diff: 4   *Page Ref: 464*

9) David, an aspiring baseball player, was struck on the left side of his face with a fastball pitch. He was not wearing a safety helmet. His zygomatic arch was crushed, as well as parts of the temporal bone. Following the accident and reconstructive surgery, he noted that his left lower eyelid was still drooping and the corner of his mouth sagged. What nerve damage did he sustain?

Answer: He suffered facial nerve damage on his left side. Due to the bone damage, branches to the eye and jaw were probably damaged. It is possible that the damage could be reversible if the nerves were not cut or crushed completely.

Diff: 4   *Page Ref: 465*

10) While working in the emergency room you receive two patients who were in an automobile accident. One is dead on arrival, having suffered a transaction of the spinal cord at the level of C_2. The other patient suffered a similar injury, but at the level of C_6, and is still alive. Explain briefly in terms of phrenic nerve origin and function why one injury was fatal and the other was not.

Answer: The phrenic nerve receives fibers from C_3 to C_5 and conveys impulses to the diaphragm. Damage to this nerve would cause respiratory arrest and death. The first patient died because damage was above C_3, making the nerve nonfunctional. The second person will be paralyzed from the neck down.

Diff: 5   *Page Ref: 471*

CHAPTER 14   The Autonomic Nervous System

Fill-in-the-Blank/Short Answer Questions

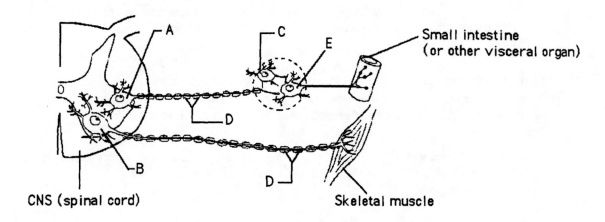

Figure 14.1

Using Figure 14.1, identify the following:

1) Myelin sheath.

   Answer: D
   Diff: 2   Page Ref: 490

2) ANS preganglionic neuron (cell body).

   Answer: A
   Diff: 2   Page Ref: 490

3) ANS ganglionic neuron (cell body).

   Answer: E
   Diff: 2   Page Ref: 490

4) Intrinsic ganglionic cell.

   Answer: C
   Diff: 2   Page Ref: 490

5) Nonmyelinated nerve.

   Answer: E
   Diff: 2   Page Ref: 490

Fill in the blank or provide a short answer:

6) The sympathetic division is referred to as the _____ system.

Answer: fight-or-flight
Diff: 1   *Page Ref: 491*

7) Ganglionic neurons must pass through _____ ramus communicantes if they exit the ventral ramus.

Answer: gray
Diff: 1   *Page Ref: 497*

8) The _____ division causes erection of the penis and clitoris.

Answer: parasympathetic
Diff: 1   *Page Ref: 501*

9) Sweat glands are innervated by the _____ fibers alone.

Answer: sympathetic
Diff: 1   *Page Ref: 502*

10) The _____ division alone stimulates the lens of the eye.

Answer: parasympathetic
Diff: 1   *Page Ref: 502*

11) The two cholinergic receptor types are _____ and _____.

Answer: nicotinic; muscarinic
Diff: 1   *Page Ref: 499–500*

12) The _____ receptor type is used by the heart, and when activated increases heart rate.

Answer: β_1
Diff: 1   *Page Ref: 500*

13) The only sympathetic preganglionic neuron to go directly to an organ is one branch of the _____ splanchnic nerve.

Answer: greater
Diff: 1   *Page Ref: 495*

14) Pain from the diaphragm will be referred to the anterior cutaneous area of the _____.

Answer: neck
Diff: 1   *Page Ref: 498–499*

15) The parasympathetic division uses only _____ as a neurotransmitter in the ganglionic neurons.

Answer: acetylcholine
Diff: 2   *Page Ref: 499*

16) What studies have suggested that the ANS can also be subject to voluntary controls?

Answer: Experimentation involving meditation and biofeedback have indicated that this is possible. Meditating yogis have indicated major physiological states, while biofeedback training suggests that we can alter certain processes such as heart rate, blood pressure, and muscle tone.

Diff: 3   *Page Ref: 504*

17) How is hypertension (high blood pressure) related to the ANS?

Answer: The ANS is involved with nearly every process that goes on within the body. Since it controls smooth muscle activity, the heart, and blood vessel constriction, it is not surprising that hypertension and ANS activity are related. Overproduction of adrenergic responses for extended periods keeps vessels constricted and heart rate and force of contraction high. This can lead to hypertension that is often stress related and can be treated with adrenergic blocking agents.

Diff: 4   *Page Ref: 504–505*

18) Describe four paths a preganglionic sympathetic fiber may take to reach its synapse point with the postganglionic neuron.

Answer: It can synapse with a ganglionic neuron in the paravertebral ganglion; ascend or descend within the chain to synapse in another ganglion; or pass through the sympathetic chain and synapse in a collateral ganglion. The fourth path is a single event in which one branch of the greater splanchnic nerve innervates the adrenal medulla, stimulating it to release the hormone norepinephrine.

Diff: 4   *Page Ref: 496–497*

Matching Questions

Match the following:

1) Column 1: Chain ganglia.

   Column 2: Autonomic

   Answer: Autonomic
   Diff: 1   *Page Ref: 489*

2) Column 1: White and gray rami
                    communicantes.

   Column 2: Autonomic

   Answer: Autonomic
   Diff: 1   *Page Ref: 496*

3) Column 1: Thoracolumbar outflow.

   Column 2: Autonomic

   Answer: Autonomic
   Diff: 1   *Page Ref: 494*

4) Column 1: Commonly acts in a
widespread and diffuse
manner.

Column 2: Autonomic

Answer: Autonomic
Diff: 1   *Page Ref: 490*

5) Column 1: Superior mesenteric and celiac
ganglia.

Column 2: Autonomic

Answer: Autonomic
Diff: 1   *Page Ref: 494*

6) Column 1: Otic and ciliary ganglia.

Column 2: Autonomic

Answer: Autonomic
Diff: 1   *Page Ref: 493–494*

7) Column 1: More specific control.

Column 2: Somatic

Answer: Somatic
Diff: 1   *Page Ref: 490*

8) Column 1: Innervates sweat glands.

Column 2: Autonomic

Answer: Autonomic
Diff: 1   *Page Ref: 490*

9) Column 1: Innervates skeletal muscles.

Column 2: Somatic

Answer: Somatic
Diff: 1   *Page Ref: 490*

10) Column 1: Innervates cardiac muscle,
smooth muscle, and glands.

Column 2: Autonomic

Answer: Autonomic
Diff: 1   *Page Ref: 490*

11) Column 1: Two–neuron efferent chain.

Column 2: Autonomic

Answer: Autonomic
Diff: 1   *Page Ref: 489*

12) Column 1: One-neuron efferent chain.

   Column 2: Somatic

   Answer: Somatic
   Diff: 1   Page Ref: 489–490

13) Column 1: Nerve cell bodies may be
              found in ganglia.

   Column 2: Autonomic

   Answer: Autonomic
   Diff: 1   Page Ref: 489

14) Column 1: Some of its fibers release
              acetylcholine; others release
              norepinephrine.

   Column 2: Autonomic

   Answer: Autonomic
   Diff: 1   Page Ref: 490

15) Column 1: Postganglionic fibers release
              ACh.

   Column 2: Somatic

   Answer: Somatic
   Diff: 2   Page Ref: 490

16) Column 1: Releases only acetylcholine.

   Column 2: Somatic

   Answer: Somatic
   Diff: 2   Page Ref: 490

Match the following:

17) Column 1: Short preganglionic, long
              postganglionic fibers.

   Column 2: Sympathetic

   Answer: Sympathetic
   Diff: 1   Page Ref: 492

18) Column 1: Collateral ganglia.

   Column 2: Sympathetic

   Answer: Sympathetic
   Diff: 1   Page Ref: 492

19) Column 1: Increases blood pressure.

Column 2: Sympathetic

Answer: Sympathetic
Diff: 1   *Page Ref: 502*

20) Column 1: Decreases heart rate.

Column 2: Parasympathetic

Answer: Parasympathetic
Diff: 1   *Page Ref: 502*

21) Column 1: Causes erection of the penis.

Column 2: Parasympathetic

Answer: Parasympathetic
Diff: 1   *Page Ref: 502*

22) Column 1: Stimulates ciliary muscles of
the eye.

Column 2: Parasympathetic

Answer: Parasympathetic
Diff: 1   *Page Ref: 502*

23) Column 1: Active after you have eaten a
meal.

Column 2: Parasympathetic

Answer: Parasympathetic
Diff: 1   *Page Ref: 491*

Match the following:

24) Column 1: Preganglionic sympathetic.

Column 2: Acetylcholine (ACh)

Answer: Acetylcholine (ACh)
Diff: 1   *Page Ref: 499*

25) Column 1: Preganglionic
parasympathetic.

Column 2: Acetylcholine (ACh)

Answer: Acetylcholine (ACh)
Diff: 1   *Page Ref: 499*

26) Column 1: Postganglionic sympathetic to
sweat glands.

Column 2: Acetylcholine (ACh)

Answer: Acetylcholine (ACh)
Diff: 1   *Page Ref: 499*

27) Column 1: Postganglionic
              parasympathetic.

   Column 2: Acetylcholine (ACh)

   Answer: Acetylcholine (ACh)
   Diff: 1   *Page Ref: 499*

28) Column 1: Most postganglionic
              sympathetic.

   Column 2: Norepinephrine (NE)

   Answer: Norepinephrine (NE)
   Diff: 1   *Page Ref: 499*

True/False Questions

1) Since the ANS is a visceral motor system, afferent pathways are of no importance and actually are rarely found.

   Answer: FALSE
   Diff: 1   *Page Ref: 498*

2) The gray rami communicantes consist of myelinated postganglionic fibers.

   Answer: FALSE
   Diff: 1   *Page Ref: 497*

3) Splanchnic nerves are mixed motor and sensory nerves.

   Answer: FALSE
   Diff: 1   *Page Ref: 494*

4) The autonomic nervous system may cause activation or inhibition, depending on the division that is active and the target that is affected.

   Answer: TRUE
   Diff: 1   *Page Ref: 490*

5) The celiac ganglion is primarily associated with the sympathetic division.

   Answer: TRUE
   Diff: 1   *Page Ref: 495*

6) The sympathetic chain is composed of collateral ganglia.

   Answer: FALSE
   Diff: 1   *Page Ref: 495–497*

7) A vagotomy would be cutting the vagus nerve so the intestines can increase secretion of gastric juices.

   Answer: FALSE
   Diff: 1   *Page Ref: 494*

8) Thermoregulatory responses to increased heat are mediated by the sympathetic nervous division.

Answer: TRUE
Diff: 1   *Page Ref: 502*

9) Most disorders of the autonomic nervous system reflect abnormalities of smooth muscle control.

Answer: TRUE
Diff: 1   *Page Ref: 504*

10) Alpha–adrenergic effects are usually stimulatory and mediatory.

Answer: TRUE
Diff: 1   *Page Ref: 500*

11) The adrenal medulla is considered a "misplaced sympathetic ganglion" by some.

Answer: TRUE
Diff: 1   *Page Ref: 498*

12) Acetylcholine is the substance released by the axonal endings of the somatic efferent fibers and by the parasympathetic nerve fiber endings.

Answer: TRUE
Diff: 1   *Page Ref: 490*

13) Most body organs are innervated by only the sympathetic division of the nervous system.

Answer: FALSE
Diff: 1   *Page Ref: 491*

14) Through direct neural stimulation, the sympathetic division promotes many metabolic effects via hormone release.

Answer: TRUE
Diff: 1   *Page Ref: 503*

15) Cranial nerves VII, IX, and X contain postganglionic fibers of the parasympathetic nervous system.

Answer: TRUE
Diff: 1   *Page Ref: 493–494*

16) In contrast to the parasympathetic division, the sympathetic division has numerous ganglionic neurons in the gray matter of the spinal cord.

Answer: FALSE
Diff: 1   *Page Ref: 494–497*

17) Norepinephrine–releasing fibers are called cholinergic fibers.

Answer: FALSE
Diff: 1   *Page Ref: 499*

18) The parasympathetic division is a branch of the somatic nervous system.

Answer: FALSE
Diff: 1   Page Ref: 491

19) The craniosacral division is the same as the parasympathetic division.

Answer: TRUE
Diff: 1   Page Ref: 493

20) The chain ganglion, like the dorsal root ganglion, contains soma from sensory neurons.

Answer: FALSE
Diff: 1   Page Ref: 489

21) Most blood vessels are innervated by the sympathetic division alone.

Answer: TRUE
Diff: 1   Page Ref: 501

22) All splanchnic nerves are sympathetic.

Answer: TRUE
Diff: 1   Page Ref: 497–498

23) Splanchnic nerves pass through the abdominal aortic plexus.

Answer: TRUE
Diff: 2   Page Ref: 497

24) The structures that specifically exhibit vasomotor tone are mostly under sympathetic control.

Answer: TRUE
Diff: 2   Page Ref: 501

25) Since many of the same cardiac cells are innervated by both parasympathetic and sympathetic fibers, the influence of the two divisions on the heart is synergistic.

Answer: FALSE
Diff: 2   Page Ref: 502

26) β–adrenergic receptors are the only receptors found on the heart.

Answer: FALSE
Diff: 2   Page Ref: 500

27) Autonomic reflex centers occur in the spinal cord, medulla, and midbrain.

Answer: TRUE
Diff: 3   Page Ref: 503

Multiple-Choice Questions

1) The secretions of the adrenal medulla act to supplement the effects of:

   A) parasympathetic innervation.   B) sympathetic stimulation.

   C) vagus nerve activity.   D) neurosecretory substances.

   Answer: B
   Diff: 1   Page Ref: 498

2) In contrast to the somatic nervous system, the autonomic nervous system:

   A) has two efferent neurons.   B) has two afferent neurons.

   C) stimulates its effector cells.   D) has both afferent and efferent fibers.

   Answer: A
   Diff: 1   Page Ref: 489

3) Preparing the body for the "fight-or-flight" response is the role of the:

   A) sympathetic nervous system.   B) cerebrum.

   C) parasympathetic nervous system.   D) somatic nervous system.

   Answer: A
   Diff: 1   Page Ref: 491

4) The parasympathetic nervous system is characterized by peripheral ganglia near the:

   A) organs and by short postganglionic fibers.

   B) organs and by long postganglionic fibers.

   C) spinal cord and by short postganglionic fibers.

   D) spinal cord and by long postganglionic fibers.

   Answer: A
   Diff: 1   Page Ref: 493

5) A drug that might be used specifically to reduce heart rate in cardiac patients could be:

   A) anticholinesterase.   B) epinephrine.

   C) norepinephrine.   D) a beta blocker.

   Answer: D
   Diff: 1   Page Ref: 500-501

6) The parasympathetic ganglion that serves the eye is the:

   A) ciliary ganglion.   B) pterygopalatine ganglion.

   C) submandibular ganglion.   D) otic ganglion.

   Answer: A
   Diff: 1   Page Ref: 493

7) Cardiovascular effects of the sympathetic division include all but:

A) constriction of most blood vessels.

B) dilation of the vessels serving the skeletal muscles.

C) increase of heart rate and force.

D) dilation of the blood vessels serving the skin and digestive viscera.

Answer: D
Diff: 1   *Page Ref: 502*

8) Over 90% of all parasympathetic fibers are derived from cranial nerve number:

A) V.   B) VII.   C) X.   D) XII.

Answer: C
Diff: 1   *Page Ref: 494*

9) The "resting and digesting" division of the autonomic nervous system is the:

A) parasympathetic division.   B) sympathetic division.

C) somatic division.   D) peripheral nervous system.

Answer: A
Diff: 1   *Page Ref: 491*

10) Control of temperature, endocrine activity, and thirst are functions associated with the:

A) medulla.   B) cerebellum.   C) hypothalamus.   D) thalamus.

Answer: C
Diff: 1   *Page Ref: 503–504*

11) Which of these effectors is not directly controlled by the autonomic nervous system?

A) smooth muscle   B) cardiac muscle   C) skeletal muscle   D) most glands

Answer: C
Diff: 1   *Page Ref: 490, 502*

12) Which of the following is not a result of parasympathetic stimulation?

A) salivation

B) dilation of the pupils

C) increased peristalsis of the digestive viscera

D) relaxation of the urethral sphincter

Answer: B
Diff: 1   *Page Ref: 502*

13) The site of origin of the preganglionic fibers of the parasympathetic nervous system is the:

A) thoracolumbar region of the spinal cord.

B) higher brain centers.

C) sympathetic chain.

D) brain stem and the sacral region of the cord.

Answer: D
Diff: 1   Page Ref: 493

14) Sympathetic responses generally are widespread because:

A) inactivation of ACh is fairly slow.

B) single preganglionic axons make multiple synapses with ganglionic neurons.

C) preganglionic fibers are short.

D) preganglionic fibers are long.

Answer: B
Diff: 1   Page Ref: 496, 503

15) Sympathetic nerves may leave the spinal cord at which vertebrae?

A) second cervical   B) third lumbar   C) first coccyx   D) first thoracic

Answer: D
Diff: 1   Page Ref: 494–496

16) Autonomic ganglia contain:

A) an outer connective tissue capsule around the cell bodies of preganglionic motor neurons.

B) synapses between postganglionic fibers and their effectors.

C) the cell bodies of motor neurons.

D) both somatic afferent and efferent neurons.

Answer: C
Diff: 1   Page Ref: 489

17) The parasympathetic fibers of the _____ nerves innervate smooth muscles of the lens of the eye, the muscles that cause the eye to bulge to accommodate close vision.

A) optic   B) oculomotor   C) trochlear   D) abducens

Answer: B
Diff: 1   Page Ref: 493

18) Fibers that enter and leave the sympathetic chain without synapsing form structures called:

A) white rami communicantes.   B) gray rami communicantes.

C) spinal nerves.   D) splanchnic nerves.

Answer: D
Diff: 1   Page Ref: 496–497

19) Which is not a plexus of the vagus nerve?

   A) cardiac   B) pulmonary   C) celiac   D) esophageal

   Answer: C
   Diff: 1   Page Ref: 494

20) Visceral reflex arcs differ from somatic in that:

   A) visceral arcs contain two sensory neurons.

   B) somatic arcs contain one additional component that visceral arcs do not possess.

   C) visceral arcs involve two motor neurons.

   D) visceral arcs do not use integration centers.

   Answer: C
   Diff: 1   Page Ref: 498–499

21) The parasympathetic tone:

   A) prevents unnecessary heart deceleration.

   B) accelerates activity of the digestive tract.

   C) determines normal activity of the urinary tract.

   D) causes blood pressure to rise.

   Answer: C
   Diff: 1   Page Ref: 501

22) The autonomic nervous system:

   A) cannot be self-controlled.

   B) has one primary division.

   C) is not affected by drugs.

   D) is directly controlled by the reticular formation of the brain stem.

   Answer: D
   Diff: 1   Page Ref: 503

23) The vagus nerve branches to all of the following plexuses except the:

   A) cardiac.   B) solar.   C) pulmonary.   D) esophageal.

   Answer: B
   Diff: 1   Page Ref: 494

24) The white rami:

   A) are found only in the C_1–T_1 cord segments.

   B) are unmyelinated.

   C) carry preganglionic axons to the sympathetic chain.

   D) carry postganglionic fibers to the periphery.

   Answer: C
   Diff: 1   Page Ref: 495–496

25) Tricyclic antidepressants work by:

   A) prolonging activity of norepinephrine on postsynaptic membranes.

   B) inhibiting reuptake of norepinephrine.

   C) increasing axonal release of serotonin.

   D) opening postsynaptic NMDA receptors.

   Answer: A
   Diff: 1   *Page Ref: 501*

26) Beta-blockers:

   A) increase a dangerously low heart rate.

   B) attach mainly to the β_1 receptors of cardiac muscle.

   C) have widespread sympathetic effects.

   D) are potent antidepressants.

   Answer: B
   Diff: 1   *Page Ref: 500–501*

27) Erection of the penis or clitoris:

   A) is primarily under sympathetic control.

   B) is primarily under parasympathetic control.

   C) is the result of coordinated activation by both sympathetic and parasympathetic input.

   D) depends very little on autonomic activation.

   Answer: B
   Diff: 1   *Page Ref: 501*

28) Which is a uniquely sympathetic function?

   A) regulation of pupil size   B) regulation of cardiac rate

   C) regulation of respiratory rate   D) regulation of body temperature

   Answer: D
   Diff: 1   *Page Ref: 502*

29) The most direct control over autonomic function is exerted by:

   A) the brain stem reticular formation.   B) the hypothalamus.

   C) the cerebral cortex.   D) the basal nuclei.

   Answer: A
   Diff: 1   *Page Ref: 503*

30) Raynaud's disease:

   A) is characterized by exaggerated vasoconstriction in the extremities.

   B) is induced by heat stress.

   C) occurs primarily in association with injury to the spinal cord.

   D) is frequently life–threatening.

   Answer: A
   Diff: 1   *Page Ref: 505*

31) The mass reflex reaction:

    A) is also known as autonomic areflexia.

    B) represents a return of reflex activity with no controls from higher centers.

    C) usually precedes spinal shock.

    D) results from overexcitatory input from the cortex.

Answer: B
Diff: 1   *Page Ref: 505*

32) Sympathetic fibers leave the spinal cord in the:

    A) craniosacral regions, and the postganglionic fibers secrete norepinephrine.

    B) thoracolumbar region, and the postganglionic fibers secrete acetylcholine.

    C) craniosacral region, and the postganglionic fibers secrete acetylcholine.

    D) thoracolumbar region, and the postganglionic fibers secrete norepinephrine.

Answer: D
Diff: 2   *Page Ref: 494*

33) Where would you not find an autonomic ganglion?

    A) in the head   B) in the cervical region

    C) close to the visceral effectors they serve   D) in the armpit

Answer: D
Diff: 2   *Page Ref: 493, 495*

34) Sympathetic division stimulation causes:

    A) decreased blood glucose, increased GI peristalsis, and increased heart rate and blood pressure.

    B) increased blood glucose, increased GI peristalsis, and decreased heart rate and blood pressure.

    C) increased blood glucose, decreased GI peristalsis, and increased heart rate and blood pressure.

    D) decreased blood glucose, increased GI peristalsis, and decreased heart rate and blood pressure.

Answer: C
Diff: 2   *Page Ref: 502*

35) The smooth muscle of the digestive viscera is served largely by the:

    A) lumbar splanchnic nerves.   B) cephalic plexus.

    C) pelvic nerves.   D) tenth cranial nerve.

Answer: D
Diff: 2   *Page Ref: 494*

36) The route of major parasympathetic outflow from the head is the:

A) sympathetic trunk.   B) phrenic nerve.

C) vagus nerve.   D) sacral nerve.

Answer: C
Diff: 2   Page Ref: 494

37) Parasympathetic functions include:

A) a stimulation of heart rate and force of contraction.

B) allowing the body to cope with an external threat.

C) constriction of bronchioles.

D) mobilizing storage energy sources.

Answer: C
Diff: 2   Page Ref: 502

38) All preganglionic axons of the autonomic nervous system release:

A) dopamine.

B) serotonin.

C) the same transmitter as the only one released by the sympathetic postganglionic axons.

D) the same transmitter as the one released by parasympathetic postganglionic axons.

Answer: D
Diff: 2   Page Ref: 490

39) Emotions influence autonomic reactions primarily through integration in the:

A) lateral horn of the spinal cord.   B) hypothalamus.

C) lateral geniculate of the thalamus.   D) inferior colliculus.

Answer: B
Diff: 2   Page Ref: 503

40) The possibility of cordical control over autonomic responses is demonstrated by:

A) split brain studies.   B) stress–induced hypertension.

C) biofeedback.   D) nightmares.

Answer: C
Diff: 2   Page Ref: 504

Clinical Questions

1) Carla was startled by an extremely loud bang that sounded like a gunshot. Her heartbeat accelerated rapidly. When she found that the noise was only a car backfiring, she felt greatly relieved but her heart kept beating heavily for over half an hour. Why did this happen?

Answer: The effects of sympathetic activators are long lasting, since norepinephrine is inactivated slowly. Also, the adrenal medulla releases this neurotransmitter, which adds to the long-lasting effects of adrenergic stimulation.
Diff: 3   Page Ref: 503

2) Ms. Johnson, an automobile whiplash victim, has been suffering spinal shock but is looking forward to complete recovery. One night on evening rounds, her nurse discovered her in a fetal position, her body drenched with sweat. She was incontinent of feces and urine and her blood pressure was dangerously high (over 200 mm Hg). After a while she was stabilized. How could these events happen and what is this response called?

Answer: The mass reflex reaction is a life-threatening condition involving both somatic and autonomic nerves in most quadriplegics and victims of spinal shock. The symptoms can precipitate a stroke.
Diff: 3   *Page Ref: 505*

3) Mark eats a very big meal in the evening. After the meal his wife would like him to share cleanup, but Mark explains that he is "too tired" and promptly goes to sleep. What seems to be his problem?

Answer: After a meal, parasympathetic influences dominate, which increase digestive functions while decreasing cardiac and respiratory activity. This causes the individual to feel sleepy.
Diff: 4   *Page Ref: 502*

4) Richard has been under great stress and has complained of migraine headaches for weeks. He tried all kinds of drugs, with little effect. When he was at the end of his rope, a friend suggested yoga and meditation. Having nothing to lose, he tried them and after several months, felt like a new person. How could these practices help him?

Answer: The practitioner of meditation and biofeedback techniques seems to enter a physiological state of concentration that can reduce sympathetic-induced hypertension. By concentrating on relaxing thoughts, the practitioner can slow heart and respiratory rates. The effects are more widespread than can be explained by parasympathetic influences; the control could be consciously induced.
Diff: 5   *Page Ref: 504*

5) Mrs. Oberhaus needs surgery to correct a severe case of Raynaud's disease, affecting one of her hands. What surgical procedure will be performed? After the surgery, will she be more likely to suffer from anhidrosis (lack of sweating) or hyperhidrosis (profuse sweating) in the affected hand?

Answer: Mrs. Oberhaus' doctor will perform a sympathectomy. Cutting the sympathetic fibers will result in dilation of the affected blood vessels. Since sweating is stimulated by sympathetic nerves, after they are cut, the affected hand will suffer from anhidrosis.
Diff: 5   *Page Ref: 505*

CHAPTER 15   The Endocrine System

Fill-in-the-Blank/Short Answer Questions

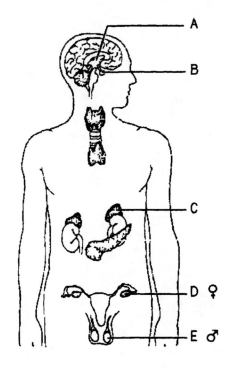

Figure 15.1

Using Figure 15.1, identify the following:

1) Produces the hormones that promote the development of the female secondary sexual characteristics at puberty.

   Answer: D
   Diff: 1   Page Ref: 514

2) Storehouse for the hormones produced by the hypothalamus of the brain.

   Answer: B
   Diff: 1   Page Ref: 514

3) Produces the hormones that direct the production of the secondary male sex characteristics.

   Answer: E
   Diff: 1   Page Ref: 514

4) Produces steroid hormones and glucocorticoids and mineralocorticoids.

   Answer: C
   Diff: 1   *Page Ref: 514*

5) Produces hormones that are stored in the neurohypophysis.

   Answer: A
   Diff: 1   *Page Ref: 514*

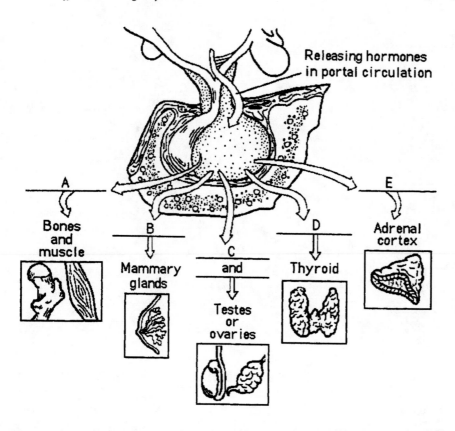

Figure 15.2

Using Figure 15.2, match the following hypothalamic hormones with the pituitary hormone targets:

6) Growth hormone-releasing hormone (GHRH).

   Answer: A
   Diff: 1   *Page Ref: 517*

7) Gonadotropin-releasing hormone (GnRH).

   Answer: C
   Diff: 1   *Page Ref: 518*

8) Prolactin-releasing hormone (PRH).

   Answer: B
   Diff: 1   *Page Ref: 518*

9) Corticotropin–releasing hormone (CRH).

   Answer: E
   Diff: 1   Page Ref: 518

10) Thyrotropin–releasing hormone (TRH).

   Answer: D
   Diff: 1   Page Ref: 518

Fill in the blank or provide a short answer:

11) _____ are hormones synthesized from cholesterol.

   Answer: Steroids
   Diff: 1   Page Ref: 507

12) _____ is a hormone that has only one known effect: to stimulate milk production by the breasts.

   Answer: Prolactin
   Diff: 1   Page Ref: 518-519

13) _____ is the result of hypersecretion of growth hormone.

   Answer: Acromegaly
   Diff: 1   Page Ref: 518

14) The largest pure endocrine gland in the body is the _____.

   Answer: thyroid
   Diff: 1   Page Ref: 514

15) Catecholamines are produced by _____ cells.

   Answer: chromaffin
   Diff: 1   Page Ref: 533

16) Alpha islet cells produce _____, an extremely potent hyperglycemic hormone.

   Answer: glucagon
   Diff: 1   Page Ref: 534

17) The _____ gland may influence our day/night cycles and even regulate the onset of sexual maturity.

   Answer: pineal
   Diff: 1   Page Ref: 537

18) The _____ gland declines in size and function with age.

   Answer: thymus
   Diff: 1   Page Ref: 538

19) Endocrine gland stimuli include hormonal, _____, and _____ stimuli.

Answer: humoral; neural
Diff: 2   *Page Ref: 512–513*

20) As a result of stress the adenohypophysis releases _____, which targets the adrenal cortex to retain sodium and water, increase blood sugar, and begin breaking down fats.

Answer: ACTH
Diff: 2   *Page Ref: 516*

21) Compare the structure and function of endocrine and exocrine glands.

Answer: Endocrine glands are ductless glands that release hormones into the blood to be transported to other organs. Exocrine glands have ducts through which products are released.
Diff: 3   *Page Ref: 507*

22) Why should the hypothalamus instead of the adenohypophysis be called the "master endocrine gland?"

Answer: Although the adenohypophysis has many hormonal products, the hypothalamus controls anterior pituitary activity through regulatory factors.
Diff: 3   *Page Ref: 516*

23) Why would one not expect to continue increasing in height with age?

Answer: The amount of growth hormone secreted declines with age and the closure of the epiphyseal plates prohibits further growth in length of the long bones.
Diff: 3   *Page Ref: 516–517*

24) A person who drinks a lot of alcoholic beverages must urinate frequently. Why?

Answer: Alcohol inhibits ADH secretion.
Diff: 3   *Page Ref: 521–522*

25) How is the heart involved as an endocrine gland?

Answer: A few cardiac cells secrete atrial natriuretic peptide (ANP), which helps regulate salt output by the kidney. ANP inhibits aldosterone and signals the kidney to remove more salt.
Diff: 3   *Page Ref: 538*

26) Briefly discuss target cell activation by hormone–receptor interaction.

Answer: The first step is hormone–receptor binding to target cells, but interaction depends on blood levels of the hormone, relative number of receptors for that hormone on or in the target cells, and the strength of the union between the hormone and the receptor.
Diff: 4   *Page Ref: 511–512*

27) List the four mechanisms involved in the regulation of aldosterone secretion.

Answer: The four mechanisms are: (1) the renin–angiotensin system, (2) plasma concentrations of sodium and potassium ions, (3) control exerted by ACTH, and (4) plasma concentration of atrial natriuretic peptide.

Diff: 4   Page Ref: 530–531

Matching Questions

Match the following:

1) Column 1: An autoimmune problem involving the thyroid gland.

   Column 2: Graves' disease

   Answer: Graves' disease
   Diff: 1   Page Ref: 525

2) Column 1: Hyposecretion of growth hormone.

   Column 2: Pituitary dwarfism

   Answer: Pituitary dwarfism
   Diff: 1   Page Ref: 518

3) Column 1: Hyposecretion of the pancreas.

   Column 2: Diabetes mellitus

   Answer: Diabetes mellitus
   Diff: 1   Page Ref: 535–536

4) Column 1: Hyposecretion of the adrenal gland.

   Column 2: Addison's disease

   Answer: Addison's disease
   Diff: 1   Page Ref: 532

5) Column 1: Hypersecretion of growth hormone.

   Column 2: Acromegaly

   Answer: Acromegaly
   Diff: 2   Page Ref: 518

Match the following:

6) Column 1: Hyposecretion of the thyroid in adults.

   Column 2: Myxedema

   Answer: Myxedema
   Diff: 1   Page Ref: 524

7) Column 1: Hypersecretion of the adrenal
        cortex.

   Column 2: Cushing's disease

   Answer: Cushing's disease
   Diff: 1   Page Ref: 531

8) Column 1: Hypersecretion of growth
        hormone.

   Column 2: Giantism

   Answer: Giantism
   Diff: 1   Page Ref: 518

9) Column 1: Hyposecretion of the thyroid
        in infants.

   Column 2: Cretinism

   Answer: Cretinism
   Diff: 1   Page Ref: 524

10) Column 1: Hyposecretion of growth
         hormone.

    Column 2: Progeria

    Answer: Progeria
    Diff: 1   Page Ref: 518

Match the following:

11) Column 1: Sometimes called the "master
         gland"; produces hormones
         that stimulate other endocrine
         glands.

    Column 2: Hypophysis

    Answer: Hypophysis
    Diff: 1   Page Ref: 516

12) Column 1: The gland that controls the
         fright, flight, or fight reaction.

    Column 2: Adrenal medulla

    Answer: Adrenal medulla
    Diff: 1   Page Ref: 533

13) Column 1: Produces hormones that
         regulate glucose levels in the
         body.

    Column 2: Pancreas

    Answer: Pancreas
    Diff: 1   Page Ref: 534

14) Column 1: Produces a hormone that controls blood levels of calcium and potassium by their removal from bone tissue.

Column 2: Parathyroid

Answer: Parathyroid
Diff: 1   Page Ref: 526

15) Column 1: Produces the body's major metabolic hormones.

Column 2: Thyroid

Answer: Thyroid
Diff: 1   Page Ref: 522

True/False Questions

1) In humans, melatonin may inhibit sexual maturation.

Answer: TRUE
Diff: 1   Page Ref: 537

2) The antagonistic hormones that regulate the blood calcium level are calcitonin–parathormone.

Answer: TRUE
Diff: 1   Page Ref: 526-527

3) The hormone that raises blood sugar levels is insulin.

Answer: FALSE
Diff: 1   Page Ref: 534

4) Both "turn on" factors (hormonal, humoral, and neural stimuli) and "turn off" factors (feedback inhibition and others) may be modulated by the activity of the nervous system.

Answer: TRUE
Diff: 1   Page Ref: 513-514

5) ACTH stimulates the adrenal cortex to release corticosteroid hormones.

Answer: TRUE
Diff: 1   Page Ref: 518

6) LH in males is sometimes referred to as ICSH.

Answer: TRUE
Diff: 1   Page Ref: 518

7) The only known effect of prolactin in humans is to produce impotence in males.

Answer: FALSE
Diff: 1   Page Ref: 518

8) Oxytocin is a strong stimulant of uterine contractions.

Answer: TRUE
Diff: 1   *Page Ref: 519*

9) Follicle cells of the thyroid gland produce thyroglobulin, while follicle cells of the parathyroid produce calcitonin.

Answer: FALSE
Diff: 1   *Page Ref: 526–527*

10) The thyroid gland is embedded in the parathyroid tissue.

Answer: FALSE
Diff: 1   *Page Ref: 526*

11) The prime metabolic effect of cortisol is gluconeogenesis.

Answer: TRUE
Diff: 1   *Page Ref: 531*

12) The beta cells are the pancreatic islet cells that produce insulin.

Answer: TRUE
Diff: 1   *Page Ref: 534*

13) Type II diabetes lacks insulin activity.

Answer: FALSE
Diff: 1   *Page Ref: 536*

14) Peptide hormones enter the target cells and elicit a response by mediating neurotransmitter effects.

Answer: FALSE
Diff: 1   *Page Ref: 508–509*

15) The only function of oxytocin release is to promote uterine contractions.

Answer: FALSE
Diff: 1   *Page Ref: 519–520*

16) When an individual suffers severe hemorrhage, an exceptionally high amount of ACTH is usually released.

Answer: FALSE
Diff: 1   *Page Ref: 530–531*

17) Calcitonin is a peptide hormone that has destructive effects on the skeletal system.

Answer: FALSE
Diff: 1   *Page Ref: 526*

18) The adrenal glands synthesize amines.

Answer: TRUE
Diff: 1   Page Ref: 533

19) Aldosterone is the most potent mineralocorticoid produced in the adrenals but the least abundant.

Answer: FALSE
Diff: 1   Page Ref: 529–530

20) Atrial natriuretic peptide is a hormone that controls blood pressure in part by increasing the urinary secretion of sodium.

Answer: TRUE
Diff: 1   Page Ref: 538

21) While glucagon is a small polypeptide, it is nevertheless very potent in its regulatory effects.

Answer: TRUE
Diff: 1   Page Ref: 534

22) The thyroid gland is a large gland that controls metabolic functions throughout the life of an individual.

Answer: TRUE
Diff: 1   Page Ref: 522

23) Many hormones synthesized in the gastrointestinal tract are chemically identical to brain neurotransmitters.

Answer: TRUE
Diff: 1   Page Ref: 538

24) All of the following hormones are secreted by the adenohypophysis: ACTH, FSH, and LH.

Answer: TRUE
Diff: 2   Page Ref: 518

25) Iodine is an essential element required for the synthesis of thyroxine.

Answer: TRUE
Diff: 2   Page Ref: 525

26) The endocrine gland that is probably malfunctioning if a person has a high metabolic rate is the parathyroid.

Answer: FALSE
Diff: 2   Page Ref: 522–523

27) Growth hormone always exerts its influence by targeting other endocrine glands to produce hormones.

Answer: FALSE
Diff: 2   Page Ref: 516–517

28) Diabetes insipidus and diabetes mellitus are both caused by a genetic mutation involving the synthesis of insulin.

Answer: FALSE
Diff: 2   *Page Ref: 522, 535–536*

29) The stimulus for calcitonin release is usually excessive amounts of growth hormone synthesis.

Answer: FALSE
Diff: 2   *Page Ref: 526*

30) Glucocorticoids are steroid hormones that usually enhance the immune responses when an individual is suffering from severe stress.

Answer: FALSE
Diff: 2   *Page Ref: 531*

31) Direct gene activation involves a second-messenger system.

Answer: FALSE
Diff: 3   *Page Ref: 511–512*

32) All peptide hormone synthesis requires gene activation that produces mRNA.

Answer: TRUE
Diff: 3   *Page Ref: 511*

33) All adenohypophyseal hormones affect their target cells via a cyclic AMP second-messenger system.

Answer: TRUE
Diff: 3   *Page Ref: 516–519*

Multiple-Choice Questions

1) Gluconeogenesis occurs in the liver due to the action of:
    A) aldosterone.   B) insulin.   C) glucagon.   D) cortisol.

Answer: D
Diff: 1   *Page Ref: 531*

2) Normal development of the immune response is due in part to hormones produced by the:
    A) adrenal medulla.   B) pancreas.
    C) thyroid gland.   D) thymus gland.

Answer: D
Diff: 1   *Page Ref: 538*

3) Virtually all of the protein or amino acid–based hormones exert their effects through intracellular:

A) ions.

B) deactivators.

C) nucleotides.

D) second messengers.

Answer: D
Diff: 1   Page Ref: 508

4) Which of the following is not a category of endocrine gland stimulus?

A) enzyme   B) humoral   C) neural   D) hormonal

Answer: A
Diff: 1   Page Ref: 512–513

5) Chemical substances, secreted by cells into the extracellular fluids, that regulate the metabolic function of other cells in the body are called:

A) enzymes.   B) antibodies.   C) proteins.   D) hormones.

Answer: D
Diff: 1   Page Ref: 507

6) Endocrine glands have three different mechanisms to stimulate themselves; _____ is not one of them.

A) humoral   B) mechanical   C) neural   D) hormonal

Answer: B
Diff: 1   Page Ref: 512–513

7) The hypothalamic–hypophyseal tract:

A) connects the hypophysis to the pituitary gland.

B) is partly contained within the infundibulum.

C) conducts aldosterone to the hypophysis.

D) is the site of prolactin synthesis.

Answer: B
Diff: 1   Page Ref: 516

8) Tropic hormones:

A) include ACTH and TSH.

B) do not regulate the function of other endocrine glands.

C) exert their effects on cells by direct gene activation.

D) include GH and PRL.

Answer: A
Diff: 1   Page Ref: 516

9) Growth hormone:

A) is also called somatostatin.

B) is regulated by humoral mechanisms.

C) secretion results in a decrease in muscle mass.

D) promotes long bone growth during the formative years.

Answer: D
Diff: 1   Page Ref: 516–517

10) Oxytocin:

A) release is an example of a positive feedback control mechanism.

B) is an adenohypophyseal secretion.

C) exerts its most important effects during menstruation.

D) controls milk production.

Answer: A
Diff: 1   Page Ref: 519–520

11) ADH:

A) increases urine production.

B) promotes dehydration.

C) is produced in the adenohypophysis.

D) is inhibited by alcohol.

Answer: D
Diff: 1   Page Ref: 521–522

12) Thyroid hormone exerts its influence by:

A) entering some cells and binding to intracellular receptors within the nuclei.

B) exerting only a minor effect on body metabolism.

C) causing a reduction in the number of blood vessel adrenergic receptors, and therefore decreasing blood pressure.

D) acting to decrease basal metabolic rate.

Answer: A
Diff: 1   Page Ref: 522–523

13) Gonadocorticoid(s):

A) synthesized by the adrenal medulla are primarily androgens.

B) production by the adrenal gland is insignificant compared with sex hormone release from the gonads during late puberty.

C) secretion inhibition is highly dependent on a negative feedback loop involving ACTH.

D) hypersecretion can result in androgenital syndrome, also called feminization.

Answer: B
Diff: 1   Page Ref: 532

14) Sometimes prolonged excessive exposure to high hormone concentrations causes a phenomenon known as:

A) diabetes mellitus.

B) cellular inhibition.

C) down-regulation.

D) metabolism of protein kinases.

Answer: C
Diff: 1   Page Ref: 512

15) Which of the following is not a change that may be caused by hormonal stimulus?

A) a change in membrane potential

B) the stimulation of a genetic event resulting in protein synthesis

C) an increase in enzymatic activity

D) direct control of the nervous system

Answer: D
Diff: 1   Page Ref: 508

16) The ability of a specific tissue or organ to respond to the presence of a hormone is dependent on:

A) the location of the tissue or organ with respect to the circulatory path.

B) the membrane potential of the cells of the target organ.

C) the prescence of the appropriate receptors on the cells of the target tissue or organ.

D) nothing—all hormones of the human body are able to stimulate any and all cell types because hormones are powerful and nonspecific.

Answer: C
Diff: 1   Page Ref: 511-512

17) Several hormones are synthesized in the hypothalamus and transported to the anterior pituitary gland. The mechanism of transportation from hypothalamus to anterior pituitary gland is through the:

A) hepatic portal system.

B) general circulatory system.

C) hypophyseal portal system.

D) feedback loop.

Answer: C
Diff: 1   Page Ref: 516

18) The neurohypophysis or posterior lobe of the pituitary gland is not a true endocrine gland because:

A) it is strictly a part of the neural system and has little or nothing to do with hormonal release.

B) embryonically it was an endocrine tissue, but in the adult human it is no longer functional.

C) it is unable to function as an endocrine tissue because it is actually part of the neural system due to its location.

D) it is only a hormone storage area that receives hormones from the hypothalamus for release.

Answer: D
Diff: 1   *Page Ref: 519*

19) Insulin, a small (51-amino-acid) protein, is synthesized by the beta cells of the pancreas. This hormone is released:

A) in excessive amounts in obese people.

B) in response to severe physical stress (i.e., a ten-mile marathon).

C) when the body's glucose level rises.

D) when the body's glucose level drops.

Answer: C
Diff: 1   *Page Ref: 534-535*

20) Steroid hormones exert their action by:

A) entering the nucleus of a cell and initiating or altering the expression of a gene.

B) finding an appropriate cell receptor and initiating cAMP activity.

C) stimulating the synthesis of a glycogen.

D) increasing blood pressure.

Answer: A
Diff: 1   *Page Ref: 510-511*

21) The "second-messenger" mechanism of hormone action operates through:

A) synthesizing more of the hormone than is actually needed.

B) increasing the basal metabolic rate in the target organ.

C) not responding to a feedback mechanism.

D) binding to specific receptors and employing the services of G proteins and cAMP.

Answer: D
Diff: 1   *Page Ref: 508*

22) Hormones often cause a cell to elicit multiple responses; this is because:

   A) there are thousands of receptors on the cell membrane.

   B) the receptors bind to several hormones at the same time.

   C) the protein kinases are rapidly metabolized.

   D) most cells have many different protein kinases with distinct substrates.

   Answer: D
   Diff: 1   Page Ref: 511-513

23) Cells that respond to peptide hormones usually do so through a sequence of biochemical reactions involving receptor and kinase activation. In order for cells to respond, it is necessary for first and second messengers to communicate. This is possible because:

   A) peptide hormones always enter the cell membrane and elicit a response without assistance from other messengers.

   B) hormones alter cellular operations through stimulation of a gene directly.

   C) G protein acts as the link between first and second messengers.

   D) the hormone receptor complex moves into the cytoplasm as a unit.

   Answer: C
   Diff: 1   Page Ref: 509-510

24) Thyroid hormone (a small iodinated amine) enters target cells in a manner similar to:

   A) insulin, because insulin is a small peptide.

   B) steroid hormones, because both diffuse easily into target cells.

   C) growth hormone, because the thyroid works synergistically with thyroid hormone.

   D) glucagon, because the structure of glucagon is similar to that of thyroid hormone.

   Answer: B
   Diff: 1   Page Ref: 523

25) When it becomes necessary to enlist the "fight-or-flight" response, a hormone that is released during the alarm phase of the general adaptation syndrome is:

   A) estrogen.   B) epinephrine.

   C) angiotensinogen.   D) renin.

   Answer: B
   Diff: 1   Page Ref: 533

26) One of the least complicated of the endocrine control systems directly responds to changing blood levels of ions and nutrients. Which of the following describes this mechanism?

   A) the rapid oxidation of carbohydrates   B) catabolic inhibition

   C) protein synthesis   D) humoral stimulation

   Answer: D
   Diff: 1   Page Ref: 512-513

27) The adenohypophysis is often referred to as the "master endocrine gland." What gives this small gland such distinction?

A) Its products initiate and maintain milk secretion via mammary glands.

B) Its products stimulate sperm production in the testes.

C) It is the only gland producing eicosanoids.

D) Its products often regulate the release of hormones by other endocrine glands.

Answer: D
Diff: 1   Page Ref: 516

28) The major targets of growth hormone are:

A) the blood vessels.   B) the adrenal glands.

C) the liver.   D) bones and skeletal muscles.

Answer: D
Diff: 1   Page Ref: 516–517

29) The parathyroid glands maintain adequate levels of blood calcium. This is accomplished through:

A) blocking the action of growth hormone.

B) targeting the bone and activating osteoclasts so that calcium will be released.

C) antagonizing the synthesis of calcitonin.

D) slowing the activity of tissues that require calcium for activity.

Answer: B
Diff: 1   Page Ref: 526–527

30) Which organ is responsible for synthesizing ANP?

A) the heart   B) the kidney   C) the skin   D) the spleen

Answer: A
Diff: 1   Page Ref: 538

31) Mineralocorticoid is to aldosterone as glucocorticoid is to:

A) testosterone.   B) estrogen.   C) cortisol.   D) epinephrine.

Answer: C
Diff: 2   Page Ref: 529–531

32) Individuals with type II diabetes:

A) have an absolute requirement for insulin injections.

B) are often in ketosis.

C) may often control their disease by diet and exercise.

D) Both B and C are correct.

Answer: C
Diff: 2   Page Ref: 536

33) Leptin is secreted by:

    A) lymphocytes.   B) adipocytes.   C) goblet cells.   D) fibroblasts.

Answer: B
Diff: 2   Page Ref: 538

34) Which of the following endocrine glands is capable of storing its hormones extracellularly and then slowly releasing them?

    A) thyroid gland   B) pituitary gland   C) adrenal gland   D) pancreas

Answer: A
Diff: 2   Page Ref: 522–523

35) The most important regulator of electrolyte concentrations in extracellular fluids is:

    A) insulin.   B) aldosterone.   C) glucagon.   D) cortisol.

Answer: B
Diff: 2   Page Ref: 529–530

36) Which of the following is not a steroid-based hormone?

    A) estrogen   B) aldosterone   C) epinephrine   D) cortisone

Answer: C
Diff: 2   Page Ref: 533

37) Which of the following does not act as a second messenger in second-messenger systems of hormone action?

    A) cyclic AMP   B) calmodulin

    C) cyclic GMP   D) inositol triphosphate

Answer: B
Diff: 2   Page Ref: 510

38) Select the correct statement about hormonal structure or function.

    A) Prostaglandins are biologically active peptides.

    B) Modified cholesterol forms the main structural component of the peptone hormones.

    C) An amino acid derivative can be a hormone.

    D) An example of a local hormone is testosterone.

Answer: C
Diff: 2   Page Ref: 507–511

39) Which of the following would be associated with the action of steroids on cells?

    A) extracellular receptors with a specificity for only a single amino acid sequence on the hormone

    B) an enzyme that catalyzes the formation of cyclic AMP

    C) second-messenger systems

    D) a hormone-receptor complex that interacts directly with the cell's DNA

Answer: D
Diff: 2   Page Ref: 510–511

40) Cellular responses to hormones that initiate second–messenger systems include:

A) possible activation of several different second–messenger systems.

B) cyclic AMP phosphodiesterase formation of an active second messenger.

C) formation of a specific protein kinase that acts on a series of extracellular intermediates.

D) hormone binding to intracellular receptors.

Answer: A
Diff: 2   Page Ref: 508-510

41) Regulating hormones from the hypothalamus:

A) enter venous circulation and travel to the heart, which pumps the hormone–containing blood to the pituitary.

B) enter the hepatic portal system, which feeds the pituitary.

C) travel by arteries to the pituitary.

D) first enter into the hypophyseal portal system.

Answer: D
Diff: 2   Page Ref: 516-517

42) Enzyme action converts pro–opiomelanocortin into:

A) ACTH.   B) beta endorphin.

C) carotene-stimulating hormone.   D) ADH.

Answer: B
Diff: 2   Page Ref: 516

43) ACTH:

A) is secreted by the posterior pituitary.

B) secretion is regulated by a hypothalamic secretion.

C) causes the release of hormones from the adrenal medulla.

D) is not a tropic hormone.

Answer: B
Diff: 2   Page Ref: 516

44) Prolactin:

A) is a steroid hormone.

B) is regulated by releasing hormones.

C) hyposecretion is more common than hypersecretion.

D) inhibiting hormone release is caused by the nursing infant.

Answer: B
Diff: 2   Page Ref: 518-519

45) Which of the following is true about calcium homeostasis?

A) Increased calcitonin levels will cause increased blood calcium levels.

B) High calcium levels cause bone resorption.

C) Parathyroid hormone causes an increase in osteoblast activity.

D) Parathyroid hormone is the single most important regulator of calcium levels in the blood.

Answer: D
Diff: 2   Page Ref: 526–527

46) Aldosterone:

A) is secreted by the neurohypophysis.

B) functions to increase sodium resorption.

C) presence increases potassium concentration in the blood.

D) production is greatly influenced by ACTH.

Answer: B
Diff: 2   Page Ref: 529–530

47) The only amine hormone to act like a steroid is:

A) TH.   B) ACTH.   C) GH.   D) ADH.

Answer: A
Diff: 2   Page Ref: 523

48) Which organ below does not have hormone production?

A) heart   B) kidney   C) liver   D) skin

Answer: C
Diff: 2   Page Ref: 538

49) In circumstances where the body requires prolonged or increased levels of a hormone, the DNA of target cells will specify the synthesis of more receptors on the surface of the cells of the target organ. This is known as:

A) the cell's sensitivity reaction.   B) cellular affinity.

C) up-regulation.   D) a reaction to a stressor.

Answer: C
Diff: 2   Page Ref: 512

50) Eicosanoids do not include:

A) paracrines.   B) leukotrienes.

C) hydrocortisones.   D) prostaglandins.

Answer: C
Diff: 2   Page Ref: 508

51) A man has been told that he is not synthesizing enough follicle-stimulating hormone (FSH), and for this reason he may be unable to father a child. Choose the correct statement to explain this problem.

A) FSH stimulates estrogen secretion by ovarian cells; therefore it is not synthesized by males.

B) The physician is wrong—a hormone made in the adenohypophysis could not influence fertility.

C) FSH stimulates sperm production in the testes.

D) The man must be producing progesterone, which inhibits the synthesis of FSH.

Answer: C
Diff: 2   Page Ref: 518

52) Which of the following organs is affected by thyroid hormone?

A) liver   B) spleen   C) testes   D) brain

Answer: A
Diff: 3   Page Ref: 522–523

53) Thyroxine is a peptide hormone, but its mechanism is different from other peptide hormones. Which of the following statements is true concerning this difference?

A) It causes positive feedback.

B) It does not require a second messenger to effect a response.

C) It is very specific in the cell type it targets.

D) It is a stimulant of cellular metabolism and targets all cells.

Answer: B
Diff: 3   Page Ref: 522–523

54) Catecholamines and/or peptide hormones bind to receptors on the surface of cells that comprise target organs. This binding causes:

A) an immediate change in genetic activity.

B) the opening of a sodium pump.

C) the activation of a potassium pump.

D) adenylate cyclase to generate cyclic AMP from ATP.

Answer: D
Diff: 3   Page Ref: 533

55) Glucocorticoids enable the body to deal appropriately with stress. They accomplish this by:

A) increasing blood glucose, fatty acid, and amino acid levels and enhancing blood pressure.

B) decreasing the heart rate, thus decreasing blood pressure.

C) stimulating the pancreas to release insulin.

D) blocking the neurotransmitters that prepare the body for the stress response.

Answer: A
Diff: 3   Page Ref: 531

Clinical Questions

1) A woman with excessive body hair, a deep voice, and an enlarged clitoris shows the outward symptoms of which hormonal dysfunction?

   Answer: The hormonal dysfunction is hypersecretion of gonadocorticoids.
   Diff: 2   *Page Ref: 532–533*

2) Mrs. James appeared at the clinic complaining of extreme nervousness and sweating, saying that she could feel and hear her heart thumping when she tried to sleep at night. Laboratory testing revealed hyperglycemia and increased basal metabolic rate. Although she also proved to have high blood pressure, tests of thyroid function were normal. What is your diagnosis? What treatment should be used?

   Answer: The diagnosis is hypersecretion of catecholamines, sometimes arising from a rare chromaffin cell tumor called a pheochromocytoma. Treatment is removal of the tumor and/or irradiation of the adrenal medulla.
   Diff: 3   *Page Ref: 534*

3) Mr. Sanchez makes an appointment to see his doctor for pain in his abdominal area. Tests and x-rays reveal kidney stones as well as bones with a moth-eaten appearance. Further questioning reveals a medical history of abnormal reflexes and weakness. What is the problem and what treatment would be recommended?

   Answer: The problem is hyperparathyroidism resulting from a parathyroid gland tumor. The treatment is removal of the tumor.
   Diff: 4   *Page Ref: 527*

4) A woman trying to lose weight buys diet pills off the shelf. She takes them as recommended and notes a quick weight loss. What could cause this sudden weight loss? (The label on the diet pills lists a chemical known to be a strong diuretic.)

   Answer: The diuretic antagonized the effect of ADH, causing water to be flushed from the body; the "weight loss" was simply water loss.
   Diff: 4   *Page Ref: 521–522*

5) Henry is a 53–year–old healthy male. He was advised by his physician that he was synthesizing excess amounts of growth hormone. What is an early symptom that may lead the physician to make this diagnosis?

   Answer: Hyperglycemia is often observed in people who are synthesizing excess growth hormone.
   Diff: 4   *Page Ref: 516–518*

6) It was often rumored that one of our deceased presidents was suffering from Addison's disease (inadequate synthesis of mineralocorticoids and glucocorticoids). What symptoms may have led to the diagnosis of this condition?

   Answer: Hypoglycemia, a bronzing of the skin, low body weight, low plasma glucose and sodium levels, high potassium levels, hypotension, and some dehydration would all have been observed in the patient.
   Diff: 4   *Page Ref: 532*

7) Glucagon and insulin both target the cells of the liver and are both made in the pancreas, yet they have very different effects on the cells they target. What accounts for this fact?

Answer: Glucagon and insulin use different cell surface receptors.
Diff: 4   *Page Ref: 534–535*

8) Due to a recent head injury, a client is told that his pituitary is hypersecreting prolactin. Is there need for concern about this young man?

Answer: Yes; there should be great concern, because hypersecretion of prolactin will lead to impotence.
Diff: 4   *Page Ref: 519*

9) The parents of a 17-year-old boy are concerned about his height because he is only 5 feet tall and they are both close to 6 feet tall. After tests by their doctor, certain hormones are prescribed for the boy. What is the probable diagnosis, and what hormones were prescribed? Why might the child still expect to reach his growth potential?

Answer: The diagnosis is insufficient growth hormone. The prescription is commercial pituitary growth hormone. The reason the child might reach his growth potential is that the epiphyseal plates of the long bones have not yet closed, allowing additional growth of the long bones.
Diff: 5   *Page Ref: 518*

10) John is a 26-year-old man who begins to notice a progressive enlargement of feet, hands, cranium, nose, and lower jawbone. His doctor recommends irradiation of the pituitary gland. What is the most likely diagnosis? Why?

Answer: The diagnosis is acromegaly. The condition results from excess secretion of growth hormone from the pituitary gland postpuberty and after the epiphyseal plates of the long bones have fused.
Diff: 5   *Page Ref: 518*

CHAPTER 16   Blood

Fill-in-the-Blank/Short Answer Questions

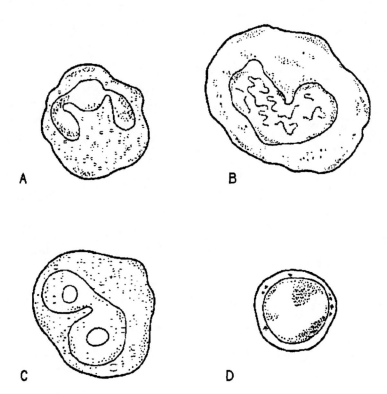

Figure 16.1

Using Figure 16.1, identify the following:

　　1) Monocyte.

　　　　Answer: B
　　　　Diff: 1   Page Ref: 554

　　2) Lymphocyte.

　　　　Answer: D
　　　　Diff: 1   Page Ref: 554

　　3) Eosinophil.

　　　　Answer: C
　　　　Diff: 1   Page Ref: 554

4) Neutrophil.

Answer: A
Diff: 1   *Page Ref:* 554

5) Most common white blood cell found in whole blood.

Answer: A
Diff: 1   *Page Ref:* 554

6) Mounts an immune response by direct cell attack or via antibodies.

Answer: D
Diff: 1   *Page Ref:* 554

7) Kills parasitic worms.

Answer: C
Diff: 1   *Page Ref:* 554

8) Become macrophages.

Answer: B
Diff: 1   *Page Ref:* 554

9) Phagocytize bacteria.

Answer: A
Diff: 1   *Page Ref:* 554

Fill in the blank or provide a short answer:

10) The formed element _____ can kill parasitic worms.

Answer: eosinophil
Diff: 2   *Page Ref:* 553

11) A _____ is a committed granular leukocyte stem cell.

Answer: myeloblast
Diff: 2   *Page Ref:* 555

12) The rarest leukocyte is the _____.

Answer: basophil
Diff: 2   *Page Ref:* 553–554

13) The potent platelet aggregate that attracts more platelets to the site of an injury is _____.

Answer: adenosine diphosphate (ADP)
Diff: 2   *Page Ref:* 558

14) _____ is an antiprostaglandin drug that inhibits thromboxane A_2 formation (platelet plug formation).

Answer: Aspirin
Diff: 2   *Page Ref:* 562

15) The universal recipient blood type is _____.

Answer: AB
Diff: 2   *Page Ref:* 564

16) When monocytes migrate into the interstitial spaces, they are called _____.

Answer: macrophages
Diff: 2   *Page Ref:* 555

17) Destruction of the hematopoietic components of red marrow leads to a condition called _____.

Answer: aplastic anemia
Diff: 2   *Page Ref:* 550

18) _____ is the stage of development in the life of an erythrocyte during which the nucleus is ejected.

Answer: Normoblast
Diff: 2   *Page Ref:* 546–547

19) Hemoglobin is composed of _____ polypeptide chains.

Answer: four
Diff: 2   *Page Ref:* 545

20) List the general factors that limit normal clot growth.

Answer: Rapid removal of coagulation factors and inhibition of activated clotting factors.
Diff: 2   *Page Ref:* 562

21) When are whole blood transfusions routinely given?

Answer: When there is substantial blood loss or to treat severe anemia or thrombocytopenia.
Diff: 2   *Page Ref:* 563

22) List the most common causes of bleeding disorders.

Answer: Platelet deficiency (thrombocytopenia); deficiency of procoagulants due to liver disorders; or certain genetic conditions (hemophilias).
Diff: 3   *Page Ref:* 563

23) List one example for each of these three functions of blood: distribution, regulation, and protection.

Answer: Distribution: deliver oxygen from lungs and nutrients from the digestive system to cells, transport hormones, remove wastes. Regulation: maintain body temperature, pH, fluid volume. Protection: prevent blood loss and infection.
Diff: 3   *Page Ref: 543*

24) What are the granulocytes and what are their life spans?

Answer: Neutrophils live 6–9 days. Eosinophils also live 6–9 days. Basophils live 3–7 days.
Diff: 3   *Page Ref: 554*

25) Why is iron not stored or transported in its free form? In what form(s) is it stored or transported in blood?

Answer: Because free iron is toxic to body cells, iron is stored within cells as protein–iron complexes such as ferritin and hemosiderin. It is transported loosely bound to a protein called transferrin.
Diff: 4   *Page Ref: 549*

26) Explain why blood is classified as a connective tissue.

Answer: It has both solid (cells) and liquid (extracellular) components. The formed elements (cells) are suspended in a nonliving fluid matrix (extracellular matrix).
Diff: 4   *Page Ref: 542*

27) What determines whether blood is bright red (scarlet) or a dull brick–red (dark red)?

Answer: In bright red blood, oxygen is bound to hemoglobin (oxygenated blood). In dull brick–red blood, oxygen has been released from the hemoglobin (deoxygenated blood).
Diff: 4   *Page Ref: 545*

28) Why is hemoglobin enclosed in erythrocytes rather than existing free in plasma?

Answer: Enclosed within erythrocytes, hemoglobin is prevented from breaking into fragments that would leak out of the vascular system through porous capillaries. Additionally, since it's enclosed, hemoglobin cannot contribute to blood viscosity and osmotic pressure.
Diff: 4   *Page Ref: 545*

Matching Questions

Match the following:

1) Column 1: Nucleus with 2 lobes; contains granules of lysosomal enzymes; function in phagocytosis of antigen-antibody complex.

Column 2: Eosinophil

Answer: Eosinophil
Diff: 1   *Page Ref: 554*

2) Column 1: Nucleus with 3–6 lobes; functions as a phagocyte; contains fine indistinct granules.

   Column 2: Neutrophil

   Answer: Neutrophil
   Diff: 1   *Page Ref: 554*

3) Column 1: Transports CO_2 and oxygen.

   Column 2: Erythrocyte

   Answer: Erythrocyte
   Diff: 1   *Page Ref: 554*

4) Column 1: Contains a U– or an S–shaped nucleus; granules stain very dark; releases histamine and heparin.

   Column 2: Basophil

   Answer: Basophil
   Diff: 1   *Page Ref: 554*

5) Column 1: Largest of the WBCs; crucial in defense against viruses; associated with chronic infections.

   Column 2: Monocyte

   Answer: Monocyte
   Diff: 1   *Page Ref: 554*

6) Column 1: Most common formed element in the bloodstream.

   Column 2: Erythrocyte

   Answer: Erythrocyte
   Diff: 1   *Page Ref: 554*

Match the following:

7) Column 1: Cell fragments; function as part of the blood–clotting mechanism.

   Column 2: Thrombocytes

   Answer: Thrombocytes
   Diff: 1   *Page Ref: 554*

8) Column 1: The major contributor to
              plasma osmotic pressure.

   Column 2: Albumin

   Answer: Albumin
   Diff: 1   Page Ref: 543

9) Column 1: Thrombin catalyzes the
              joining of these molecules
              present in plasma to this
              insoluble mesh, which traps
              blood cells.

   Column 2: Fibrinogen

   Answer: Fibrinogen
   Diff: 1   Page Ref: 560

10) Column 1: Forms the structural
               framework of a blood clot.

    Column 2: Fibrinogen

    Answer: Fibrinogen
    Diff: 1   Page Ref: 560

11) Column 1: Plasma protein that plays a
               role in the formation of a
               blood clot.

    Column 2: Prothrombin

    Answer: Prothrombin
    Diff: 1   Page Ref: 559

Match the following:

12) Column 1: Floating intravascular clot.

    Column 2: Embolus

    Answer: Embolus
    Diff: 1   Page Ref: 562

13) Column 1: Any decrease in
               oxygen–carrying ability of the
               blood.

    Column 2: Anemia

    Answer: Anemia
    Diff: 1   Page Ref: 550

14) Column 1: Coagulation.

    Column 2: Clotting

    Answer: Clotting
    Diff: 1   Page Ref: 559

Match the following:

15) Column 1: Polymorphonuclear leukocyte.

    Column 2: Neutrophil

    Answer: Neutrophil
    Diff: 1   Page Ref: 553

16) Column 1: Agranular white blood cells.

    Column 2: Monocyte

    Answer: Monocyte
    Diff: 1   Page Ref: 555

17) Column 1: Protein capable of changing
                shape and color in the
                presence of O_2.

    Column 2: Hemoglobin

    Answer: Hemoglobin
    Diff: 1   Page Ref: 545

18) Column 1: Adverse reaction of donor
                blood cells with recipient
                plasma.

    Column 2: Agglutination

    Answer: Agglutination
    Diff: 1   Page Ref: 565

19) Column 1: Lacking in hemophilia type A.

    Column 2: Factor VIII

    Answer: Factor VIII
    Diff: 2   Page Ref: 563

Match the following:

20) Column 1: Constitutes 90% of plasma
                volume.

    Column 2: Water

    Answer: Water
    Diff: 1   Page Ref: 543

21) Column 1: Plasma and formed elements.

    Column 2: Whole blood

    Answer: Whole blood
    Diff: 1   Page Ref: 563

22) Column 1: Liquid portion of the blood.

   Column 2: Plasma

   Answer: Plasma
   Diff: 1   Page Ref: 543

23) Column 1: A clot that develops in an
                   unbroken blood vessel.

   Column 2: Thrombus

   Answer: Thrombus
   Diff: 1   Page Ref: 562

Match the following:

24) Column 1: Stem cell from which all
                   formed elements arise.

   Column 2: Hematopoietic stem cell

   Answer: Hematopoietic stem cell
   Diff: 1   Page Ref: 546

25) Column 1: Interferes with blood–clotting
                   ability.

   Column 2: Heparin

   Answer: Heparin
   Diff: 1   Page Ref: 562

26) Column 1: A hormone-stimulating
                   erythropoiesis.

   Column 2: Erythropoietin

   Answer: Erythropoietin
   Diff: 1   Page Ref: 547

27) Column 1: Found in basophils.

   Column 2: Heparin

   Answer: Heparin
   Diff: 1   Page Ref: 562

28) Column 1: Deficient erythrocyte
                   production due to lack of
                   intrinsic factor and failure to
                   absorb vitamin B_{12}.

   Column 2: Pernicious anemia

   Answer: Pernicious anemia
   Diff: 2   Page Ref: 550

29) Column 1: Released from platelets.

Column 2: Prostaglandin derivatives

Answer: Prostaglandin derivatives
Diff: 3   Page Ref: 558

True/False Questions

1) Most of the body's iron supply is in heparin.

Answer: FALSE
Diff: 1   Page Ref: 562

2) The most important plasma proteins involved in maintaining the proper osmotic pressure of the blood are the gamma globulins.

Answer: FALSE
Diff: 1   Page Ref: 543

3) Hemoglobin is found within red blood cells.

Answer: TRUE
Diff: 1   Page Ref: 545

4) The primary source of RBCs in the adult human being is the bone marrow in the shafts of the long bones.

Answer: FALSE
Diff: 1   Page Ref: 545–546

5) An Rh incompatibility in infants due to the mother having Rh-positive blood and the infant having Rh-negative blood is called erythroblastosis fetalis.

Answer: FALSE
Diff: 1   Page Ref: 565

6) Clumping of red blood cells can occur when mismatched blood is transfused.

Answer: TRUE
Diff: 1   Page Ref: 565

7) Transfusion of type O blood always triggers a transfusion reaction.

Answer: FALSE
Diff: 1   Page Ref: 564

8) Leukemia refers to cancerous conditions of white blood cells.

Answer: TRUE
Diff: 1   Page Ref: 557

9) The immediate response to blood vessel injury is clotting.

Answer: FALSE
Diff: 1   Page Ref: 557–558

10) Platelets form a plug that seals a break in a blood vessel.

Answer: TRUE
Diff: 1   *Page Ref: 557*

11) The process of fibrinolysis disposes of bacteria when healing has occurred.

Answer: FALSE
Diff: 1   *Page Ref: 561–562*

12) The RBC "graveyard" is the liver.

Answer: FALSE
Diff: 1   *Page Ref: 549–550*

13) Hemorrhagic anemias result from blood loss.

Answer: TRUE
Diff: 1   *Page Ref: 550*

14) White blood cells are produced through the action of colony–stimulating factors.

Answer: TRUE
Diff: 1   *Page Ref: 555*

15) Hemoglobin is made up of the protein heme and the red pigment globin.

Answer: FALSE
Diff: 1   *Page Ref: 545*

16) The globin molecule for hemoglobin consists of four polypeptide chains.

Answer: TRUE
Diff: 1   *Page Ref: 545*

17) Each heme contains an atom of iron and can transport one molecule of oxygen.

Answer: TRUE
Diff: 1   *Page Ref: 545*

18) Each hemoglobin molecule can transport two molecules of oxygen.

Answer: FALSE
Diff: 1   *Page Ref: 545*

19) Diapedesis is the process by which red blood cells move into tissue spaces from the interior of blood capillaries.

Answer: FALSE
Diff: 1   *Page Ref: 552*

20) Positive chemotaxis is a feedback system that signals leukocyte migration into damaged areas.

Answer: TRUE
Diff: 1   *Page Ref: 552*

21) Basophils increase in number when parasitic invasion occurs.

Answer: FALSE
Diff: 1   Page Ref: 553-554

22) Leukopenia is an abnormally low number of leukocytes.

Answer: TRUE
Diff: 1   Page Ref: 555

23) A person with type B blood could receive blood from a person with either type B or O blood.

Answer: TRUE
Diff: 1   Page Ref: 564

24) The erythrocyte count increases when an individual goes from a low to a high altitude because the concentration of oxygen and total atmospheric pressure is lower at high altitudes.

Answer: TRUE
Diff: 2   Page Ref: 551

25) Clot retraction is usually followed by fibrinolysis.

Answer: TRUE
Diff: 2   Page Ref: 561

26) The least numerous of the white blood cells are basophils.

Answer: TRUE
Diff: 2   Page Ref: 554

27) Leukocytes move through the circulatory system by amoeboid motion.

Answer: FALSE
Diff: 2   Page Ref: 552

28) Granulocytes called neutrophils are phagocytic and the most numerous of all white blood cell types.

Answer: TRUE
Diff: 2   Page Ref: 554

29) All lymphocytes are leukocytes, but not all leukocytes are lymphocytes.

Answer: TRUE
Diff: 2   Page Ref: 555

30) Myelocytic leukemia involves a cancerous condition of lymphocytes.

Answer: FALSE
Diff: 2   Page Ref: 557

Multiple–Choice Questions

1) What is the average normal pH of blood?

   A) 8.4   B) 7.8   C) 7.4   D) 4.7

   Answer: C
   Diff: 1   Page Ref: 543

2) Which blood type is called the universal donor?

   A) A   B) B   C) AB   D) O

   Answer: D
   Diff: 1   Page Ref: 564

3) Which of the following is a regulatory function of blood?

   A) delivery of oxygen to body cells

   B) transport of metabolic wastes from cells

   C) prevention of blood loss

   D) maintenance of normal pH in body tissues

   Answer: D
   Diff: 1   Page Ref: 543

4) Which of the following is a protective function of blood?

   A) prevention of blood loss

   B) maintenance of adequate fluid volume

   C) maintenance of normal pH in body tissue

   D) maintenance of body temperature

   Answer: A
   Diff: 1   Page Ref: 543

5) Which of the following is not a phase of erythropoiesis?

   A) production of ribosomes   B) synthesis of hemoglobin
   C) ejection of the erythrocyte nucleus   D) production of vacuoles

   Answer: D
   Diff: 1   Page Ref: 545–547

6) Which of the following might trigger erythropoiesis?

   A) increased tissue demand for oxygen

   B) decreased tissue demand for oxygen

   C) an increased number of RBCs

   D) moving from a high altitude to a low altitude

   Answer: A
   Diff: 1   Page Ref: 547–548

7) As red blood cells age:

    A) ATP production increases.

    B) membranes "wear out" and the cells become damaged.

    C) they will eventually be excreted by the digestive system.

    D) iron will be excreted by the kidneys.

Answer: B
Diff: 1   *Page Ref: 549*

8) An individual who is blood type AB negative:

    A) can receive any blood type in moderate amounts except that with the Rh antigen.

    B) can donate to all blood types in moderate amounts.

    C) can receive types A, B, and AB, but not type O.

    D) can donate to types A, B, and AB, but not to type O.

Answer: A
Diff: 1   *Page Ref: 564*

9) The most abundant plasma protein is:

    A) globulin.   B) clotting protein.   C) albumin.   D) bile.

Answer: C
Diff: 1   *Page Ref: 543*

10) When neither anti-A nor anti-B clots on a blood plate, the blood is type:

    A) A.   B) B.   C) AB.   D) O.

Answer: D
Diff: 1   *Page Ref: 566*

11) Select the correct statement regarding blood cell formation.

    A) The main sites of blood cell production in adults are the spleen and the liver.

    B) Before the seventh month of fetal development, yellow marrow is the main site of blood cell formation.

    C) Red marrow is the main site of blood cell formation throughout adult life.

    D) Yellow marrow is the main site of leukocyte formation.

Answer: C
Diff: 1   *Page Ref: 545–546*

12) Blood volume expanders include all of the following except:

    A) dextran.   B) albumin.   C) packed cells.   D) saline solutions.

Answer: C
Diff: 2   *Page Ref: 566*

13) James has a hemoglobin measurement of 16 g / 100 ml blood. This is:
   A) above normal.   B) normal only if James is an infant.
   C) abnormally low.   D) within the normal range.

   Answer: D
   Diff: 2   *Page Ref: 545*

14) Which of these is not a normal plasma protein?
   A) fibrinogen   B) gamma globulin   C) thromboplastin   D) albumin

   Answer: C
   Diff: 2   *Page Ref: 561*

15) All of the following can be expected with polycythemia except:
   A) high hematocrit.   B) low blood viscosity.
   C) increased blood volume.   D) high blood pressure.

   Answer: B
   Diff: 2   *Page Ref: 551*

16) No visible cytoplasmic granules are present in:
   A) monocytes.   B) basophils.   C) eosinophils.   D) neutrophils.

   Answer: A
   Diff: 2   *Page Ref: 554*

17) Which of the following is not a phase of hemostasis?
   A) vascular spasm   B) fibrinolysis
   C) platelet plug formation   D) coagulation

   Answer: B
   Diff: 2   *Page Ref: 557–561*

18) Which of the following are not currently known red blood cell antigens?
   A) Carson   B) Lewis   C) Kell   D) Duffy

   Answer: A
   Diff: 2   *Page Ref: 564*

19) Place the following in correct developmental sequence:

   1. reticulocyte
   2. proerythroblast
   3. normoblast
   4. late erythroblast

   A) 1, 2, 3, 4   B) 1, 3, 2, 4   C) 2, 1, 3, 4   D) 2, 4, 3, 1

   Answer: D
   Diff: 2   *Page Ref: 545–547*

20) A lack of intrinsic factor, leading to a deficiency of vitamin B$_{12}$ and large pale cells called macrocytes, is characteristic of:

A) aplastic anemia.   B) polycythemia.

C) pernicious anemia.   D) sickle–cell anemia.

Answer: C
Diff: 2   *Page Ref: 550*

21) The slowest step in the clotting process is:

A) formation of prothrombin activator.   B) production of fibrin strands.

C) binding fibrin strands.   D) release of PF$_3$.

Answer: A
Diff: 2   *Page Ref: 559–561*

22) Thromboembolytic disorders:

A) result in uncontrolled bleeding.

B) include thrombus formation, a clot in a broken blood vessel.

C) include embolus formation, a clot moving within the circulatory system.

D) are caused by vitamin K deficiency.

Answer: C
Diff: 2   *Page Ref: 562*

23) Which of the following is not a cause of bleeding disorders?

A) thrombocytopenia, a condition of decreased circulating platelets

B) excess secretion of platelet–derived growth factor (PDGF)

C) a defect in the clotting cascade

D) vitamin K deficiency

Answer: B
Diff: 2   *Page Ref: 562–563*

24) Which of the following is characteristic of all leukocytes?

A) They are nucleated.

B) They have cytoplasmic granules.

C) They are phagocytic.

D) They are the most numerous of the formed elements in blood.

Answer: A
Diff: 2   *Page Ref: 552*

25) Which of the following is true about blood plasma?

    A) It is the same as serum but without the clotting proteins.

    B) The main protein component is hemoglobin.

    C) It is about 90% water.

    D) It contains about 20 dissolved components.

Answer: C
Diff: 2   *Page Ref: 543*

26) Platelets:

    A) stick to the damaged area of a blood vessel and help seal the break.

    B) have a life span of about 120 days.

    C) are the precursors of leukocytes.

    D) have multiple nuclei.

Answer: A
Diff: 2   *Page Ref: 557*

27) Which sequence is correct for the following events?

    1. fibrinogen-->fibrin
    2. clot retraction
    3. formation of thromboplastin
    4. prothrombin-->thrombin

    A) 3, 4, 1, 2   B) 1, 2, 3, 4   C) 4, 3, 1, 2   D) 3, 2, 1, 4

Answer: A
Diff: 3   *Page Ref: 557-561*

28) Fred's blood was determined to be AB positive. What does this mean?

    A) There are no antibodies to A, to B, or to Rh antigens in the plasma.

    B) Antibodies to A and B are present in the red cells.

    C) His blood lacks Rh factor.

    D) All of the above are correct.

Answer: A
Diff: 3   *Page Ref: 564-566*

29) Which of the following is a precursor of a basophil?

    A) megakaryoblast   B) myeloblast   C) lymphoblast   D) monoblast

Answer: B
Diff: 3   *Page Ref: 555*

30) Sickling of red blood cells can be produced in those with sickle-cell anemia by:
   A) travel at high altitude.
   B) vigorous exercise.
   C) malaria and travel at high altitude.
   D) travel at high altitude and vigorous exercise.

   Answer: D
   Diff: 3   Page Ref: 550

31) All of the following conditions impair coagulation except:
   A) vascular spasm.   B) vitamin K deficiency.
   C) severe hypocalcemia.   D) liver disease.

   Answer: A
   Diff: 3   Page Ref: 562–563

32) When can erythroblastosis fetalis not possibly happen in the child of an Rh negative mother?
   A) if the child is type O positive   B) if the child is Rh$^+$
   C) if the father is Rh$^+$ D) if the father is Rh$^-$

   Answer: D
   Diff: 3   Page Ref: 565

33) Complications of aplastic anemia generally do not include:
   A) hemorrhage.
   B) suppressed immunity.
   C) impaired formation of all formed elements.
   D) bleeding disorders.

   Answer: A
   Diff: 3   Page Ref: 550

Clinical Questions

1) Why would there be cause for concern if a young pregnant mother is Rh$^-$ and her husband is Rh$^+$ and this is their second child?

   Answer: If the mother was given RhoGAM before or shortly after birth of the first child, there is little concern, because the RhoGAM prevented the mother from sensitizing herself against her child. If she did not take RhoGAM, there is a chance the second child will develop erythroblastosis fetalis and die before birth.
   Diff: 4   Page Ref: 565

2) A total WBC count and a differential WBC count have been ordered for Mrs. Johnson. What information is obtained from the differential count that the total count does not provide?

   Answer: The differential count determines the relative proportion of individual leukocyte types (a valuable diagnostic tool). The total WBC count indicates an increase or decrease in number of WBCs.
   Diff: 5   Page Ref: 567

3) List three blood tests that might be ordered if anemia is suspected.

   Answer: The tests for anemia are hematocrit, complete blood count, and microscopic study of
           erythrocytes.
   Diff: 5   *Page Ref: 567*

4) List three blood tests that might be done if a person has bleeding problems.

   Answer: The tests for bleeding problems include prothrombin time, platelet count, hematocrit,
           and CBC.
   Diff: 5   *Page Ref: 567*

5) An elderly man has been receiving weekly injections of vitamin B_{12} ever since nearly all of his
   stomach was removed 6 months ago because of stomach cancer. Why is he receiving the
   vitamin injections? Why can't the vitamin be delivered in tablet form? What is the function of
   the vitamin in hematopoiesis?

   Answer: He is receiving the injections because he can't absorb the vitamin through dietary
           intake. Intrinsic factor produced by the stomach mucosa must be present for the
           absorption of the vitamin through the wall of the intestine. The vitamin is not delivered
           in tablet form for the same reason. B–complex vitamins are necessary for DNA synthesis,
           essential to hematopoiesis.
   Diff: 5   *Page Ref: 550*

6) A person complains of no energy, a chronic sore throat, a low–grade fever, and is tired and
   achy. His doctor notes an enlarged spleen upon examination. What diagnosis would you
   expect and what definitive test would you request?

   Answer: The test would be a differential white blood cell count to look for elevated numbers of
           monocytes and atypical lymphocytes. The diagnosis would be possible infectious
           mononucleosis, pending test results.
   Diff: 5   *Page Ref: 557*

7) A man of Mediterranean ancestry goes to his doctor with the following symptoms. He is very
   tired all of the time. He has difficulty catching his breath after even mild exercise. His doctor
   orders the following tests: CBC, hematocrit, differential WBC count. The tests show immature
   erythrocytes, fragile erythrocytes, and less than 2 million RBC per cubic millimeter. What
   would be a tentative diagnosis and suggested treatment?

   Answer: The diagnosis is thalassemia. The treatment is blood transfusion.
   Diff: 5   *Page Ref: 550*

CHAPTER 17   The Cardiovascular System: The Heart

Fill-in-the-Blank/Short Answer Questions

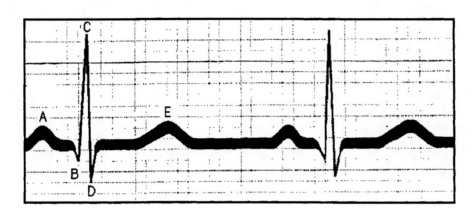

Figure 17.1

Using Figure 17.1, identify the following:

1) Atrial depolarization.

   Answer: A
   Diff: 1   Page Ref: 587–588

2) Point after which pressure begins to rise in the aorta.

   Answer: D
   Diff: 2   Page Ref: 587–588

3) Point of the least ventricular volume.

   Answer: E
   Diff: 2   Page Ref: 588

4) Point that represents the "dup" sound made by the heart.

   Answer: E
   Diff: 3   Page Ref: 588

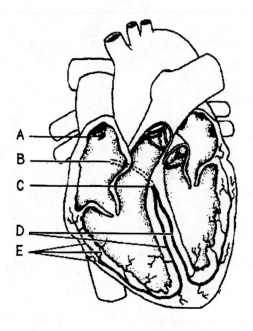

A

B

C

D

E

Figure 17.2

Using Figure 17.2, identify the following:

5) Purkinje fibers.

   Answer: E
   Diff: 1   Page Ref: 585

6) SA node.

   Answer: A
   Diff: 1   Page Ref: 585

7) AV bundle.

   Answer: C
   Diff: 1   Page Ref: 585

8) AV node.

   Answer: B
   Diff: 1   Page Ref: 585

9) Bundle branches.

   Answer: D
   Diff: 1   Page Ref: 585

Fill in the blank or provide a short answer:

10) The enlarged coronary vessel outside the heart that empties blood into the right atrium is the
_____.

Answer: coronary sinus
Diff: 1   Page Ref: 577

11) The _____ cells of the heart do not maintain stable resting membrane potentials; therefore,
they continually depolarize.

Answer: autorhythmic
Diff: 1   Page Ref: 584

12) Specialized conductive cells of the ventricles are called _____ fibers.

Answer: Purkinje
Diff: 1   Page Ref: 584–585

13) The ECG T wave interval represents _____.

Answer: ventricular repolarization
Diff: 1   Page Ref: 588

14) CO = _____ x SV.

Answer: HR or heart rate
Diff: 1   Page Ref: 591

15) The _____ membrane covers the heart.

Answer: parietal pericardium
Diff: 1   Page Ref: 570

16) The _____ valve of the heart has three valves with chordae tendineae.

Answer: tricuspid
Diff: 1   Page Ref: 577

17) _____ valves of the heart have no chordae tendineae attached.

Answer: Semilunar
Diff: 1   Page Ref: 579

18) Define *systole* and *diastole*. Which heart chambers are usually referenced when these terms are
used?

Answer: Systole is contraction of the muscle. Diastole is relaxation of the muscle. The contraction
and relaxation of the ventricles are normally described with the terms systole and
diastole.
Diff: 1   Page Ref: 588

19) Define the terms *end diastolic volume* (EDV) and *end systolic volume* (ESV) and relate them to the calculation of stroke volume.

   Answer: EDV is the amount of blood that collects in a ventricle during diastole. ESV is the volume of blood remaining in a ventricle after it has contracted. Stroke volume (ml/beat) equals EDV – ESV.
   Diff: 1   *Page Ref: 588–590*

20) What is the difference between the auricle and the atrium?

   Answer: Auricles are the flaplike appendages attached to the atria that allow them to expand or increase the atrial volume.
   Diff: 1   *Page Ref: 571*

21) The heart is called a "double pump" because there are two functionally separate circulations. Trace the pathway of each of these circulations and include the following information: heart chambers involved, major blood vessels involved, and general areas through which the blood flows. Begin with the right atrium.

   Answer: Right atrium to right ventricle to pulmonary arteries to lungs (pulmonary circuit pump); pulmonary veins to left atrium to left ventricle to aorta to body to venae cavae (systemic circuit pump).
   Diff: 2   *Page Ref: 575–576*

22) What two important functions does the cardiac conduction system perform?

   Answer: The important functions of the cardiac conduction system are to initiate impulses (pacemaker) and to distribute impulses throughout the heart so that it depolarizes and contracts in an orderly, sequential manner.
   Diff: 2   *Page Ref: 584–585*

23) Explain autorhythmicity in cardiac muscle cells.

   Answer: Autorhythmic cells do not maintain a stable resting membrane potential. Instead, they have an unstable resting potential that continuously depolarizes, drifting toward threshold for firing.
   Diff: 3   *Page Ref: 584*

24) Of what functional importance are the intercalated discs of cardiac muscle? Of what functional importance is the fibrous skeleton of the heart?

   Answer: Intercalated disks contain anchoring desmosomes, which prevent cell separation, and gap junctions, which allow ions to travel from cell to cell. The fibrous skeleton is connective tissue that reinforces the myocardium internally.
   Diff: 3   *Page Ref: 581, 571*

Matching Questions

Match the following:

1) Column 1: The lining of the heart.

   Column 2: Endocardium

   Answer: Endocardium
   Diff: 1   *Page Ref: 571*

2) Column 1: Heart muscle.

   Column 2: Myocardium

   Answer: Myocardium
   Diff: 1   *Page Ref: 571*

3) Column 1: Serous layer covering the
             heart muscle.

   Column 2: Epicardium

   Answer: Epicardium
   Diff: 1   *Page Ref: 571*

4) Column 1: The outermost layer of the
             serous pericardium.

   Column 2: Parietal pericardium

   Answer: Parietal pericardium
   Diff: 2   *Page Ref: 570*

Match the following:

5) Column 1: The pacemaker of the heart.

   Column 2: SA node

   Answer: SA node
   Diff: 1   *Page Ref: 584*

6) Column 1: Found in the interventricular
             septum.

   Column 2: AV bundle

   Answer: AV bundle
   Diff: 1   *Page Ref: 584*

7) Column 1: Network found in the
             ventricular myocardium.

   Column 2: Purkinje fibers

   Answer: Purkinje fibers
   Diff: 2   *Page Ref: 584*

8) Column 1: The point in the conduction
             system of the heart where the
             impulse is temporarily
             delayed.

   Column 2: AV node

   Answer: AV node
   Diff: 2   *Page Ref: 584*

Match the following:

9) Column 1: Prevents backflow into the left
ventricle.

Column 2: Aortic semilunar valve

Answer: Aortic semilunar valve
Diff: 1   Page Ref: 579

10) Column 1: Prevents backflow into the
right atrium.

Column 2: Tricuspid valve

Answer: Tricuspid valve
Diff: 1   Page Ref: 577

11) Column 1: Prevents backflow into the left
atrium.

Column 2: Mitral valve

Answer: Mitral valve
Diff: 1   Page Ref: 577

12) Column 1: Prevents backflow into the
right ventricle.

Column 2: Pulmonary semilunar valve

Answer: Pulmonary semilunar valve
Diff: 1   Page Ref: 579

13) Column 1: AV valve with two flaps.

Column 2: Mitral valve

Answer: Mitral valve
Diff: 1   Page Ref: 577

14) Column 1: AV valve with three flaps.

Column 2: Tricuspid valve

Answer: Tricuspid valve
Diff: 1   Page Ref: 577

True/False Questions

1) The myocardium receives its blood supply from the coronary arteries.

Answer: TRUE
Diff: 1   Page Ref: 576

2) A heart rate of less than 60 beats per minute is called tachycardia.

Answer: FALSE
Diff: 1   Page Ref: 595

3) The heart lies anterior to the vertebral column and posterior to the sternum.

Answer: TRUE
Diff: 1   *Page Ref: 569–570*

4) The atria receive blood returning to the heart.

Answer: TRUE
Diff: 1   *Page Ref: 571*

5) Cardiac muscle has more mitochondria and depends less on a continual supply of oxygen than does skeletal muscle.

Answer: FALSE
Diff: 1   *Page Ref: 581*

6) Proper function of the heart is dependent upon blood levels of ionic sodium.

Answer: FALSE
Diff: 1   *Page Ref: 584*

7) Congestive heart failure means that the pumping efficiency of the heart is depressed so that there is inadequate delivery of blood to body tissues.

Answer: TRUE
Diff: 1   *Page Ref: 595*

8) Tissues damaged by myocardial infarction are replaced by connective tissue.

Answer: TRUE
Diff: 1   *Page Ref: 577*

9) The left side of the heart pumps the same volume of blood as the right.

Answer: TRUE
Diff: 1   *Page Ref: 576*

10) In an ECG, the electrical activity associated with atrial repolarization is usually obscured by the QRS complex.

Answer: TRUE
Diff: 1   *Page Ref: 587–588*

11) Chronic release of excess thyroxine can cause a sustained increase in heart rate and a weakened heart.

Answer: TRUE
Diff: 1   *Page Ref: 593–594*

12) The mitral valve has chordae but the tricuspid valve does not.

Answer: FALSE
Diff: 1   *Page Ref: 577*

13) Trabeculae carneae are found in the ventricles and never the atria.

Answer: TRUE
Diff: 1   *Page Ref: 574*

14) The aortic semilunar valve opens when pressure in the aorta is higher than the ventricular pressure.

Answer: FALSE
Diff: 2   *Page Ref: 579*

15) The "lub" sounds of the heart are valuable in diagnosis because they provide information about the function of the heart's semilunar valves.

Answer: FALSE
Diff: 2   *Page Ref: 590*

16) Autonomic regulation of heart rate is via two reflex centers found in the pons.

Answer: FALSE
Diff: 2   *Page Ref: 593*

17) The dicrotic notch refers to the brief rise in pressure caused by the closure of the AV valves during ventricular systole.

Answer: FALSE
Diff: 2   *Page Ref: 590*

18) An ECG provides direct information about valve function.

Answer: FALSE
Diff: 3   *Page Ref: 587*

19) As pressure in the aorta rises due to atherosclerosis, more ventricular pressure is required to open the aortic semilunar valve.

Answer: TRUE
Diff: 3   *Page Ref: 595*

Multiple-Choice Questions

1) Normal heart sounds are caused by which of the following events?
   A) excitation of the SA node
   B) closure of the heart valves
   C) friction of blood against the chamber walls
   D) contraction of ventricular muscle

Answer: B
Diff: 1   *Page Ref: 590*

2) Cardiac reserve:
   A) is determined by your genes and not subject to improvement.
   B) is unrelated to health.
   C) can be improved by regular exercise.
   D) can be determined by auscultation.

   Answer: C
   Diff: 1   Page Ref: 591

3) Hemorrhage with a large loss of blood causes:
   A) a lowering of blood pressure due to change in cardiac output.
   B) a rise in blood pressure due to change in cardiac output.
   C) no change in blood pressure but a slower heart rate.
   D) no change in blood pressure but a change in respiration.

   Answer: A
   Diff: 1   Page Ref: 591–592

4) The left ventricular wall of the heart is thicker than the right wall in order to:
   A) accommodate a greater volume of blood.
   B) expand the thoracic cage during diastole.
   C) pump blood with greater pressure.
   D) pump blood through a smaller valve.

   Answer: C
   Diff: 1   Page Ref: 576

5) Damage to the _____ is referred to as heart block.
   A) SA node   B) AV valves   C) AV bundle   D) AV node

   Answer: D
   Diff: 1   Page Ref: 586

6) The P wave of a normal electrocardiogram indicates:
   A) ventricular repolarization.   B) ventricular depolarization.
   C) atrial repolarization.   D) atrial depolarization.

   Answer: D
   Diff: 1   Page Ref: 587–588

7) Blood within the pulmonary veins returns to the:
   A) right atrium.   B) left atrium.   C) right ventricle.   D) left ventricle.

   Answer: B
   Diff: 1   Page Ref: 575–576

8) Small muscle masses attached to the chordae tendineae are the:
   A) trabeculae carneae.   B) pectinate muscles.
   C) papillary muscles.   D) venae cavae.

   Answer: C
   Diff: 1   *Page Ref: 574*

9) The term for pain associated with deficient blood delivery to the heart that may be caused by the transient spasm of coronary arteries is:
   A) ischemia.   B) pericarditis.
   C) myocardial infarct.   D) angina pectoris.

   Answer: D
   Diff: 1   *Page Ref: 577*

10) To auscultate the aortic semilunar valve, you would place your stethoscope:
    A) in the second intercostal space to the right of the sternum.
    B) in the second intercostal space to the left of the sternum.
    C) in the fifth intercostal space inferior to the left nipple.
    D) in the fifth right intercostal space.

    Answer: A
    Diff: 1   *Page Ref: 590*

11) Blood is carried to capillaries in the myocardium by way of:
    A) the coronary sinus.   B) the fossa ovalis.
    C) coronary arteries.   D) coronary veins.

    Answer: C
    Diff: 1   *Page Ref: 576*

12) When the heart is beating at a rate of 75 times per minute, the duration of one cardiac cycle is _____ second(s).
    A) 0.8   B) 1.0   C) 1.2   D) 1.8

    Answer: A
    Diff: 1   *Page Ref: 590*

13) Which of the following factors does not influence heart rate?
    A) skin color   B) age
    C) gender   D) body temperature

    Answer: A
    Diff: 1   *Page Ref: 593*

14) If cardiac muscle is deprived of its normal blood supply, damage would primarily result from:

A) decreased delivery of oxygen.

B) a decrease in the number of available mitochondria for energy production.

C) a lack of nutrients to feed into metabolic pathways.

D) an inadequate supply of lactic acid.

Answer: A
Diff: 1   Page Ref: 577

15) Cardiac muscle cells are like skeletal muscle cells in that they:

A) have gap junctions.   B) have end walls.

C) have I and A bands.   D) have intercalated disks.

Answer: C
Diff: 1   Page Ref: 581

16) Cardiac output is about _____ L/min.

A) 7.27   B) 6.26   C) 5.25   D) 4.25

Answer: C
Diff: 1   Page Ref: 591

17) Select the correct statement about heart anatomy.

A) Approximately one-third of the mass of the heart is to the left of the midsternal line.

B) The point between the fifth and sixth ribs just below the left nipple is referred to as the point of maximal intensity (PMI).

C) The typical human heart weighs between 650 and 750 grams.

D) The heart lies posterior to the vertebral column.

Answer: B
Diff: 1   Page Ref: 570

18) The pericardial cavity:

A) is another name for the chambers of the heart.

B) is a space between the fibrous pericardium and the serous pericardium.

C) is the region of the thoracic cavity that contains the heart.

D) contains a lubricating fluid called serous fluid.

Answer: D
Diff: 1   Page Ref: 570

19) If the length of the absolute refractory period in cardiac muscle cells was the same as it is for skeletal muscle cells:
    A) it would be much longer before cardiac cells could respond to a second stimulation.
    B) contractions would last as long as the refractory period.
    C) tetanic contractions might occur, which would stop the heart's pumping action.
    D) The length of the absolute refractory period in cardiac muscle is the same as it is in skeletal muscle.

Answer: C
Diff: 1   Page Ref: 582

20) Norepinephrine acts on heart muscle cells by:
    A) decreasing heart contractility.
    B) causing a decrease in stroke volume.
    C) blocking the action of calcium.
    D) causing threshold to be reached more quickly.

Answer: D
Diff: 1   Page Ref: 593

21) If the vagal nerves to the heart were cut, the result would be that:
    A) the heart would stop, since the vagal nerves trigger the heart to contract.
    B) the heart rate would increase by about 25 beats per minute.
    C) the AV node would become the pacemaker of the heart.
    D) parasympathetic stimulation would increase, causing a decrease in heart rate.

Answer: B
Diff: 1   Page Ref: 593

22) The stroke volume for a normal resting heart is _____ ml/beat.
    A) 30   B) 50   C) 70   D) 90

Answer: C
Diff: 1   Page Ref: 591

23) Which vessel of the heart receives blood during right ventricular systole?
    A) venae cavae   B) pulmonary artery
    C) aorta   D) pulmonary veins

Answer: B
Diff: 1   Page Ref: 588

24) Blood enters which of these vessels during ventricular systole?
    A) aorta   B) pulmonary arteries
    C) pulmonary vein   D) Both A and B are correct.

Answer: D
Diff: 2   Page Ref: 588

25) Which of the following is not part of the conduction system of the heart?

A) AV node   B) bundle of His   C) AV valve   D) SA node

Answer: C
Diff: 2   Page Ref: 584

26) The tricuspid valve is closed:

A) while the ventricle is in diastole.

B) when the ventricle is in systole.

C) while the atrium is contracting.

D) by the movement of blood from atrium to ventricle.

Answer: B
Diff: 2   Page Ref: 588

27) When holding a dissected heart in your hands, it is easy to orient the right and left side by:

A) tracing out where the vena cava enters the heart.

B) noticing the thickness of the ventricle walls.

C) locating the aorta.

D) finding the pulmonary semilunar valves.

Answer: B
Diff: 2   Page Ref: 576

28) Select the correct statement about the heart valves.

A) The mitral valve separates the right atrium from the right ventricle.

B) The tricuspid valve divides the left atrium from the left ventricle.

C) Semilunar valves control the flow of blood into the heart.

D) The AV valves are supported by chordae tendineae so that they do not blow back up into the atria during ventricular contraction.

Answer: D
Diff: 2   Page Ref: 577–580

29) Select the correct statement about the structure of the heart wall.

A) The fibrous skeleton forms the bulk of the heart.

B) Connective tissue in the heart wall aids in the conduction of the action potential.

C) The heart chambers are lined by the endomysium.

D) The myocardium is the layer of the heart that actually contracts.

Answer: D
Diff: 2   Page Ref: 571

30) Compared to skeletal muscle, cardiac muscle:

   A) has gap junctions that allow it to act as a functional syncytium.

   B) lacks striations.

   C) has more nuclei per cell.

   D) cells are larger than skeletal muscle cells.

   Answer: A
   Diff: 2   Page Ref: 582

31) Cardiac muscle:

   A) has fewer mitochondria than skeletal muscle.

   B) relies mostly on glycolysis for energy.

   C) has sarcomeres with A bands and I bands.

   D) can operate for long periods without oxygen as long as lactic acid is present.

   Answer: C
   Diff: 2   Page Ref: 580–581

32) The deflection waves in an ECG tracing include:

   A) the P wave, which is present only in patients who have had a heart attack.

   B) the Q–T interval, which indicates the time of atrial contraction.

   C) the PQRS complex, which follows ventricular contraction.

   D) the T wave, which indicates ventricular repolarization.

   Answer: D
   Diff: 2   Page Ref: 587–588

33) During the period of ventricular filling:

   A) pressure in the heart is at its peak.

   B) blood flows passively through the atria and the open AV valves.

   C) the atria remain in diastole.

   D) it is represented by the P wave on the ECG.

   Answer: B
   Diff: 2   Page Ref: 588

34) The effect of endurance–type athletic training may be to lower the heart rate. This phenomenon:

   A) is a sign of dangerous overexertion.

   B) is caused by hypertrophy of the heart muscle.

   C) results in decreased cardiac output.

   D) does not occur in aerobic training.

   Answer: B
   Diff: 2   Page Ref: 594

35) The second heart sound is heard during which phase of the cardiac cycle?

   A) isovolumetric relaxation   B) isovolumetric contraction

   C) ventricular ejection   D) ventricular filling

   Answer: A
   Diff: 3   *Page Ref: 590*

36) Stenosis of the mitral valve may initially cause a pressure increase in the:

   A) venae cavae.   B) left ventricle.

   C) pulmonary circulation.   D) coronary circulation.

   Answer: C
   Diff: 3   *Page Ref: 580*

37) If a significant amount of connective tissue were to develop connecting the visceral and parietal pericardial layers together, which of the following would be a likely consequence?

   A) interference with normal mechanical cardiac activity

   B) strengthening of the delicate pericardial layers and an improvement of cardiac function

   C) decreased production of fluid in the pericardial cavity since it is no longer necessary

   D) decreased friction between the visceral and parietal layers

   Answer: A
   Diff: 3   *Page Ref: 570*

38) If we were able to artificially alter the membrane permeability of pacemaker cells so that sodium influx is more rapid:

   A) heart rate would increase due to a decreased time for depolarization of the pacemaker cells.

   B) slow calcium channels in the pacemaker tissue would be cycling at a greater rate.

   C) heart rate would decrease, but blood pressure would rise due to the excess sodium present.

   D) tetanic contraction would occur due to the short absolute refractory period of cardiac muscle.

   Answer: B
   Diff: 3   *Page Ref: 584*

39) Select the correct statement about cardiac output.

   A) A slow heart rate increases end diastolic volume, stroke volume, and force of contraction.

   B) Decreased venous return will result in increased end diastolic volume.

   C) If a semilunar valve were partially obstructed, the end systolic volume in the affected ventricle would be decreased.

   D) Stroke volume increases if end diastolic volume decreases.

   Answer: A
   Diff: 3   *Page Ref: 591–593*

40) During contraction of heart muscle cells:

A) the action potential is initiated by voltage-regulated slow calcium channels.

B) some calcium enters the cell from the extracellular space and triggers the release of larger amounts of calcium from intracellular stores.

C) the action potential is prevented from spreading from cell to cell by gap junctions.

D) calcium is prevented from entering cardiac fibers that have been stimulated.

Answer: B
Diff: 3   Page Ref: 582–583

41) Isovolumetric contraction:

A) refers to the short period during ventricular systole when the ventricles are completely closed chambers.

B) occurs while the AV valves are open.

C) occurs immediately after the semilunar valves close.

D) occurs only in people with heart valve defects.

Answer: A
Diff: 3   Page Ref: 588

Clinical Questions

1) A 14-year-old girl undergoing a physical examination prior to being admitted to summer camp was found to have a loud heart murmur at the second intercostal space to the left side of the sternum. Explain the reason for the loud heart murmur associated with this girl's condition.

Answer: The heart murmur is due to incomplete closing of the pulmonary valve.
Diff: 4   Page Ref: 591

2) A man enters the hospital complaining of chest pain. His history includes smoking, a stressful job, a diet heavy in saturated fats, lack of exercise, and high blood pressure. Although he is not suffering from a heart attack, his doctor explains to him that a heart attack is quite possible. What did the chest pain indicate? Why is this man a prime candidate for a heart attack?

Answer: His symptoms indicate angina pectoris, possibly due to either atherosclerosis or stress-induced spasms of the coronary arteries. If the arteries are occluded (atherosclerosis), the heart muscle could be deprived of blood, and therefore oxygen. A heart attack could occur if the coronary vessels experience further (or progressive) occlusion.
Diff: 5   Page Ref: 577

3) An older woman complains of shortness of breath and intermittent fainting spells. Her doctor runs various tests and finds that the AV node is not functioning properly. What is the suggested treatment?

Answer: The suggested treatment is surgery to implant an artificial pacemaker.
Diff: 5   Page Ref: 586

CHAPTER 18 The Cardiovascular System: Blood Vessels

Fill-in-the-Blank/Short Answer Questions

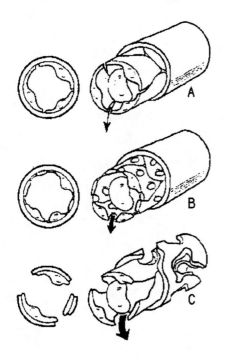

Figure 18.1

Using Figure 18.1, identify the following:

1) Sinusoid capillary.

   Answer: C
   Diff: 1   Page Ref: 602

2) Capillary found in endocrine organs that allows hormones to gain rapid entry into the blood.

   Answer: B
   Diff: 2   Page Ref: 602

3) Capillary with intercellular clefts.

   Answer: A
   Diff: 2   Page Ref: 602

4) Capillary that may contain Kupffer cells.

   Answer: C
   Diff: 2   Page Ref: 602

5) Capillaries found where active capillary absorption on filtrate occurs.

> Answer: B
> *Diff: 2*   *Page Ref: 602*

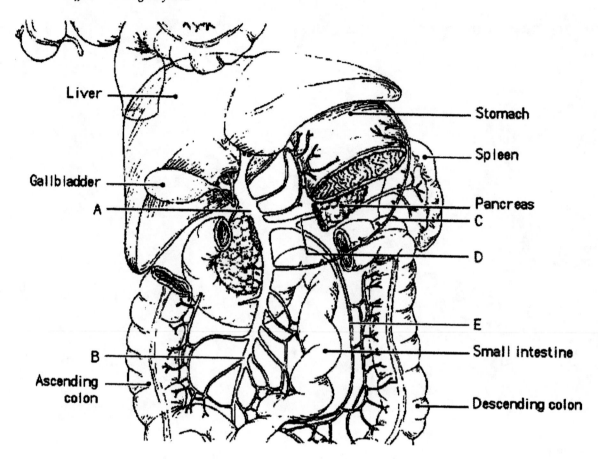

Figure 18.2

Using Figure 18.2, identify the following:

6) Splenic vein.

> Answer: D
> *Diff: 1*   *Page Ref: 645*

7) Superior mesenteric vein.

> Answer: B
> *Diff: 1*   *Page Ref: 645*

8) Inferior mesenteric vein.

> Answer: E
> *Diff: 1*   *Page Ref: 645*

9) Hepatic portal vein.

> Answer: A
> *Diff: 1*   *Page Ref: 645*

10) Gastroepiploic vein.

Answer: C
Diff: 1   *Page Ref: 645*

Fill in the blank or provide a short answer:

11) The first major branch of the aortic arch is the _____ branch.

Answer: brachiocephalic
Diff: 1   *Page Ref: 626*

12) A _____ capillary has many oval holes in it.

Answer: fenestrated
Diff: 1   *Page Ref: 603*

13) Arterial _____ provide alternate pathways for blood to get to an organ.

Answer: anastomoses
Diff: 1   *Page Ref: 605*

14) The _____ in the carotid sinuses and aortic arch detect raises in blood pressure.

Answer: baroreceptors
Diff: 1   *Page Ref: 610*

15) The hormones _____ and _____ alone stimulate the heart to increase blood pressure.

Answer: epinephrine; norepinephrine
Diff: 1   *Page Ref: 611*

16) The _____ artery is a blood vessel on the arm used as a pressure point.

Answer: brachial
Diff: 1   *Page Ref: 614-615*

17) _____ shock is due to abnormal expansion of blood vessels and a rapid drop in blood pressure.

Answer: Vascular
Diff: 1   *Page Ref: 623*

18) The third major branch of the aortic arch is the _____ artery.

Answer: left subclavian
Diff: 1   *Page Ref: 626*

19) The _____ supply the brain with blood.

Answer: internal carotid arteries
Diff: 1   *Page Ref: 628*

20) _____ pressure is the difference between systolic and diastolic pressure.

Answer: Pulse
Diff: 1   Page Ref: 614

21) Blood flow equals the difference in blood pressure divided by _____.

Answer: peripheral resistance
Diff: 2   Page Ref: 609

22) The lowest venous blood pressure is found in the _____.

Answer: venae cavae
Diff: 2   Page Ref: 608

23) As a cuff is deflated on the arm, sounds of _____ can be heard.

Answer: Korotkoff
Diff: 2   Page Ref: 615

24) Which type of blood vessels contain valves and what is their function?

Answer: Veins and venules contain valves to prevent blood from flowing backward. This is
necessary because the venous vessels are a low-pressure system and the blood must
sometimes flow against gravity, particularly in the limbs.
Diff: 2   Page Ref: 604–605

25) Describe the forces that determine fluid movements across capillary walls.

Answer: (1) Capillary hydrostatic pressure (equal to capillary blood pressure) tends to force fluid
out of capillaries into the interstitial spaces. (2) Osmotic pressure, created by large
nondiffusible particles in the blood, tends to draw water into the capillaries. At the
arterial end of the capillary bed, hydrostatic forces dominate and fluid moves out, while
at the venous end, osmotic forces dominate and the net fluid movement is into the
capillaries.
Diff: 3   Page Ref: 620–622

26) Define *vasoconstriction* and *vasodilation*. What is the mechanism of regulation?

Answer: Vasoconstriction is a reduction in the lumen diameter of a blood vessel due to smooth
muscle contraction. Vasodilation is a widening of the lumen due to smooth muscle
relaxation. This is regulated by vasomotor nerve fibers of the sympathetic division of the
autonomic nervous system.
Diff: 3   Page Ref: 609–610

27) Consider a 4–mm blood vessel and two 2–mm blood vessels. Would the two 2–mm vessels
carry more, less, or the same amount of fluids, given that pressure is a constant?

Answer: The two 2–mm vessels would deliver considerably less fluids for two reasons: (1) the
resistance in the smaller vessels is much greater and (2) the volume of the 4–mm vessel is
greater than that of two 2–mm vessels. Draw a 4–inch circle; then put two 2–inch circles
in it and notice the volume difference.
Diff: 3   Page Ref: 606

28) Based on what we have learned about the regulation of blood flow to various organs, do you think it is wiser to rest or exercise after a heavy meal? Explain your answer.

Answer: At rest, the abdominal organs receive approximately 24% of the total blood flow. With exercise, blood flow is shifted away from abdominal organs to skeletal muscles. It would therefore be wiser to rest after a heavy meal to allow optimum function of the organs of digestion and absorption of nutrients.

Diff: 4   *Page Ref: 618*

Matching Questions

Match the following:

1) Column 1: Largest artery of the body.

   Column 2: Aorta

   Answer: Aorta
   Diff: 1   *Page Ref: 626*

2) Column 1: Supplies the kidneys.

   Column 2: Renal artery

   Answer: Renal artery
   Diff: 1   *Page Ref: 634*

3) Column 1: Supplies the duodenum and stomach.

   Column 2: Common hepatic artery

   Answer: Common hepatic artery
   Diff: 2   *Page Ref: 633*

4) Column 1: Supplies the distal areas of the large intestine.

   Column 2: Inferior mesenteric artery

   Answer: Inferior mesenteric artery
   Diff: 2   *Page Ref: 634*

5) Column 1: Supplies pelvic structures.

   Column 2: Common iliac artery

   Answer: Common iliac artery
   Diff: 2   *Page Ref: 634*

6) Column 1: Artery that does not anastomose.

   Column 2: Renal artery

   Answer: Renal artery
   Diff: 3   *Page Ref: 634*

Match the following:

7) Column 1: Gives rise to the right common
carotid and right subclavian
artery.

Column 2: Brachiocephalic artery

Answer: Brachiocephalic artery
Diff: 1   Page Ref: 626

8) Column 1: Supplies the lower limbs.

Column 2: Iliac artery

Answer: Iliac artery
Diff: 2   Page Ref: 634

9) Column 1: Common "pulse-taking"
artery.

Column 2: Radial artery

Answer: Radial artery
Diff: 2   Page Ref: 630

10) Column 1: Major supply to the cerebral
hemispheres.

Column 2: Interior carotid artery

Answer: Interior carotid artery
Diff: 2   Page Ref: 628

11) Column 1: Large unpaired branch of the
abdominal aorta.

Column 2: Celiac artery

Answer: Celiac artery
Diff: 2   Page Ref: 633

12) Column 1: Abdominal aorta splits to
form two.

Column 2: Iliac artery

Answer: Iliac artery
Diff: 2   Page Ref: 634

Match the following:

13) Column 1: Receives blood from all areas
superior to the diaphragm,
except the lungs.

Column 2: Superior vena cava

Answer: Superior vena cava
Diff: 2   Page Ref: 638

14) Column 1: Carries oxygen–poor blood to
                    the lungs.

Column 2: Pulmonary artery

Answer: Pulmonary artery
Diff: 2   Page Ref: 624

15) Column 1: Drains the scalp.

Column 2: Exterior jugular vein

Answer: Exterior jugular vein
Diff: 2   Page Ref: 638

16) Column 1: Runs through the armpit.

Column 2: Axillary artery

Answer: Axillary artery
Diff: 2   Page Ref: 630

17) Column 1: Drains the upper extremities,
                    deep vein.

Column 2: Subclavian vein

Answer: Subclavian vein
Diff: 2   Page Ref: 638

Match the following:

18) Column 1: Artery usually palpated to
                    take the blood pressure.

Column 2: Brachial artery

Answer: Brachial artery
Diff: 1   Page Ref: 630

19) Column 1: Major artery of the thigh.

Column 2: Femoral artery

Answer: Femoral artery
Diff: 1   Page Ref: 636

20) Column 1: Supplies the small intestine.

Column 2: Superior mesenteric artery

Answer: Superior mesenteric artery
Diff: 1   Page Ref: 634

21) Column 1: Carries oxygen–rich blood
                    from the lungs.

Column 2: Pulmonary vein

Answer: Pulmonary vein
Diff: 1   Page Ref: 624

22) Column 1: Longest vein in the body,
        superficial.

   Column 2: Great saphenous vein

   Answer: Great saphenous vein
   Diff: 2   *Page Ref: 646*

Match the following:

23) Column 1: Site where resistance to blood
        flow is greatest.

   Column 2: Arterioles

   Answer: Arterioles
   Diff: 1   *Page Ref: 601*

24) Column 1: Site where exchanges of food
        and gases are made.

   Column 2: Capillaries

   Answer: Capillaries
   Diff: 1   *Page Ref: 602*

25) Column 1: Site where blood pressure is
        least.

   Column 2: Large veins

   Answer: Large veins
   Diff: 1   *Page Ref: 604*

26) Column 1: Site where the velocity of
        blood flow is greatest.

   Column 2: Large arteries

   Answer: Large arteries
   Diff: 2   *Page Ref: 600–601*

27) Column 1: Site where the velocity of
        blood flow is least.

   Column 2: Capillaries

   Answer: Capillaries
   Diff: 2   *Page Ref: 602*

28) Column 1: Site where the blood volume
        contained is greatest.

   Column 2: Large veins

   Answer: Large veins
   Diff: 2   *Page Ref: 604*

29) Column 1: Site where the blood pressure
      is greatest.

   Column 2: Large arteries

   Answer: Large arteries
   Diff: 2   Page Ref: 600–601

30) Column 1: Site that is the major
      determinant of peripheral
      resistance.

   Column 2: Arterioles

   Answer: Arterioles
   Diff: 2   Page Ref: 601

True/False Questions

1) All arteries of the systemic circulation branch from the superior vena cava.

   Answer: FALSE
   Diff: 1   Page Ref: 626

2) Arteries that provide the major supply of the cerebral hemispheres are the internal carotid arteries.

   Answer: TRUE
   Diff: 1   Page Ref: 628–629

3) The adjustment of blood flow to each tissue in proportion to its requirements at any point in time is termed autoregulation.

   Answer: TRUE
   Diff: 1   Page Ref: 617

4) Arterial pressure in the pulmonary circulation is much higher than in the systemic circulation because of its proximity to the heart.

   Answer: FALSE
   Diff: 1   Page Ref: 619

5) Osmotic pressure is the force exerted by a fluid pressing against a wall.

   Answer: FALSE
   Diff: 1   Page Ref: 622

6) Osmotic pressure is created by the presence in a fluid of small diffusible molecules that easily move through the capillary membrane.

   Answer: FALSE
   Diff: 1   Page Ref: 622

7) The circle of Willis is an arterial anastomosis.

Answer: TRUE
Diff: 1   Page Ref: 629

8) The outermost layer of a blood vessel is the tunica intima.

Answer: FALSE
Diff: 1   Page Ref: 599

9) The thick-walled arteries close to the heart are called muscular arteries.

Answer: FALSE
Diff: 1   Page Ref: 600

10) Hypotension is generally considered systolic blood pressure that is below 100 mm Hg.

Answer: TRUE
Diff: 1   Page Ref: 615

11) Persistent or chronic hypertension can contribute to varicose veins.

Answer: FALSE
Diff: 1   Page Ref: 615-616

12) A precapillary sphincter is a cuff of smooth muscle that regulates the flow of blood into the capillaries.

Answer: TRUE
Diff: 1   Page Ref: 604

13) Thoroughfare channels indirectly connect an arteriole to a venule.

Answer: FALSE
Diff: 1   Page Ref: 603

14) Vasodilation is a widening of the lumen due to smooth muscle contraction.

Answer: FALSE
Diff: 1   Page Ref: 610

15) The pulmonary circulation does not directly serve the metabolic needs of body tissues.

Answer: TRUE
Diff: 1   Page Ref: 624

16) The most common form of shock is hypovolemic shock.

Answer: TRUE
Diff: 1   Page Ref: 622

17) Every minute, about 1.5 ml of fluid leaks out of the capillaries.

Answer: TRUE
Diff: 1   Page Ref: 622

18) The pancreas is an example of an organ that does not anastomose.

Answer: FALSE
Diff: 1   *Page Ref: 605*

19) The largest of the circulatory routes is the pulmonary route.

Answer: FALSE
Diff: 2   *Page Ref: 624–625*

20) An obstruction in the superior vena cava would decrease the flow of blood from the head and neck to the heart.

Answer: TRUE
Diff: 2   *Page Ref: 638*

21) Arteries supplying the same territory are often parallel with one another, forming arterial anastomoses.

Answer: FALSE
Diff: 2   *Page Ref: 605*

22) An increase in blood viscosity will cause an increase in peripheral resistance.

Answer: TRUE
Diff: 2   *Page Ref: 606*

23) The first major branch of the femoral artery is the pedis artery.

Answer: FALSE
Diff: 2   *Page Ref: 636*

24) Reflexes that regulate blood pressure are integrated at the brain stem (medulla) level.

Answer: TRUE
Diff: 3   *Page Ref: 609*

25) The azygos vein originates in the abdomen.

Answer: TRUE
Diff: 3   *Page Ref: 642*

Multiple-Choice Questions

1) Which of the following is not one of the three main factors influencing blood pressure?
   A) cardiac output   B) peripheral resistance
   C) emotional state   D) blood volume

Answer: C
Diff: 1   *Page Ref: 605–606*

2) Which of the following chemicals does not control blood pressure?

A) ADH

B) atrial natriuretic peptide

C) nitric oxide

D) nitric acid

Answer: D
Diff: 1   *Page Ref: 611–612*

3) Which statement best describes arteries?

A) All carry oxygenated blood to the heart.

B) All carry blood away from the heart.

C) All contain valves to prevent the backflow of blood.

D) Only large arteries are lined with endothelium.

Answer: B
Diff: 1   *Page Ref: 600–601*

4) Which tunic of an artery contains endothelium?

A) tunica interna (intima)

B) tunica media

C) tunica externa

D) tunica adventitia

Answer: A
Diff: 1   *Page Ref: 599*

5) Permitting the exchange of nutrients and gases between the blood and tissue cells is the primary function of:

A) arterioles.   B) arteries.   C) veins.   D) capillaries.

Answer: D
Diff: 1   *Page Ref: 602–603*

6) The circulatory route that runs from the digestive tract to the liver is called:

A) hepatic portal circulation.

B) pulmonary circulation.

C) coronary circulation.

D) cerebral circulation.

Answer: A
Diff: 1   *Page Ref: 644*

7) The arteries that are also called distributing arteries are the:

A) elastic arteries.

B) muscular arteries.

C) arterioles.

D) capillaries.

Answer: B
Diff: 1   *Page Ref: 601*

8) Aldosterone will:

A) promote an increase in blood pressure.

B) promote a decrease in blood volume.

C) result in a larger output of urine.

D) decrease sodium reabsorption.

Answer: A
Diff: 1   *Page Ref: 613*

9) The pulse pressure is:

A) systolic pressure plus diastolic pressure.

B) systolic pressure minus diastolic pressure.

C) systolic pressure divided by diastolic pressure.

D) diastolic pressure plus 1/3 (systolic pressure plus diastolic pressure).

Answer: B
Diff: 1   Page Ref: 607

10) Which of the following signs of hypovolemic shock is a relatively late sign?

A) cold, clammy skin	B) increased heart rate
C) rapid thready pulse	D) rapidly falling blood pressure

Answer: D
Diff: 1   Page Ref: 622

11) Which of the following is likely during vigorous exercise?

A) Blood will be diverted to the digestive organs.

B) The skin will be cold and clammy.

C) Capillaries of the active muscles will be engorged with blood.

D) Blood flow to the kidneys increases.

Answer: C
Diff: 1   Page Ref: 618

12) Continuous capillaries:

A) have oval pores to facilitate the delivery of oxygen and nutrients to tissues.

B) are abundant in the skin and skeletal muscles.

C) have a thin layer of muscle tissue to autoregulate blood flow.

D) contain a layer of connective tissue to prevent protein leakage.

Answer: B
Diff: 1   Page Ref: 602

13) Which of the following is true about veins?

A) Venous valves are formed from the tunica media.

B) Up to 35% of total body blood is in venous circulation at any given time.

C) Veins have a small lumen in relation to the thickness of the vessel wall.

D) Veins are called capacitance vessels or blood reservoirs.

Answer: D
Diff: 1   Page Ref: 604–605

14) Venous anastomoses:

   A) often occlude, causing death if located in a vital area.

   B) connect veins together along their entire length.

   C) form more freely than arterial anastomoses.

   D) occur only in the brain.

   Answer: C
   Diff: 1   Page Ref: 605

15) Peripheral resistance:

   A) decreases with increasing length of the blood vessel.

   B) increases as blood vessel diameter increases.

   C) increases as blood viscosity increases.

   D) is not a major factor in blood pressure in healthy individuals.

   Answer: C
   Diff: 1   Page Ref: 605

16) Brain blood flow autoregulation:

   A) is less sensitive to pH than to a decreased oxygen level.

   B) causes constriction of cerebral blood vessels in response to a drop in systemic blood pressure.

   C) is abolished when abnormally high CO_2 levels persist.

   D) is controlled by cardiac centers in the pons.

   Answer: C
   Diff: 1   Page Ref: 619

17) Blood flow to the skin:

   A) is controlled mainly by decreasing pH.

   B) increases when environmental temperature rises.

   C) increases when body temperature drops so that the skin does not freeze.

   D) is not an important source of nutrients and oxygen for skin cells.

   Answer: B
   Diff: 1   Page Ref: 619

18) Select the correct statement about the movement of materials at the capillary level.

   A) Oxygen diffuses up its concentration gradient.

   B) Chemical waste products follow the same general path as oxygen.

   C) Carbon dioxide moves from its production site into the interstitial fluid.

   D) If the osmotic pressure in the blood vessels is relatively higher than that in the tissues, tissue edema will result.

   Answer: C
   Diff: 1   Page Ref: 607-608

19) Which of the following is a type of circulatory shock?

    A) hypovolemic, caused by increased blood volume

    B) cardiogenic, which results from any defect in blood vessels

    C) vascular, due to extreme vasodilation as a result of loss of vasomotor tone

    D) circulatory, where blood volume is normal and constant

Answer: C
Diff: 1   Page Ref: 622–623

20) Which tunic of an artery is most responsible for maintaining blood pressure and continuous blood circulation?

    A) tunica interna (intima)   B) tunica media

    C) tunica externa   D) tunica adventitia

Answer: B
Diff: 1   Page Ref: 599

21) The influence of blood vessel diameter on peripheral resistance is:

    A) the only factor that influences resistance.

    B) very large because resistance is inversely proportional to the fourth power of vessel radius.

    C) very large because resistance is directly proportional to the blood vessel diameter.

    D) very small because vessel diameter does not vary.

Answer: B
Diff: 1   Page Ref: 606

22) The form of circulatory shock known as hypovolemic shock is:

    A) only that form of shock caused by large–scale loss of blood.

    B) any condition in which blood vessels are inadequately filled and blood cannot circulate normally.

    C) shock that results from large–scale loss of blood volume, such as might follow severe vomiting or diarrhea.

    D) always fatal.

Answer: C
Diff: 1   Page Ref: 622

23) In the dynamics of blood flow through capillaries, hydrostatic pressure:

    A) does not play a role.

    B) is the same as capillary blood pressure.

    C) generally forces fluid from the interstitial space into the capillaries.

    D) is completely canceled out by osmotic pressure.

Answer: B
Diff: 1   Page Ref: 621–622

24) The hepatic portal vein:

    A) is actually an artery.

    B) carries nutrient–rich blood to the liver.

    C) carries oxygen–rich blood from the liver to the viscera.

    D) carries blood from the liver to the inferior vena cava.

Answer: B
Diff: 1   Page Ref: 644

25) One of the following has an anastomosing vessel.

    A) retina   B) kidney   C) heart   D) spleen

Answer: C
Diff: 1   Page Ref: 605

26) Which of the following do not influence arterial pulse rate?

    A) activity   B) postural changes

    C) emotions   D) sleep

Answer: D
Diff: 2   Page Ref: 607

27) Which of the following are involved directly in pulmonary circulation?

    A) superior vena cava, right atrium, and left ventricle

    B) right ventricle, pulmonary artery, and left atrium

    C) left ventricle, aorta, and inferior vena cava

    D) right atrium, aorta, left ventricle

Answer: B
Diff: 2   Page Ref: 624–625

28) Histologically, the _____ is squamous epithelium underlain by a sparse connective tissue layer.

    A) tunica intima (interna)   B) tunica media

    C) tunica externa   D) tunica adventitia

Answer: A
Diff: 2   Page Ref: 599

29) The arteries that directly feed into the capillary beds are called:

    A) muscular arteries.   B) elastic arteries.

    C) arterioles.   D) venules.

Answer: C
Diff: 2   Page Ref: 601

30) Fenestrated capillaries:

   A) are not more permeable than continuous capillaries.

   B) are not common in endocrine organs and in areas where capillary absorption is an important function.

   C) do not occur in the glomerular capillaries of the kidneys.

   D) are not found in the brain.

Answer: D
Diff: 2   Page Ref: 603

31) Modified capillaries that are lined with phagocytes are called:

   A) sinuses.   B) sinusoids.

   C) thoroughfare channels.   D) anastomoses.

Answer: B
Diff: 2   Page Ref: 603

32) Factors that aid venous return include all except:

   A) activity of skeletal muscles.   B) pressure changes in the thorax.

   C) venous valves.   D) urinary output.

Answer: D
Diff: 2   Page Ref: 608

33) Which of the following blood pressure readings would be indicative of hypertension?

   A) 120/80 in a 30-year-old man   B) 140/90 in a 70-year-old woman

   C) 170/96 in a 50-year-old man   D) 110/60 in a 20-year-old woman

Answer: C
Diff: 2   Page Ref: 615-616

34) Select the correct statement about factors that influence blood pressure.

   A) An increase in cardiac output corresponds to a decrease in blood pressure, due to the increased delivery.

   B) Systemic vasodilation would increase blood pressure, due to diversion of blood to essential areas.

   C) Excess protein production would decrease blood pressure.

   D) Excess red cell production would cause a blood pressure increase.

Answer: D
Diff: 2   Page Ref: 615-616

35) Mechanisms that do not help autoregulate blood pressure include:

A) nervous control that operates via reflex arcs involving pressoreceptors, chemoreceptors, and higher brain centers.

B) alcohol.

C) renal regulation via the renin–angiotensin system of vasoconstriction.

D) chemical controls such as atrial natriuretic peptide.

Answer: B
Diff: 2   Page Ref: 609–612

36) The velocity of blood flow:

A) is in direct proportion to the total cross–sectional area of the blood vessels.

B) is slower in the arteries than capillaries since they possess a relatively large diameter.

C) is slower in the veins than in the capillaries since veins have a large diameter.

D) is slowest in the capillaries since the total cross–sectional area is the greatest.

Answer: D
Diff: 2   Page Ref: 617

37) Select the correct statement about autoregulation of blood flow.

A) Spending some time at high altitudes can result in the formation of additional blood vessels.

B) Precapillary sphincters contract to divert blood into needy areas.

C) Long–term autoregulation exists in the form of decreased numbers of blood vessels forming when conditions of hypoxia predominate.

D) In most tissues the strongest stimulus for vasoconstriction is decreased oxygen levels.

Answer: A
Diff: 2   Page Ref: 617–618

38) Select the correct statement about blood flow.

A) It is relatively constant through all body organs.

B) It is measured in mm Hg.

C) It is greatest where resistance is highest.

D) Blood flow through the entire vascular system is equivalent to cardiac output.

Answer: D
Diff: 2   Page Ref: 616–618

39) A thrombus (blood clot) in the first branch of the arch of the aorta would affect the flow of blood to the:

A) left side of the head and neck.

B) myocardium of the heart.

C) left upper arm.

D) right side of the head and neck and right upper arm.

Answer: D
Diff: 3   Page Ref: 626

40) Cerebral blood flow is regulated by:

   A) skin temperature.   B) ADH.

   C) intrinsic autoregulatory mechanisms.   D) the hypothalamic "thermostat."

Answer: C
Diff: 3   Page Ref: 619

41) A patient with essential hypertension might have pressures of 200/120 mm Hg. This hypertensive state could result in all of the following changes except:

   A) increased work of the left ventricle.

   B) increased incidence of coronary artery disease.

   C) increased damage to blood vessel endothelium.

   D) decreased size of the heart muscle.

Answer: D
Diff: 3   Page Ref: 616

42) One of the following is not a blood vessel attached to the circle of Willis.

   A) anterior cerebral artery   B) posterior cerebral artery

   C) posterior communicating artery   D) anterior communicating artery

Answer: B
Diff: 3   Page Ref: 629

Clinical Questions

1) Describe the effect of hypovolemic shock on the blood vessels and the heart.

   Answer: Hypovolemic shock causes blood vessels to constrict to increase venous return and maintain pressure. Heart rate increases to compensate for loss of blood pressure and to maintain cardiac output. If volume loss continues, pressure eventually drops sharply and the shock becomes irreversible, leading to death.
   Diff: 3   Page Ref: 622

2) For each of the following situations, describe the anticipated effect on blood pressure and the physiological basis of the response: (1) a high–salt diet, (2) a blow on the head that damages (disables) the vasomotor center, (3) an attack by a mugger, and (4) a hypothalamic tumor resulting in excess ADH production.

   Answer: (1) A high–salt diet causes increased sodium in the blood, which increases osmotic pressure in the capillaries and thus increases blood volume and blood pressure. (2) Damage to the vasomotor center will cause a loss of vasomotor tone and a drop in blood pressure, since the vasomotor center is the integrating center for blood pressure control. (3) During the mugger attack, blood pressure would increase due to sympathetic nervous system stimulation (the "fight–or–flight" response) triggered by the hypothalamus. (4) Excess ADH production would cause an increase in blood pressure through increased water retention and therefore increased blood volume. ADH also stimulates vasoconstriction.
   Diff: 4   Page Ref: 609–612

3) Mrs. Gray, a 50-year-old mother of seven children, is complaining of dull, aching pains in her legs, which she reports have been getting progressively worse since the birth of her last child. During her physical examination, numerous varicosities are seen in both legs. How are varicosities recognized? What veins are most likely involved? What pathologic changes have occurred in these veins, and what is the most likely causative factor in this patient's case?

Answer: Varicosities are recognized by the enlargement of the veins. Superficial veins are most likely involved because they have little support from surrounding tissues. The veins have become tortuous and dilated because of incompetent valves that allow the blood to pool, stretching the vein walls. The likely causative agent in this patient's case is her pregnancies, because the enlarged uterus exerts downward pressure on groin vessels, restricting return blood flow to the heart.

Diff: 4   *Page Ref: 604–605*

4) Mr. Wilson is a 45-year-old stockbroker with essential hypertension. He is African American, obese, and he smokes 2–3 packs of cigarettes daily. What risk factors for hypertension are typified by Mr. Wilson? What steps should be taken to treat Mr. Wilson, and what lifestyle changes should he make? What complications are likely if corrective steps are not taken?

Answer: The risk factors are obesity, race, a high-stress job, and smoking. Mr. Wilson should lose weight, reduce salt intake, quit smoking, and try to reduce his stress level, perhaps by relaxation training. Medical intervention could include treatment with diuretics, sympathetic nerve blockers, calcium channel blockers, and angiotensin–converting enzyme inhibitors. Complications could include atherosclerosis, heart failure, renal failure, and stroke.

Diff: 4   *Page Ref: 616*

5) A pregnant patient comes into a clinic and asks about a small dark bulge that is becoming more apparent on her leg. What is it and what caused it?

Answer: The patient is getting a varicose vein. Due to the growing fetus putting downward pressure on the vessels of the groin and restricting the return of blood to the heart, the valves in the peripheral veins begin to fail. This causes blood pooling, which enlarges these veins and puts additional strain on other peripheral vein valves down the line.

Diff: 4   *Page Ref: 604–605*

6) At the battle of Shiloh in the American Civil War, Confederate General A. S. Johnston was killed when he was shot in the thigh. Witnesses reported that he bled to death almost before he realized that he was wounded. Which blood vessel was most likely to have been injured? Why is a tourniquet usually ineffective in stopping the bleeding from this wound?

Answer: The wound severed his femoral artery, the largest artery serving the lower limb. A tourniquet may be ineffective because it is a high pressure, deep artery with a large diameter. It is therefore difficult to exert enough pressure through the thigh muscles to stop the bleeding.

Diff: 5   *Page Ref: 636*

CHAPTER 19 The Lymphatic System

Fill–in–the–Blank/Short Answer Questions

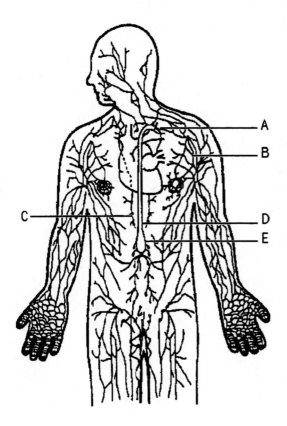

Figure 19.1

Using Figure 19.1, identify the following:

1) Axillary node(s).

   Answer: B
   Diff: 2   Page Ref: 651

2) Cisterna chyli.

   Answer: E
   Diff: 2   Page Ref: 651

3) Entrance of thoracic duct into subclavian vein.

   Answer: A
   Diff: 2   Page Ref: 651

4) Thoracic duct.

   Answer: D
   Diff: 2   Page Ref: 651

5) Thoracic node(s).

   Answer: C
   Diff: 3   Page Ref: 651

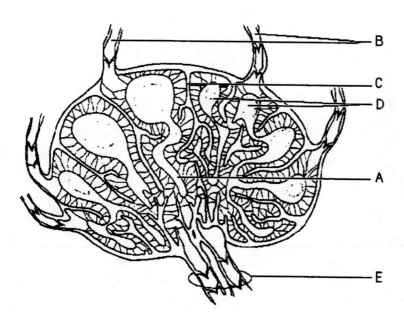

Figure 19.2

Using Figure 19.2, identify the following:

   6) Efferent vessels.

      Answer: E
      Diff: 2   Page Ref: 653

   7) Cortex.

      Answer: D
      Diff: 2   Page Ref: 653

   8) Cords.

      Answer: A
      Diff: 2   Page Ref: 653

   9) Trabecula.

      Answer: C
      Diff: 2   Page Ref: 653

10) Afferent vessels.

> Answer: B
> *Diff: 2   Page Ref: 653*

11) Medulla.

> Answer: A
> *Diff: 2   Page Ref: 653*

Fill in the blank or provide a short answer:

12) The _____ are the simplest lymphoid organs and are found at the entrance to the pharynx.

> Answer: tonsils
> *Diff: 2   Page Ref: 656–657*

13) The appendix, tonsils, and Peyer's patches are collectively called _____.

> Answer: MALT
> *Diff: 2   Page Ref: 657*

14) Highly specialized lymph capillaries called _____ are present in the villi of the intestinal mucosa.

> Answer: lacteals
> *Diff: 2   Page Ref: 650*

15) The thoracic duct of the lymphatic system empties into the _____.

> Answer: left subclavian vein
> *Diff: 2   Page Ref: 650*

16) Lymph nodes have more _____ lymphatic vessels than _____ lymphatic vessels.

> Answer: afferent; efferent
> *Diff: 2   Page Ref: 654*

17) Of the organs in the lymphatic system, only the _____ becomes less important as you get older.

> Answer: thymus
> *Diff: 2   Page Ref: 656*

18) Tonsils have blind-ended structures called _____.

> Answer: crypts
> *Diff: 2   Page Ref: 657*

19) Hassall's corpuscles are always found in the lighter-colored _____ regions of the thymus.

> Answer: medullary
> *Diff: 2   Page Ref: 656*

20) The _____ pulp of the spleen forms cuffs around the central arteries.

Answer: white
Diff: 2   *Page Ref: 655*

21) Lymphatic _____ are formed from the union of the largest collecting vessels.

Answer: trunks
Diff: 2   *Page Ref: 650*

22) Describe the structural and functional relationship of the vessels of the blood vascular system and the lymphatic system.

Answer: Vessels of the blood vascular system are relatively high–pressure conduits compared to vessels of the lymphatic system. The same mechanisms that promote venous return in blood vessels act within lymphatic vessels. Because lymphatics are usually packaged together in connective tissue sheaths with blood vessels, the pulsating expansions of the nearby arteries also promote lymph flow.
Diff: 3   *Page Ref: 649–650*

23) Describe the mechanisms by which lymphatic fluid is moved through the lymphatics.

Answer: Lymphatic fluid is moved through the lymphatics by the milking action of active skeletal muscles, pressure changes within the thorax during breathing, valves to prevent backflow, and pulsation of adjacent arteries.
Diff: 3   *Page Ref: 650–651*

24) What is the consequence of obstruction of the lymphatics?

Answer: Obstruction of the lymphatics results in edema distal to the obstruction.
Diff: 3   *Page Ref: 651*

25) Where are the lymph node aggregations most dense?

Answer: Lymph node aggregations are most dense near the body surface in the inguinal, axillary, and cervical regions of the body.
Diff: 3   *Page Ref: 653*

26) What is the special role of the thymus gland?

Answer: By secreting hormones, the thymus gland causes T lymphocytes to become immunocompetent.
Diff: 3   *Page Ref: 656*

27) Name the tonsils and state their body locations.

Answer: Palatine tonsils are located on either side at the posterior end of the oral cavity. The lingual tonsils lie at the base of the tongue. The pharyngeal tonsils are in the posterior wall of the nasopharynx.
Diff: 3   *Page Ref: 656–657*

28) List the functions of the spleen.

Answer: The spleen's main functions are to remove aged or defective blood cells and platelets from the blood and to store or release some of the breakdown products of RBCs to the blood for processing by the liver. Other functions include acting as a blood filter and reservoir, serving as a site for erythrocyte production in developing embryos, storing blood platelets, and providing a site for lymphocyte proliferation and immune surveillance and response.
Diff: 3   Page Ref: 654-655

29) Characterize lymph transport as to rate, volume, and ability to change.

Answer: Lymph transport is sporadic and much slower than that occurring in veins. About 3 liters of lymph enters the bloodstream in a 24-hour period. An increase in physical activity will cause lymph flow to increase, balancing the greater rate of fluid outflow from the vascular system.
Diff: 3   Page Ref: 650-651

30) In the thymus, what is the difference in the lymphocyte density of the cortex versus the medulla?

Answer: The cortex contains densely packed, rapidly dividing lymphocytes; the medulla contains fewer lymphocytes.
Diff: 3   Page Ref: 656

31) Contrast the structure of blood and lymph capillaries.

Answer: Lymphatic capillaries weave between the tissue cells and blood capillaries. Although similar to blood capillaries, lymphatic capillaries differ structurally in the following ways: (1) The endothelial cells forming the walls of lymphatic capillaries are not tightly joined. Their edges loosely overlap one another, forming flaplike minivalves. (2) Bundles of fine filaments anchor the endothelial cells to surrounding structures so that any increase in interstitial fluid volume separates the cell flaps, exposing gaps in the wall rather than causing the lymphatic capillary to collapse. (3) Lymphatic capillaries are blind-ended.
Diff: 4   Page Ref: 649-650

32) How does the lymphatic system both help and hinder the spread of cancer through the body?

Answer: Lymph nodes help rid the body of cancer cells by immune mechanisms. Lymph vessels may also be used to spread cancer cells throughout the body if immunity is not effective against the cancer cells.
Diff: 4   Page Ref: 653

33) How does the structure of a lymph node allow lymphocytes and macrophages to perform their protective function?

Answer: Macrophages ingest microorganisms and cellular debris. Lymphocytes monitor the lymphatic stream for the presence of antigens and mount an immune response. Because there are fewer efferent vessels draining the node than afferent vessels that feed it, the flow of lymph through the node stagnates somewhat, allowing time for the lymphocytes and macrophages to work.
Diff: 4   Page Ref: 653-654

34) Explain the term MALT. What is its function?

> Answer: MALT is an acronym for mucosa–associated lymphatic tissue. It includes Peyer's patches, the appendix, and the tonsils in the digestive tract, and lymphoid follicles in the walls of the bronchi. Collectively, MALT acts to protect these systems from foreign material.
>
> *Diff: 4   Page Ref: 657*

Matching Questions

Match the following:

1) Column 1: Protein–containing fluid within lymphatic vessels.

   Column 2: Spleen

   Answer: Spleen
   Diff: 1   Page Ref: 654–655

2) Column 1: Stores blood platelets.

   Column 2: Spleen

   Answer: Spleen
   Diff: 1   Page Ref: 654–655

3) Column 1: Part of MALT.

   Column 2: Peyer's patches

   Answer: Peyer's patches
   Diff: 1   Page Ref: 657

4) Column 1: Receives lymph from most of the body.

   Column 2: Thoracic duct

   Answer: Thoracic duct
   Diff: 2   Page Ref: 650

5) Column 1: Small organs intimately associated with lymphatic vessels.

   Column 2: Lymph nodes

   Answer: Lymph nodes
   Diff: 2   Page Ref: 653

6) Column 1: Largest lymphatic organ.

   Column 2: Spleen

   Answer: Spleen
   Diff: 2   Page Ref: 654–655

7) Column 1: Isolated clusters of lymph
               follicles found in the wall of
               the small intestine.

Column 2: Peyer's patches

    Foil: Lymph

Answer: Peyer's patches
Diff: 2   *Page Ref: 657*

True/False Questions

1) Peyer's patches are clusters of lymphoid tissue found primarily in the large intestine.

Answer: FALSE
Diff: 1   *Page Ref: 657*

2) The lymphatics function to absorb the excess protein–containing interstitial fluid and return it to the bloodstream.

Answer: TRUE
Diff: 1   *Page Ref: 649*

3) Lymph always flows away from the heart.

Answer: FALSE
Diff: 1   *Page Ref: 650–651*

4) Lymphatic capillaries are permeable to proteins.

Answer: TRUE
Diff: 1   *Page Ref: 649–650*

5) The villi of the intestinal mucosa contain lymphatic capillaries called Peyer's patches.

Answer: FALSE
Diff: 1   *Page Ref: 650, 657*

6) Digested fats are absorbed from the intestine by the lymph capillaries.

Answer: TRUE
Diff: 1   *Page Ref: 650*

7) Chyle is delivered to the blood via the lymphatic system.

Answer: TRUE
Diff: 1   *Page Ref: 650*

8) Hassall's corpuscles are found in the thymus.

Answer: TRUE
Diff: 1   *Page Ref: 656*

9) About 3 liters of fluid is lost to the tissue spaces every 24 hours and is returned to the bloodstream as lymph.

Answer: TRUE
Diff: 1   Page Ref: 649

10) Because lymph vessels are very low-pressure conduits, movements of adjacent tissues are important in propelling lymph through the lymphatics.

Answer: TRUE
Diff: 1   Page Ref: 650

11) Lymphoid tissue is mainly reticular connective tissue.

Answer: TRUE
Diff: 1   Page Ref: 652

12) Lymphocytes reside permanently in lymphoid tissue, then move to other parts of the body.

Answer: TRUE
Diff: 1   Page Ref: 652

13) An infected lymph gland is called a bubo.

Answer: TRUE
Diff: 1   Page Ref: 654

14) The largest lymphatic vessels are called lacteals.

Answer: FALSE
Diff: 2   Page Ref: 650

15) The cisterna chyli collects lymph from the lumbar trunks draining the upper limbs and from the intestinal trunk draining the digestive organs.

Answer: FALSE
Diff: 2   Page Ref: 650

16) Germinal centers in lymph node follicles contain white pulp.

Answer: FALSE
Diff: 2   Page Ref: 653-654

17) Blockage of lymphatics by tumors usually results in shrinkage of the tissue distal to the blockage due to inadequate delivery of lymph to the area.

Answer: FALSE
Diff: 2   Page Ref: 651

Multiple-Choice Questions

1) Small organs associated with lymphatic vessels are termed:
   A) lymph follicles.   B) lymph nodes.   C) axillary nodes.   D) cisterna chyli.

   Answer: B
   Diff: 1   Page Ref: 653

2) Which of the following would not be classified as a lymphatic structure?
   A) pancreas   B) spleen
   C) tonsils   D) Peyer's patches of the intestine

   Answer: A
   Diff: 1   Page Ref: 654–657

3) The distal portion of the small intestine contains clumps of lymph follicles called:
   A) islets of Langerhans.   B) Peyer's patches.
   C) rugae.   D) villi.

   Answer: B
   Diff: 1   Page Ref: 657

4) Both lymph and venous blood flow are heavily dependent on:
   A) the pumping action of the heart.
   B) skeletal muscle contractions and differences in thoracic pressures due to respiratory movement.
   C) contraction of the vessels themselves.
   D) two-way valves.

   Answer: B
   Diff: 1   Page Ref: 650

5) The thymus is most active during:
   A) fetal development.   B) childhood.
   C) middle age.   D) old age.

   Answer: B
   Diff: 1   Page Ref: 656

6) Which lymphatic structure drains lymph from the right upper limb and the right side of the head and thorax?
   A) lumbar trunk   B) thoracic duct
   C) right lymphatic duct   D) cisterna chyli

   Answer: C
   Diff: 1   Page Ref: 650

7) What effect does age have on the size of the thymus?

    A) The size of the thymus increases continuously from birth to death.

    B) The size of the thymus decreases continuously from birth to death.

    C) The thymus is not affected by age.

    D) The thymus initially increases in size and then decreases in size from adolescence through old age.

  Answer: D
  Diff: 1   *Page Ref: 656*

8) The lymphatic capillaries are:

    A) more permeable than blood capillaries.   B) less permeable than blood capillaries.

    C) equally permeable to blood capillaries.   D) completely impermeable.

  Answer: A
  Diff: 1   *Page Ref: 649*

9) Red pulp consists primarily of:

    A) cords.   B) macrophages.   C) lymphocytes.   D) erythrocytes.

  Answer: D
  Diff: 1   *Page Ref: 655*

10) Antibodies that act against a particular foreign substance are released by:

    A) T lymphocytes.   B) plasma cells.

    C) lymph nodes.   D) medullary cords.

  Answer: B
  Diff: 1   *Page Ref: 652*

11) Lymph leaves a lymph node via:

    A) efferent lymphatic vessels.   B) afferent lymphatic vessels.

    C) the cortical sinus.   D) the subscapular sinus.

  Answer: A
  Diff: 1   *Page Ref: 654*

12) The outer cortex of a lymph node contains:

    A) erythrocytes.   B) leukocytes.

    C) lymphocytes.   D) dense irregular connective tissue.

  Answer: C
  Diff: 1   *Page Ref: 653–654*

13) By secreting hormones, the thymus causes what cells to become immunocompetent?

    A) basophils   B) lymphocytes   C) macrophages   D) monocytes

  Answer: B
  Diff: 1   *Page Ref: 656*

14) Functions of the spleen include all of those below except:

    A) removal of old or defective formed elements from the blood.

    B) crypts that trap bacteria.

    C) storage of blood platelets.

    D) storage of iron.

Answer: B
Diff: 1   *Page Ref: 654–656*

15) When the lymphatics are blocked due to tumors, the result is:

    A) shrinkage of tissues distal to the blockage due to inadequate delivery of lymph.

    B) severe localized edema distal to the blockage.

    C) increased pressure in the lymphatics proximal to the blockage.

    D) abnormally high lymph drainage from the distal region.

Answer: B
Diff: 1   *Page Ref: 651*

16) Select the correct statement about lymph transport.

    A) Under normal conditions, lymph vessels are very high–pressure conduits.

    B) Lymph transport is faster than that occurring in veins.

    C) Lymph transport is only necessary when illness causes tissue swelling.

    D) Lymph transport depends on the movement of adjacent tissues, such as skeletal muscles.

Answer: D
Diff: 1   *Page Ref: 650–651*

17) Select the correct statement about lymphocytes.

    A) The two main types are T cells and macrophages.

    B) B cells produce plasma cells, which secrete antibodies into the blood.

    C) T cells are the precursors of B cells.

    D) T cells are the only form of lymphocyte found in lymphoid tissue.

Answer: B
Diff: 1   *Page Ref: 652*

18) Select the correct statement about lymphoid tissue.

    A) Once a lymphocyte enters the lymphoid tissue, it resides there permanently.

    B) Lymphoid macrophages secrete antibodies into the blood.

    C) Lymphoid tissue is predominantly reticular connective tissue.

    D) T lymphocytes act by ingesting foreign substances.

Answer: C
Diff: 1   *Page Ref: 652*

19) The soft connective tissue in the spleen is called:

A) dense regular connective tissue.   B) dense irregular connective tissue.

C) loose connective tissue.   D) reticular connective tissue.

Answer: D
Diff: 1   Page Ref: 654–655

20) A ring of lymphoid tissue that appears as a swelling of the mucosa in the oral cavity is called a(n):

A) tonsil.   B) thymus.   C) Peyer's patch.   D) appendix.

Answer: A
Diff: 1   Page Ref: 656–657

21) Which is not a mucosa-associated lymphatic tissue?

A) tonsil   B) thymus   C) Peyer's patch   D) appendix

Answer: B
Diff: 1   Page Ref: 654–657

22) Peyer's patches are found in the:

A) stomach.   B) small intestine.   C) large intestine.   D) spleen.

Answer: B
Diff: 1   Page Ref: 657

23) Lymph collecting or pooling from the lower extremities would first pool in the _____ before moving on up.

A) thoracic duct   B) inguinal nodes   C) cisterna chyli   D) azygos

Answer: C
Diff: 1   Page Ref: 650

24) What is a bubo?

A) a wall in a lymph node   B) a lobe of the spleen

C) an infected Peyer's patch   D) an infected lymph node

Answer: D
Diff: 1   Page Ref: 654

25) What is the function of a Hassall's corpuscle?

A) It increases the surface area of the thymic cortex.

B) It assists in the production of lymphocytes.

C) It forms the blood–thymus barrier.

D) It has no known significant function.

Answer: D
Diff: 1   Page Ref: 656

26) Particularly large clusters of lymph nodes occur in all of the following locations except the:

    A) inguinal region.   B) cervical region.

    C) axillary region.   D) lower extremities.

Answer: D
Diff: 2   *Page Ref: 657*

27) Digestive tract–associated lymphatic tissue includes all of the following except:

    A) Peyer's patches.   B) palatine tonsils.

    C) lingual tonsils.   D) islets of Langerhans.

Answer: D
Diff: 2   *Page Ref: 657*

28) Functions of the lymphatic system include:

    A) transport of excess tissue fluid to the blood vascular system.

    B) transport of red blood cells to the blood vascular system.

    C) maintenance of blood pressure in the venous circulation.

    D) excretion of excess dietary fat.

Answer: A
Diff: 2   *Page Ref: 649*

29) The tonsils located at the base of the tongue are the:

    A) lingual tonsils.   B) palatine tonsils.

    C) pharyngeal tonsils.   D) Peyer's tonsils.

Answer: A
Diff: 2   *Page Ref: 656–657*

30) Which of the following is not a normal component of lymph?

    A) water   B) plasma proteins   C) red blood cells   D) ions

Answer: C
Diff: 2   *Page Ref: 649*

Clinical Questions

1) A mother takes her son to the doctor and describes the following symptoms that she has noted. The child is running a fever, has flulike symptoms, and his lymph glands are very swollen and sore to the touch. Of what significance are the swollen and sore lymph glands?

    Answer: When tissues are inflamed, such as due to a bacterial infection, lymphatic capillaries develop openings that permit the uptake of the pathogens. The inflammation and pain indicate lymph nodes infected by microorganisms.
    Diff: 5   *Page Ref: 653–654*

2) A woman had a mastectomy with removal of axillary lymph nodes on her left side. What can she expect regarding her left arm and why?

Answer: Removal of the axillary lymph nodes results in severe localized edema since the lymphatic vessels are also lost. She can expect chronic edema along the arm, although some lymphatic drainage is eventually reestablished by regrowth of the vessels.
Diff: 5   Page Ref: 651

3) A man involved in a traffic accident is rushed to the emergency room of a hospital with severe internal bleeding. Examination reveals a ruptured spleen. What is the treatment of choice and what is the likely long-term outcome (prognosis)?

Answer: Surgical removal of the spleen is indicated. The prognosis is very good, as the functions of the spleen are taken over by the liver and bone marrow.
Diff: 5   Page Ref: 656

CHAPTER 20   The Immune System: Innate and Adaptive Body Defenses

Fill-in-the-Blank/Short Answer Questions

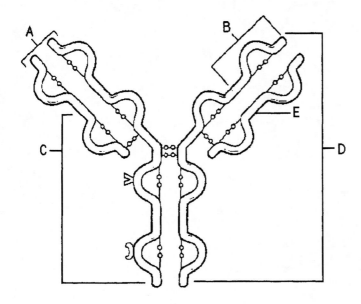

Figure 20.1

Using Figure 20.1, identify the following:

1) Heavy chain.

Answer: D
Diff: 1   Page Ref: 677

2) Light chain.

Answer: E
Diff: 1   Page Ref: 677

3) Variable region.

Answer: B
Diff: 1   Page Ref: 677

4) Constant region.

Answer: C
Diff: 1   Page Ref: 677

5) Antigen–binding site.

Answer: A
Diff: 1   *Page Ref: 677*

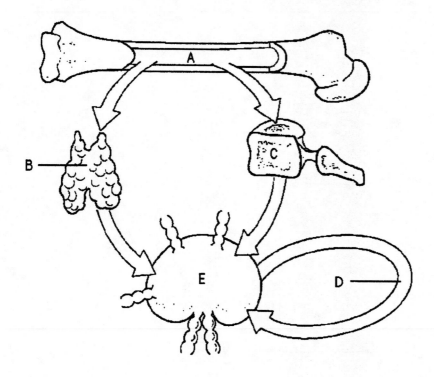

Figure 20.2

Using Figure 20.2, identify the following:

6) Area where B cells become immunocompetent.

Answer: A
Diff: 2   *Page Ref: 672*

7) Area where T cells become immunocompetent.

Answer: B
Diff: 2   *Page Ref: 672*

8) Area where immature lymphocytes arise.

Answer: A
Diff: 2   *Page Ref: 672*

9) Area seeded by immunocompetent B and T cells.

Answer: E
Diff: 2   *Page Ref: 672*

10) Area where antigen challenge and clonal selection are most likely to occur.

Answer: E
Diff: 2   Page Ref: 672

Fill in the blank or provide a short answer:

11) _____ are grafts taken from another animal species.

Answer: Xenografts
Diff: 2   Page Ref: 689

12) _____ is the most common type of immediate hypersensitivity.

Answer: Anaphylaxis
Diff: 2   Page Ref: 692

13) _____ cells can lyse and kill cancer cells and virus–infected body cells before the immune system is activated.

Answer: Natural killer
Diff: 2   Page Ref: 662

14) Harmful or disease-causing microorganisms are called _____.

Answer: pathogens
Diff: 2   Page Ref: 660

15) _____ refers to a group of at least 20 plasma proteins that normally circulate in an inactive state and are a major mechanism for destroying foreign substances in the body.

Answer: Complement
Diff: 2   Page Ref: 666–667

16) _____ becomes bound to mast cells and basophils and causes the cells to release histamine and other chemicals.

Answer: IgE
Diff: 2   Page Ref: 678

17) A _____ is a hybrid formed from the fusion of tumor cells and B lymphocytes.

Answer: hybridoma
Diff: 2   Page Ref: 680

18) _____ cells are the only T lymphocytes that can directly attack and kill other cells.

Answer: Cytoxic T
Diff: 2   Page Ref: 684

19) _____ is an autoimmune disease that severely impairs renal function.

Answer: Glomerulonephritis
Diff: 2   Page Ref: 691

20) List and briefly discuss innate body defenses to disease.

Answer: Innate body defenses to disease include surface membrane barriers, such as the skin and mucous membranes, as the first line of defense. Not only do the skin and mucous membranes act as a physical barrier to microorganisms, but they also secrete chemicals such as saliva, sebum, mucus, and HCl that kill microorganisms. Innate cellular and chemical defenses include the use of phagocytes and natural killer cells. Inflammation occurs in response to injury. The inflammation response includes vasodilation, increased vascular permeability, and phagocyte mobilization. Antimicrobial substances such as interferon and complement are also produced as innate defenses by the body.
Diff: 3   Page Ref: 660–661

21) What are monoclonal antibodies? How are they produced, and what are some of their clinical uses?

Answer: Monoclonal antibodies are pure antibody preparations that exhibit specificity for a single antigenic determinant. They are produced from the progeny of a single B cell hybridoma "clone," prepared by injecting a specific antigen into a lab animal and then harvesting sensitized B cells from its spleen. The cells are mixed with myeloma cells and incubated, and the resulting hybridoma cells (B cell fused with myeloma cells) produce the monoclonal antibody. They are used for the diagnosis of pregnancy, certain sexually transmitted diseases, hepatitis, and rabies, and for other purposes.
Diff: 3   Page Ref: 679–680

22) What is the antigen challenge, and where does it usually take place?

Answer: The antigen challenge is the first encounter between an immunocompetent lymphocyte and an invading antigen. It usually takes place in the spleen or a lymph node, but may happen in any lymphoid tissue.
Diff: 3   Page Ref: 673

23) Why are suppressor T cells important to the immune process?

Answer: They are vital in the final stopping of an immune response after the antigen is inactivated. They may also help prevent autoimmune reactions.
Diff: 3   Page Ref: 686–687

24) What is the most likely type of hypersensitivity associated with an agonizingly itchy case of poison ivy, appearance of hives after eating shellfish, or a positive TB test?

Answer: The hypersensitivity associated with poison ivy is delayed hypersensitivity allergic contact dermatitis. The hypersensitivity associated with hives is a local anaphylactic reaction. The hypersensitivity associated with a positive TB test is delayed hypersensitivity.
Diff: 4   Page Ref: 691–693

25) Children born without a thymus must be kept in a germ-free environment if they are to survive. Explain why this is necessary.

Answer: If the thymus fails to develop, the T cells will not mature and become immunocompetent. If T cell function is disrupted, there is no resistance to disease.
Diff: 4   Page Ref: 671–672

26) What are the signs of inflammation, and how does inflammation serve as a protective function?

   Answer: The four signs of inflammation are swelling, redness, heat, and pain. The signs are caused by local vasodilation and increased capillary permeability. This is of benefit because the process helps to dilute harmful substances that may be present; brings in large quantities of oxygen, nutrients, and cells necessary for the repair process; and allows the entry of clotting proteins. Pain helps immobilize the injury.
   Diff: 4   *Page Ref: 662–666*

27) A person gets a cut on his hand. After several days he notes swelling, pain, heat, and redness. Upon opening the wound to relieve the pressure, the presence of pus is noted. What has happened to the wound?

   Answer: The wound has become infected, probably with bacteria. The initial symptoms indicate acute inflammation. Pus indicates the presence of dead or dying neutrophils, broken–down tissue cells, and living and dead pathogens.
   Diff: 4   *Page Ref: 662–666*

Matching Questions

Match the following:

1) Column 1: First line of defense.

   Column 2: Skin and mucous membranes

   Answer: Skin and mucous membranes
   Diff: 1   *Page Ref: 660*

2) Column 1: Second line of defense.

   Column 2: Inflammatory response

   Answer: Inflammatory response
   Diff: 1   *Page Ref: 660*

3) Column 1: Third line of defense.

   Column 2: Immune response

   Answer: Immune response
   Diff: 1   *Page Ref: 660*

4) Column 1: Nonspecific defense system.

   Column 2: Inflammatory response *and*
   skin and mucous membranes

   Answer: Inflammatory response *and* skin and mucous membranes
   Diff: 1   *Page Ref: 660*

5) Column 1: Specific defense system.

   Column 2: Immune response

   Foil: Inflammatory response *and* immune response

   Answer: Immune response
   Diff: 1   *Page Ref: 660*

Match the following:

6) Column 1: Small proteins secreted by virus–containing cells.

   Column 2: Interferon

   Answer: Interferon
   Diff: 2   *Page Ref: 666*

7) Column 1: Major nonspecific mechanism that mediates destruction of foreign substances in the body.

   Column 2: Complement

   Answer: Complement
   Diff: 2   *Page Ref: 666*

8) Column 1: Stimulate the proliferation of other lymphocytes.

   Column 2: Helper T cells

   Answer: Helper T cells
   Diff: 2   *Page Ref: 684*

9) Column 1: Dampen the activity of both T cells and B cells.

   Column 2: Suppressor T cells

   Answer: Suppressor T cells
   Diff: 2   *Page Ref: 686*

10) Column 1: Presents the double activation signal to T cells.

    Column 2: Macrophage APC

    Answer: Macrophage APC
    Diff: 2   *Page Ref: 672–673*

Match the following:

11) Column 1: Main antibody of both
         primary and secondary
         immune response.

    Column 2: IgG

    Answer: IgG
    Diff: 2   Page Ref: 678

12) Column 1: Protects mucosal barriers.

    Column 2: IgA

    Answer: IgA
    Diff: 2   Page Ref: 678

13) Column 1: Involved in allergies.

    Column 2: IgE

    Answer: IgE
    Diff: 2   Page Ref: 678

14) Column 1: Along with IgM, this is a B cell
         receptor.

    Column 2: IgD

    Answer: IgD
    Diff: 2   Page Ref: 678

15) Column 1: Activates complement.

    Column 2: IgM

    Answer: IgM
    Diff: 2   Page Ref: 678

True/False Questions

1) A graft from a monkey to a human is an example of an allograft.

    Answer: FALSE
    Diff: 1   Page Ref: 689

2) The mechanism of the "lethal hit" of cytotoxic T cells involves a protein called perforin.

    Answer: TRUE
    Diff: 1   Page Ref: 686

3) Cellular ingestion and destruction of particulate matter is called phagocytosis.

    Answer: TRUE
    Diff: 1   Page Ref: 661

4) The respiratory burst produced by some macrophages releases free radicals.

Answer: TRUE
Diff: 1   Page Ref: 662

5) The directional movement of cells in response to chemicals is called chemotaxis.

Answer: TRUE
Diff: 1   Page Ref: 665

6) Substances capable of triggering the adaptive immune system and provoking an immune response are called antigens.

Answer: FALSE
Diff: 1   Page Ref: 669

7) Soluble proteins secreted by plasma cells are called antibodies.

Answer: TRUE
Diff: 1   Page Ref: 676

8) Tolerance for self–antigens is abnormal.

Answer: FALSE
Diff: 1   Page Ref: 670

9) Fever is seldom beneficial because it speeds up the cellular metabolic rate and will not allow antigen–antibody reactions to occur.

Answer: TRUE
Diff: 1   Page Ref: 668

10) Monocytes are the main type of phagocytic cell.

Answer: TRUE
Diff: 1   Page Ref: 661

11) Monoclonal antibodies can be specific for several antigenic determinants.

Answer: FALSE
Diff: 1   Page Ref: 679

12) Autoimmune diseases are more common in men than in women.

Answer: FALSE
Diff: 1   Page Ref: 691

13) Some immunocompetent cells will never be called to service in our lifetime.

Answer: TRUE
Diff: 1   Page Ref: 671

14) Atopy is an inherited tendency to spontaneously develop immediate (type I) allergies to certain environmental antigens.

Answer: TRUE
Diff: 1   Page Ref: 693

15) Adaptive immunity is provided by lymphocytes that secrete antibodies.

Answer: FALSE
Diff: 2   Page Ref: 669

16) The most important cells of specific immunity are the agranulocytes.

Answer: TRUE
Diff: 2   Page Ref: 660, 670

17) A transfusion reaction is a subacute hypersensitivity to foreign red blood cells.

Answer: TRUE
Diff: 2   Page Ref: 693

18) Somatic recombination by B cells allows each B cell to form its own unique antibody genes.

Answer: TRUE
Diff: 3   Page Ref: 677

19) Antibodies and complement fixation mediate delayed hypersensitivity reactions.

Answer: FALSE
Diff: 3   Page Ref: 693

20) It is possible to have several different monoclonal antibodies against one antigen.

Answer: TRUE
Diff: 3   Page Ref: 679–680

21) Perforins are cytolytic chemicals used by NK cells.

Answer: TRUE
Diff: 3   Page Ref: 662

Multiple-Choice Questions

1) Which of the following is characteristic of antibodies?
   A) carbohydrate structure
   B) composed of heavy and light polypeptide chains
   C) three binding sites per antibody monomer
   D) incapable of being transferred from one person to another

Answer: B
Diff: 1   Page Ref: 676–677

2) Which of the following is associated with passive immunity?

A) long-term immune protection

B) infusion of weakened viruses

C) passage of IgG antibodies from a pregnant mother to her fetus

D) booster shot

Answer: C
Diff: 1   Page Ref: 676

3) Which of the following is not a type of T cell?

A) cytotoxic   B) antigenic   C) helper   D) suppressor

Answer: B
Diff: 1   Page Ref: 684–687

4) B lymphocytes develop immunocompetence in the:

A) thymus.   B) spleen.   C) bone marrow.   D) lymph nodes.

Answer: C
Diff: 1   Page Ref: 672

5) Which of the following is not a function of the inflammatory response?

A) prevents the spread of the injurious agent to nearby tissue

B) replaces injured tissues with connective tissue

C) disposes of cellular debris and pathogens

D) sets the stage for repair processes

Answer: B
Diff: 1   Page Ref: 662–663

6) The redness and heat of an inflamed area are due to a local hyperemia caused by:

A) vasodilation.

B) vasoconstriction.

C) phagocyte mobilization.

D) production of complement and interferon.

Answer: A
Diff: 1   Page Ref: 663

7) The antibody molecule is held together by _____ bonds.

A) disulfide   B) hydrogen   C) amino acid   D) sodium

Answer: A
Diff: 1   Page Ref: 676

8) In clonal selection of B cells, which substance is responsible for determining which cells will eventually become cloned?

A) antigen   B) lymphocyte   C) antibody   D) macrophage

Answer: A
Diff: 1   Page Ref: 680–682

9) The system that recognizes foreign molecules and acts to immobilize, neutralize, or destroy them is the:

A) integumentary system.   B) renal system.

C) immune system.   D) lymphatic system.

Answer: C
Diff: 1   Page Ref: 660

10) The process whereby neutrophils and other white blood cells are attracted to an inflammatory site is called:

A) diapedesis.   B) chemotaxis.   C) margination.   D) phagocytosis.

Answer: B
Diff: 1   Page Ref: 665

11) Small molecules that bind with self-proteins to produce antigenic substances are called:

A) haptens.   B) antibodies.   C) ions.   D) reagins.

Answer: A
Diff: 1   Page Ref: 670

12) The chief antibody-mediated mechanism used against cellular antigens, such as bacteria, is:

A) interferon production.   B) complement fixation.

C) neutralization.   D) agglutination.

Answer: B
Diff: 1   Page Ref: 666–667

13) The only T cell population that can directly attack and kill cells are the:

A) suppressor cells.   B) helper cells.   C) cytotoxic cells.   D) plasma cells.

Answer: C
Diff: 1   Page Ref: 684–686

14) Select the correct statement about phagocytic cells.

A) Neutrophils may destroy themselves when they phagocytize large quantities of a foreign substance.

B) Macrophages release defensins during killing.

C) The respiratory burst characterizes eosinophil phagocytosis.

D) Kupffer cells are a type of neutrophil.

Answer: A
Diff: 1   Page Ref: 662

15) _____ predominate at the sites of chronic infections.

    A) Basophils   B) Eosinophils   C) Macrophages   D) B cells

Answer: C
Diff: 1   *Page Ref: 665–666*

16) Interferons:

    A) are virus–specific, so that an interferon produced against one virus could not protect cells against another virus.

    B) act by increasing the rate of cell division.

    C) interfere with virus multiplication within cells.

    D) are routinely used in nasal sprays for the common cold.

Answer: C
Diff: 1   *Page Ref: 666*

17) _____ determine(s) what specific foreign substances our adaptive immune system will be able to recognize and resist.

    A) The type of antigen

    B) Memory cell production

    C) Enzymes present at the time of the invasion

    D) Our genes

Answer: D
Diff: 1   *Page Ref: 677*

18) Suppressor T cells:

    A) release cytokines that increase the activity of cytotoxic T cells and activated B cells.

    B) decrease their activity as antigenic stimulus decreases.

    C) may function in preventing autoimmune reactions.

    D) are the most thoroughly understood T cells.

Answer: C
Diff: 1   *Page Ref: 686–687*

19) Select the correct definition about tissue grafts.

    A) Isografts are between identical twins.

    B) Allografts are between different species.

    C) Xenografts are between individuals of the same species.

    D) Autografts are between two genetically identical individuals.

Answer: A
Diff: 1   *Page Ref: 689*

20) The only immunoglobulin to exist as a pentameter is:

    A) IgD.   B) IgM.   C) IgG.   D) IgA.

Answer: B
Diff: 1   *Page Ref: 678*

21) _____ are released by helper T cells to mobilize immune cells and macrophages and attract other leukocytes into the area.

A) Cytokines   B) Perforins

C) Interleukin 1 proteins   D) Interleukin 2 proteins

Answer: A
Diff: 1   Page Ref: 684

22) Which of the following is a part of the second line of defense against microorganisms?

A) keratin   B) cilia   C) gastric juice   D) phagocytes

Answer: D
Diff: 1   Page Ref: 660

23) Grafts between identical twins are called:

A) autografts.   B) allografts.   C) isografts.   D) xenografts.

Answer: C
Diff: 1   Page Ref: 689

24) Which of the following is characteristic of complete antigens?

A) small molecules   B) reactivity with an antibody

C) contain many repeating chemical units   D) inhibit production of antibodies

Answer: B
Diff: 2   Page Ref: 669

25) B cells respond to the initial antigen challenge by:

A) reducing its size.

B) immediately producing antigen–specific antibodies.

C) forming of a large number of cells that are unlike the original B cell.

D) producing progeny cells that include plasma cells and memory cells.

Answer: D
Diff: 2   Page Ref: 673–674

26) Graft rejection may be caused by:

A) using a xenograft.   B) use of immunosuppressive drugs.

C) treatment with antilymphocyte serum.   D) total body irradiation.

Answer: A
Diff: 2   Page Ref: 669

27) Which of the following is produced by epithelial membranes as a first line of defense protection?

A) sebum   B) haptens   C) antibodies   D) complement

Answer: A
Diff: 2   Page Ref: 660–661

382 Test Bank for *Anatomy & Physiology*

28) Cancer cells and virus-infected body cells can be killed before activation of the immune system by:
   A) natural killer cells.   B) T lymphocytes.
   C) B lymphocytes.   D) pinocytosis.

   Answer: A
   Diff: 2   Page Ref: 662

29) C3b molecules coat a microorganism and roughen its surface, enabling macrophages and neutrophils to phagocytize the organism. This phenomenon is termed:
   A) diapedesis.   B) agglutination.   C) opsonization.   D) chemotaxis.

   Answer: C
   Diff: 2   Page Ref: 662

30) Which of the following is not characteristic of the adaptive immune system?
   A) It is antigen-specific.   B) It is systemic.
   C) It has memory.   D) It is specific for a given organ.

   Answer: D
   Diff: 2   Page Ref: 669

31) Which of the following is not generally considered a defensive mechanism against disease?
   A) fever   B) glycolysis   C) intact epidermis   D) phagocytosis

   Answer: B
   Diff: 2   Page Ref: 668

32) Monoclonal antibodies are used for the diagnosis of all of the following except:
   A) juvenile diabetes.   B) hepatitis.
   C) rabies.   D) pregnancy.

   Answer: A
   Diff: 2   Page Ref: 679-680

33) Which of the following would be classified as a delayed hypersensitivity reaction?
   A) immune-complex hypersensitivity   B) anaphylaxis
   C) cytotoxic hypersensitivity   D) allergic contact dermatitis

   Answer: D
   Diff: 2   Page Ref: 693

34) Innate immune system defenses include:
   A) B cells.   B) T cells.   C) plasma cells.   D) phagocytosis.

   Answer: D
   Diff: 2   Page Ref: 668

35) Select the correct statement about inflammation.

A) Only the lymphocyte functions in the transport and release of the mediators of inflammation at the site of injury.

B) Exudation is the cause of localized edema.

C) Leukopenia-inducing factors are released by damaged tissues.

D) Aspirin and other anti-inflammatory substances act by promoting histamine release.

Answer: B
Diff: 2   Page Ref: 662-663

36) Phagocyte mobilization involves:

A) diapedesis, during which cells line up against the capillary wall.

B) margination, which is the process of white cell movement through the walls of capillaries into injured tissues.

C) mainly neutrophil and macrophage migration into inflamed areas.

D) monocytes as the most active phagocyte.

Answer: C
Diff: 2   Page Ref: 665-666

37) Fever:

A) is a higher-than-normal body temperature that is always dangerous.

B) decreases the metabolic rate of the body to conserve energy.

C) production is regulated by chemicals that reset the body's thermostat to a higher setting.

D) causes the liver to release large amounts of iron, which seems to inhibit bacterial replication.

Answer: C
Diff: 2   Page Ref: 668

38) Immunocompetence:

A) occurs in one specific organ of the adaptive immune system.

B) is the ability of individual cells to recognize a specific antigen by binding to it.

C) prevents intercellular communication so that only specific cell types respond to the invader.

D) requires exposure to an antigen.

Answer: B
Diff: 2   Page Ref: 671

39) Select the correct statement about the prevention of immune attack on "self."

A) The development of tolerance is specific to B cells only.

B) Neutrophils capable of binding to self-antigens are chemically inactivated.

C) Tolerance to self is due to the action of foreign antigens that inactivate the immune response to one's own tissues.

D) Tolerance is developed during fetal life.

Answer: D
Diff: 2   Page Ref: 671

40) Select the correct statement about active and passive immunity.

A) Immunological memory is established by passive immunization.

B) A vaccination is an example of the introduction of passive immunity into the body.

C) The antibodies utilized in active immunity are acquired from another organism.

D) Active and passive humoral immunity are both mechanisms of specific immunity that use antibodies.

Answer: D
Diff: 2   *Page Ref: 676*

41) Cytotoxic T cells:

A) are the only T cells that can directly attack and kill other cells.

B) require the double recognition signal of MHC I plus MHC II on the target cell in order to function.

C) function mainly to stimulate the proliferation of other T cell populations.

D) self–destruct once the antigen has been neutralized.

Answer: A
Diff: 2   *Page Ref: 684–686*

42) Helper T cells:

A) bind tightly to target cells and release a lymphotoxin called perforin.

B) often function to decrease the immune response.

C) release B7 proteins.

D) function in the adaptive immune system activation.

Answer: D
Diff: 2   *Page Ref: 684*

43) Select the correct statement about T cells.

A) CD4 cells are cytotoxic in function.

B) T suppressor cells have the CD8 antigen.

C) B cell function is much more complex than T cell function.

D) There are four major populations of T cells based on function.

Answer: B
Diff: 2   *Page Ref: 680*

44) Select the correct statement about immunodeficiency.

A) Severe combined immunodeficiency disease (SCID) is an acquired condition.

B) The causative agent in acquired immune deficiency syndrome (AIDS) is a virus that recognizes CD4 proteins.

C) Hodgkin's disease is a hereditary immunodeficiency found in children.

D) The most common form of immunodeficiency is graft versus host (GVH) disease.

Answer: B
Diff: 2   *Page Ref: 689–691*

45) Immediate hypersensitivities:

   A) are also called type IV hypersensitivities.

   B) are adaptive immune responses.

   C) include allergic contact dermatitis.

   D) include anaphylaxis, triggered by a second (or later) exposure to an allergen to which the individual has been sensitized.

Answer: D
Diff: 2   Page Ref: 692–693

46) Delayed hypersensitivities:

   A) are mediated by B cells.

   B) include allergic contact dermatitis.

   C) include anaphylactic shock, a systemic vasodilation that results in inadequate blood delivery to all tissues.

   D) do not involve T cells.

Answer: B
Diff: 2   Page Ref: 693

47) Natural killer (NK) cells:

   A) are also called cytotoxic T cells.

   B) are a type of phagocyte.

   C) are cells of the specific immune system.

   D) can kill cancer cells before the immune system is activated.

Answer: D
Diff: 2   Page Ref: 662

48) Select the correct statement about antigens:

   A) "Self-antigens" is another name for incomplete antigens.

   B) The largest type of antigen is called a hapten.

   C) Only small antigens exhibit reactivity.

   D) One antigen may have many different antigenic determinants and may therefore cause the formation of more than one antibody.

Answer: D
Diff: 2   Page Ref: 669–670

49) Clonal selection of B cells:

   A) occurs during fetal development.

   B) results in the formation of plasma cells.

   C) cannot occur in the presence of antigens.

   D) only occurs in the secondary immune response.

Answer: B
Diff: 2   Page Ref: 680–682

50) The primary immune response:

   A) occurs more rapidly and is stronger than the secondary response.

   B) occurs when memory cells are stimulated.

   C) is another name for immunological memory.

   D) has a lag period while B cells proliferate and differentiate into plasma cells.

   Answer: D
   Diff: 2   Page Ref: 674

51) Select the correct statement about the function of antibodies.

   A) Antibodies may directly destroy "invaders."

   B) Neutralization is the process by which antibodies cause invading cells to clump together.

   C) Complement fixation is the main mechanism by which antibodies provide protection.

   D) The most potent agglutinating agent is IgG.

   Answer: C
   Diff: 2   Page Ref: 676–677

52) Which of the following is not an autoimmune disease?

   A) multiple sclerosis   B) type II diabetes

   C) systemic lupus erythematosus   D) glomerulonephritis

   Answer: B
   Diff: 2   Page Ref: 691

53) Which of the following is not a mechanism for the development of autoimmune disorders?

   A) exposure of previously "hidden" self-antigens to the adaptive immune system

   B) a second exposure to an allergen

   C) mutation followed by the appearance of membrane proteins not previously present

   D) cross-reaction of antibodies formed against foreign antigens with self-antigens

   Answer: B
   Diff: 3   Page Ref: 691

54) Select the correct statement about complement.

   A) A specific immune mechanism is often involved in directing complement to its target.

   B) Complement can be activated through three pathways: classical, secondary, and alternate.

   C) The membrane attack complex consists of complement proteins C3a through C5.

   D) Complement proteins C1 through C9 act exclusively in the classical pathway.

   Answer: A
   Diff: 3   Page Ref: 666–667

55) Which of the following is true about the number of binding sites per functional antibody unit?

   A) IgD contains 4 binding sites.   B) IgA contains 6 binding sites.

   C) IgG contains 6 binding sites.   D) IgM contains 10 binding sites.

   Answer: D
   Diff: 3   Page Ref: 678

56) Antibody functions include all of the following except:

A) binding and inactivating chemical toxins released by bacteria or other microorganisms.

B) cross-linking cell-bound antigens on red blood cells when blood types are properly matched.

C) linking soluble antigens together so that they fall out of solution.

D) targeting foreign cells so that complement proteins can cause cellular lysis.

Answer: B
Diff: 3   Page Ref: 676-679

57) Which statement is true about T cells?

A) They usually directly recognize antigens, which then activates a subpopulation of killer cells.

B) Their proliferation is enhanced by interleukins 1 and 2.

C) Once activated, they cannot secrete cytokines.

D) They will develop into cytotoxic T cells if antigen is complexed with class II MHC proteins.

Answer: B
Diff: 3   Page Ref: 683-684

Clinical Questions

1) A 36-year-old man enters the hospital in an extremely debilitated condition. He has purple-brown skin lesions (a symptom of Kaposi's sarcoma) and a persistent cough. A physical examination reveals swollen lymph nodes, and laboratory tests find a very low lymphocyte count. Information taken during the personal history reveals that he has multiple sex partners with whom he frequently engages in unprotected sex. What is likely to be the man's problem and what is his outlook?

Answer: He is probably suffering from AIDS. His outlook is extremely poor since there is currently no known cure or effective treatment for AIDS, and spontaneous remission is unknown.
Diff: 3   Page Ref: 690

2) Name four autoimmune diseases.

Answer: Multiple sclerosis, myasthenia gravis, Graves' disease, juvenile (type I) diabetes, systemic lupus erythematosus, glomerulonephritis, rheumatoid arthritis.
Diff: 3   Page Ref: 691

3) What are three mechanisms by which autoimmune diseases could arise?

Answer: (1) Ineffective lymphocyte programming. (2) Appearance of self-proteins in the circulation that have not previously been exposed to the immune system. (3) Cross-reaction of antibodies produced against foreign antigens with self-antigens.
Diff: 3   Page Ref: 691

4) A young girl requires a liver transplant due to failure of her liver to function. What is required for her to have a good prognosis and why?

Answer: At least a 75% tissue match is essential, and she must receive immunosuppressive therapy to keep her body from rejecting the new liver as foreign tissue.
Diff: 4   *Page Ref: 689*

5) Why do schools require inoculations for childhood diseases such as mumps, measles, and whooping cough? Why are the inoculations of value?

Answer: The inoculations are required to try to prevent epidemics of these microbiological infections. The inoculations are of great benefit in preventing the diseases because the vaccines cause immunity to the pathogens by stimulating both the formation of protective antibodies and the establishment of immunological memory against future infection.
Diff: 5   *Page Ref: 674–675*

6) A person is bitten by a rattlesnake while on a camping trip. His friends immediately apply ice packs to the bitten area to slow the spread of the protein–based toxin; they then rush him to an emergency facility. What treatment would be given and why?

Answer: The person could be given an immune serum to the rattlesnake venom, thereby conferring passive immunity. The reason for passive immunization is that the venom could kill the person before active immunity could be established. The passive immunity would last until the "borrowed" antibodies naturally degraded in the body. No immunological memory would be established because B cells are not activated.
Diff: 5   *Page Ref: 674–675*

CHAPTER 21   The Respiratory System

Fill-in-the-Blank/Short Answer Questions

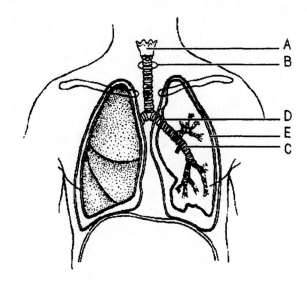

Figure 21.1

Using Figure 21.1, identify the following:

1) Primary bronchi.

Answer: D
Diff: 1   Page Ref: 705

2) Visceral pleura.

Answer: E
Diff: 1   Page Ref: 708

3) Larynx.

Answer: A
Diff: 1   Page Ref: 701

4) Secondary bronchi.

Answer: C
Diff: 1   Page Ref: 705

5) Trachea.

Answer: B
Diff: 1   Page Ref: 705

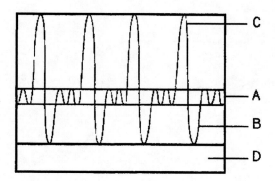

Figure 21.2

Using Figure 21.2, identify the following:

6) Tidal volume.

   Answer: A
   Diff: 1   Page Ref: 717

7) Inspiratory reserve volume.

   Answer: C
   Diff: 1   Page Ref: 717

8) Residual volume.

   Answer: D
   Diff: 1   Page Ref: 717

9) Expiratory reserve volume.

   Answer: B
   Diff: 1   Page Ref: 717

10) The Heimlich manuever uses this.

   Answer: B
   Diff: 2   Page Ref: 717

11) Air that does not participate in the exchange of gases.

   Answer: D
   Diff: 2   Page Ref: 717

Fill in the blank or provide a short answer:

12) Type II alveolar cells secrete _____.

   Answer: surfactant
   Diff: 1   Page Ref: 715

13) _____ law is called the law of partial pressure.

Answer: Dalton's
Diff: 2   Page Ref: 718

14) _____ law would apply to the amount of CO_2 you could dissolve in a Pepsi.

Answer: Henry's
Diff: 2   Page Ref: 719

15) Oxygen unloading in a RBC due to declining pH is called the _____.

Answer: Bohr effect
Diff: 2   Page Ref: 724

16) The _____ center of the pons exerts mainly inhibitory effects on breathing rates.

Answer: pneumotaxic
Diff: 2   Page Ref: 729

17) The cartilaginous flap that closes the trachea during swallowing is called the _____.

Answer: epiglottis
Diff: 2   Page Ref: 700

18) The archway in the back of the throat is called the _____.

Answer: fauces
Diff: 2   Page Ref: 700

19) The trachea is lined with _____ epithelium.

Answer: ciliated pseudostratified columnar
Diff: 3   Page Ref: 702

20) Terminal bronchioles are lined with _____ epithelium.

Answer: cuboidal
Diff: 3   Page Ref: 705

21) How is alveolar gas exchange affected by emphysema and pneumonia?

Answer: With pneumonia, if the lungs become edematous, the thickness of the exchange membrane may increase dramatically, restricting gas exchange, and body tissues begin to suffer from hypoxia. With emphysema, the lungs become progressively less elastic and more fibrous, which hinders both inspiration and expiration. Gas exchange remains adequate initially, but muscular activity must be enlisted to expire. Additionally, a symptom of emphysema is fusion of alveoli, resulting in less surface area for gas exchange.
Diff: 3   Page Ref: 734

22) Briefly differentiate between atmospheric pressure, intrapulmonary pressure, and intrapleural pressure. Which of these is always negative in a healthy individual? What happens if intrapleural pressure becomes equal to atmospheric pressure?

   Answer: Atmospheric pressure is the pressure exerted by gases of the atmosphere. Intrapulmonary pressure is the pressure within the alveoli of the lungs. Intrapleural pressure is the pressure within the intrapleural space. Intrapleural pressure is always negative relative to the other two. Equalization of the intrapleural pressure with atmospheric pressure or intrapulmonary pressure immediately causes lung collapse.

   Diff: 3   *Page Ref: 711–712*

23) The contraction of the diaphragm and the external intercostal muscles begins inspiration. Explain exactly what happens, in terms of volume and pressure changes in the lungs, when these muscles contract.

   Answer: With contraction of the diaphragm, the height of the thoracic cavity increases. Contraction of the intercostal muscles expands the diameter of the thorax. With an increase in volume of the thorax, the intrapulmonary volume increases, causing a drop in pressure relative to atmospheric pressure. Air rushes into the lungs along this pressure gradient until intrapulmonary and atmospheric pressures are equal.

   Diff: 3   *Page Ref: 712*

24) What is the *chloride shift* and why does it occur?

   Answer: The chloride shift is an ionic exchange process whereby chloride ions move from the plasma into the erythrocytes to counterbalance the net positive charge left within the erythrocytes by the rapid outrush of negative bicarbonate ions.

   Diff: 3   *Page Ref: 726*

25) How is it possible to change the pitch of our voice from high to low?

   Answer: Usually, the tenser the vocal folds, the faster they vibrate and the higher the pitch. To produce deep tones, the glottis widens, and to produce high-pitched tones, the glottis becomes a slit. Intrinsic laryngeal muscles control the true vocal folds and the size of the glottis.

   Diff: 4   *Page Ref: 702*

26) The partial pressure gradient for oxygen (in the body) is much steeper than that for carbon dioxide. Explain how equal amounts of these two gases can be exchanged (in a given time interval) in the lungs and at the tissues.

   Answer: Equal amounts of O_2 and CO_2 can be exchanged in the lungs and at the tissues because CO_2 solubility in plasma and alveolar fluid is 20 times greater than that of O_2.

   Diff: 4   *Page Ref: 721*

27) Define *anatomic dead space*. What is the relationship between anatomic and alveolar dead space? Which value is likely to increase during lung pathology?

   Answer: Anatomic dead space is the space in the conducting respiratory passageways. Alveolar dead space is the space in nonfunctional alveoli. Anatomic dead space and alveolar dead space together make up the total dead space. Alveolar dead space will increase during lung pathology.

   Diff: 4   *Page Ref: 716*

Matching Questions

Match the following:

1) Column 1: No exchange of gases occurs here.

   Column 2: Terminal bronchioles

   Answer: Terminal bronchioles
   Diff: 1   Page Ref: 705

2) Column 1: Secrete a fluid containing surfactant.

   Column 2: Type 1 cells

   Answer: Type 1 cells
   Diff: 1   Page Ref: 706

3) Column 1: Where the respiratory zone of the lungs begins.

   Column 2: Respiratory bronchioles

   Answer: Respiratory bronchioles
   Diff: 1   Page Ref: 705

4) Column 1: Composed of simple squamous epithelium.

   Column 2: Type I cells

   Answer: Type I cells
   Diff: 1   Page Ref: 706

5) Column 1: Terminates in alveoli.

   Column 2: Alveolar duct

   Answer: Alveolar duct
   Diff: 1   Page Ref: 705

6) Column 1: Composed of cuboidal cells.

   Column 2: Type II cells

   Answer: Type II cells
   Diff: 2   Page Ref: 706

7) Column 1: The respiratory membrane is composed of fused basal laminas of the capillary walls and _____.

   Column 2: Type I cells

   Answer: Type I cells
   Diff: 2   Page Ref: 706

True/False Questions

1) Internal respiration is oxygen loading and carbon dioxide unloading between the blood and the air of the alveoli.

   Answer: FALSE
   Diff: 1   Page Ref: 696

2) External respiration is the exchange of gas between the blood and tissue cells.

   Answer: FALSE
   Diff: 1   Page Ref: 696

3) The roof of the nasal cavity is formed by parts of the frontal bone.

   Answer: FALSE
   Diff: 1   Page Ref: 697

4) There is glandular tissue in the cavity of the nose.

   Answer: TRUE
   Diff: 1   Page Ref: 698

5) The olfactory mucosal lining of the nasal cavity contains the receptors for the sense of smell.

   Answer: TRUE
   Diff: 1   Page Ref: 697

6) The functions of the nasal conchae are to enhance the air turbulence in the cavity and to increase the mucosal surface area exposed to the air.

   Answer: TRUE
   Diff: 1   Page Ref: 698

7) Paranasal sinuses seem to have no useful function.

   Answer: FALSE
   Diff: 1   Page Ref: 699

8) The pleura is a thin, single-layered serosa that divides into parietal and visceral pleura.

   Answer: FALSE
   Diff: 1   Page Ref: 710

9) Intrapleural pressure is normally about 4 mm Hg less than the pressure in the alveoli.

   Answer: TRUE
   Diff: 1   Page Ref: 711

10) During normal quiet breathing, approximately 750 ml of air moves into and out of the lungs with each breath.

    Answer: FALSE
    Diff: 1   Page Ref: 717

11) Vital capacity refers to the length of time one is able to hold his or her breath.

Answer: FALSE
Diff: 1   *Page Ref: 716*

12) The alveolar ventilation rate is the best index of effective ventilation.

Answer: TRUE
Diff: 1   *Page Ref: 718*

13) At high altitudes, all partial pressure values of gases decrease in proportion to the decrease in atmospheric pressure.

Answer: FALSE
Diff: 1   *Page Ref: 719*

14) The basic pattern of breathing is set by the activity of neurons in the reticular formation of the spinal cord.

Answer: FALSE
Diff: 1   *Page Ref: 728*

15) Lowered oxygen levels are the most powerful respiratory stimulant.

Answer: FALSE
Diff: 1   *Page Ref: 720*

16) In chronic bronchitis, mucus production is decreased and this leads to the inflammation and fibrosis of the mucosal lining of the bronchial tree.

Answer: FALSE
Diff: 1   *Page Ref: 734*

17) The larynx is "roofed" by the thyroid cartilage.

Answer: FALSE
Diff: 1   *Page Ref: 700*

18) Labored breathing is termed dyspnea.

Answer: TRUE
Diff: 1   *Page Ref: 734*

19) The largest amount of carbon dioxide is transported in the bloodstream, in the form of carbonic anhydrase.

Answer: FALSE
Diff: 1   *Page Ref: 726*

20) The normal respiratory rate and rhythm is referred to as eupnea.

Answer: TRUE
Diff: 1   *Page Ref: 728*

21) Physiologically, the most important stimulus for breathing in a healthy person is the carbon dioxide level in the blood.

Answer: TRUE
Diff: 1   Page Ref: 732

22) Forced expiration is an active process.

Answer: TRUE
Diff: 1   Page Ref: 714

23) Each lung has an indention, the pelvis, through which blood vessels enter and leave the lung.

Answer: FALSE
Diff: 1   Page Ref: 709

24) Increased temperature results in decreased O_2 unloading from hemoglobin.

Answer: FALSE
Diff: 1   Page Ref: 724

25) The actual site of gas exchange in the lungs starts with the terminal bronchioles.

Answer: FALSE
Diff: 1   Page Ref: 705

26) The epiglottis is a smooth muscle that covers the glottis during swallowing.

Answer: FALSE
Diff: 1   Page Ref: 700

27) Smoking diminishes ciliary action and eventually destroys the cilia.

Answer: TRUE
Diff: 1   Page Ref: 703

28) Tracheal obstruction is life threatening.

Answer: TRUE
Diff: 1   Page Ref: 704

29) The respiratory zone begins at the terminal bronchioles.

Answer: FALSE
Diff: 1   Page Ref: 705

30) The alveolar and capillary walls and their fused basal laminas form the respiratory membrane.

Answer: TRUE
Diff: 1   Page Ref: 706

31) The paired lungs are located in the mediastinum.

Answer: FALSE
Diff: 1   Page Ref: 709

32) The parietal pleura lines the thoracic wall.

Answer: TRUE
Diff: 1   Page Ref: 710

33) The average individual has 500 ml of residual volume in his lungs.

Answer: FALSE
Diff: 1   Page Ref: 716

34) Atelectasis (lung collapse) renders the lung useless for ventilation.

Answer: TRUE
Diff: 2   Page Ref: 711–712

35) The respiratory centers in the medulla and pons are sensitive only to excitatory stimuli.

Answer: FALSE
Diff: 2   Page Ref: 728–729

36) The Hering–Breuer reflex is a potentially dangerous response that may cause overinflation of the lung.

Answer: FALSE
Diff: 2   Page Ref: 730

37) Strong emotions and pain acting through the limbic system activate sympathetic centers in the hypothalamus, thus modulating respiratory rate and depth by sending signals to the respiratory centers.

Answer: TRUE
Diff: 2   Page Ref: 730

38) As carbon dioxide enters systemic blood, it causes more oxygen to dissociate from hemoglobin (the Haldane effect), which in turn allows more CO_2 to combine with hemoglobin and more bicarbonate ion to be generated (the Bohr effect).

Answer: FALSE
Diff: 2   Page Ref: 724

39) Dalton's law states that the total pressure exerted by a mixture of gases is the sum of the pressures exerted independently by each gas in the mixture.

Answer: TRUE
Diff: 2   Page Ref: 718

40) Oxygenated hemoglobin releases oxygen more readily when the pH is more basic.

Answer: FALSE
Diff: 3   Page Ref: 724

41) Volume changes lead to pressure changes, which lead to the movement of gases to equalize the pressure.

Answer: TRUE
Diff: 3   Page Ref: 712

Multiple-Choice Questions

1) Air and food are routed into the proper channels by the:

   A) trachea.   B) pharynx.   C) larynx.   D) carina.

Answer: C
Diff: 1   Page Ref: 700

2) The loudness of a person's voice depends on:

   A) the thickness of vestibular folds.

   B) the length of the vocal folds.

   C) the strength of the intrinsic laryngeal muscles.

   D) the force with which air rushes across the vocal folds.

Answer: D
Diff: 1   Page Ref: 702

3) The walls of the alveoli are composed of two types of cells, type I and type II. The function of type II is:

   A) to secrete surfactant.

   B) to trap dust and other debris.

   C) to replace mucus in the alveoli.

   D) to protect the lungs from bacterial invasion.

Answer: A
Diff: 1   Page Ref: 706

4) After the tertiary bronchus, the next smaller branch of the respiratory passageway is the:

   A) terminal bronchiole.   B) atrium.

   C) alveolar ducts.   D) respiratory bronchiole.

Answer: A
Diff: 1   Page Ref: 705

5) The smallest macroscopic subdivision of the lung is the:

   A) lobule.   B) pleura.

   C) primary bronchiole.   D) extrinsic ligament.

Answer: A
Diff: 1   Page Ref: 710

6) The pleurae are vital to the integrity of the lungs because:

   A) they contain cilia that protect the lungs.

   B) they control the volume of the lungs.

   C) they maintain the proper temperature of the lungs during sleep.

   D) they produce a lubricating serous secretion, allowing the lungs to glide over the thorax wall during breathing.

   Answer: D
   Diff: 1   Page Ref: 710

7) Intrapulmonary pressure is the:

   A) pressure within the pleural cavity.

   B) pressure within the alveoli of the lungs.

   C) negative pressure in the intrapleural space.

   D) difference between atmospheric pressure and respiratory pressure.

   Answer: B
   Diff: 1   Page Ref: 711

8) The relationship between the pressure and volume of gases is given by:

   A) Boyle's law.   B) Henry's law.   C) Charles' law.   D) Dalton's law.

   Answer: A
   Diff: 1   Page Ref: 712

9) The statement, "in a mixture of gases, the total pressure is the sum of the individual partial pressures of gases in the mixture" paraphrases:

   A) Henry's law.   B) Boyle's law.   C) Dalton's law.   D) Charles' law.

   Answer: C
   Diff: 1   Page Ref: 712

10) Surfactant helps to prevent the alveoli from collapsing by:

   A) humidifying the air before it enters.

   B) warming the air before it enters.

   C) interfering with the cohesiveness of water molecules, thereby reducing the surface tension of alveolar fluid.

   D) protecting the surface of alveoli from dehydration and other environmental variations.

   Answer: C
   Diff: 1   Page Ref: 715

11) For gas exchange to be efficient, the respiratory membrane must be:

   A) at least 3 micrometers thick.

   B) 0.5 to 1 micrometer thick.

   C) between 5 and 6 micrometers thick.

   D) The thickness of the respiratory membrane is not important in the efficiency of gas exchange.

   Answer: B
   Diff: 1   Page Ref: 722

12) With the Bohr effect, more oxygen is released because:

   A) a decrease in pH (acidosis) strengthens the hemoglobin–oxygen bond.

   B) a decrease in pH (acidosis) weakens the hemoglobin–oxygen bond.

   C) an increase in pH (alkalosis) strengthens the hemoglobin–oxygen bond.

   D) an increase in pH (alkalosis) weakens the hemoglobin–oxygen bond.

   Answer: B
   Diff: 1   Page Ref: 724

13) The most powerful respiratory stimulus for breathing in a healthy person is:

   A) loss of oxygen in tissues.   B) increase of carbon dioxide.
   C) pH (acidosis).   D) pH (alkalosis).

   Answer: B
   Diff: 1   Page Ref: 732

14) Nerve impulses from _____ will result in inspiration.

   A) the dorsal respiratory group

   B) the chemoreceptor center

   C) Broca's center

   D) the preoptic nucleus of the hypothalamus

   Answer: A
   Diff: 1   Page Ref: 728

15) In the plasma, the quantity of oxygen in solution is:

   A) only about 1.5% of the oxygen is carried in dissolved form.

   B) about equal to the oxygen combined with hemoglobin.

   C) greater than the oxygen combined with hemoglobin.

   D) not present except where it is combined with carrier molecules.

   Answer: A
   Diff: 1   Page Ref: 723

16) Another name for the inflation reflex is:

   A) Bohr.

   C) Hering–Breuer.

   B) Haldane.

   D) pulmonary irritant.

Answer: C
Diff: 1   *Page Ref: 730*

17) Which of the following does not influence the increase in ventilation that occurs as exercise is initiated?

   A) psychic stimuli

   B) fall in lactic acid levels

   C) proprioceptors

   D) simultaneous cortical motor activation of the skeletal muscles and respiratory center

Answer: B
Diff: 1   *Page Ref: 733*

18) Which of the following is not a form of lung cancer?

   A) adenocarcinoma

   C) small cell carcinoma

   B) Kaposi's sarcoma

   D) squamous cell carcinoma

Answer: B
Diff: 1   *Page Ref: 736*

19) Which of the following is not an event necessary to supply the body with O_2 and dispose of CO_2?

   A) pulmonary ventilation

   C) internal respiration

   B) blood pH adjustment

   D) external respiration

Answer: B
Diff: 1   *Page Ref: 696*

20) Which of the following changes occurs as the conducting tubes of the lungs become smaller?

   A) Cartilage rings are gradually replaced by regular plates of cartilage.

   B) Resistance to air flow decreases due to the increased number of tubes.

   C) Smooth muscle amount increases.

   D) Lining of the tubes changes from ciliated columnar to simple squamous epithelium which lines the alveoli.

Answer: C
Diff: 1   *Page Ref: 704–705*

21) Which of the following does not diminish compliance?
    A) factors that block the bronchi
    B) factors that impair the flexibility of the thoracic cage
    C) factors that reduce the natural resilience of the lungs
    D) factors that decrease the surface tension of the fluid film of the alveoli

Answer: D
Diff: 1   *Page Ref: 715–716*

22) Tidal volume is air:
    A) remaining in the lungs after forced expiration.
    B) exchanged during normal breathing.
    C) inhaled after normal inspiration.
    D) forcibly expelled after normal expiration.

Answer: B
Diff: 1   *Page Ref: 716*

23) The ideal vital capacity of an adult male is around:
    A) 1200 ml.   B) 3100 ml.   C) 4800 ml.   D) 6600 ml.

Answer: C
Diff: 1   *Page Ref: 717*

24) Possible causes of hypoxia include:
    A) too little oxygen in the atmosphere.   B) obstruction of the esophagus.
    C) taking several rapid deep breaths.   D) getting very cold.

Answer: A
Diff: 1   *Page Ref: 725*

25) The lung volume that represents the total volume of exchangeable air is the:
    A) tidal volume.   B) vital capacity.
    C) inspiratory capacity.   D) expiratory reserve volume.

Answer: B
Diff: 1   *Page Ref: 716*

26) Which of the following is not a stimulus for breathing?
    A) rising carbon dioxide levels   B) rising blood pressure
    C) arterial P_{O_2} below 60 mm Hg   D) arterial pH resulting from CO_2 retention

Answer: B
Diff: 1   *Page Ref: 730–733*

27) Respiratory control centers are located in the:

    A) midbrain and medulla.   B) medulla and pons.

    C) pons and midbrain.   D) upper spinal cord and medulla.

Answer: B
Diff: 1   *Page Ref: 730–731*

28) The amount of air that can be inspired above the tidal volume is called:

    A) reserve air.   B) expiratory reserve.

    C) inspiratory reserve.   D) vital capacity.

Answer: C
Diff: 1   *Page Ref: 716–717*

29) Which statement about CO_2 is incorrect?

    A) Its concentration in the blood is decreased by hyperventilation.

    B) Its accumulation in the blood is associated with a decrease in pH.

    C) More CO_2 dissolves in the blood plasma than is carried on the RBCs.

    D) CO_2 concentrations are greater in venous blood than arterial blood.

Answer: C
Diff: 1   *Page Ref: 726–728*

30) Oxygen and carbon dioxide are exchanged in the lungs and through all cell membranes by:

    A) osmosis.   B) diffusion.   C) filtration.   D) active transport.

Answer: B
Diff: 1   *Page Ref: 718*

31) Select the correct statement about the pharynx.

    A) The adenoids are located in the laryngopharynx.

    B) The auditory tube drains into the nasopharynx.

    C) The oropharynx blends posteriorly into the nasopharynx.

    D) The palatine tonsils are embedded in the lateral walls of the nasopharynx.

Answer: B
Diff: 1   *Page Ref: 699–700*

32) The larynx contains:

    A) the thyroid cartilage.

    B) a cricoid cartilage also called the Adam's apple.

    C) an upper pair of avascular mucosal folds called true vocal folds.

    D) lateral cartilage ridges called false vocal folds.

Answer: A
Diff: 1   *Page Ref: 700–701*

33) Which respiratory-associated muscles would contract if you were to blow up a balloon?

A) diaphragm would contract, external intercostals would relax

B) internal intercostals and abdominal muscles would contract

C) external intercostals would contract and diaphragm would relax

D) diaphragm contracts, internal intercostals would relax

Answer: B
Diff: 1   *Page Ref: 714*

34) The oropharynx does not include:

A) fauces.   B) palatine tonsils.

C) lingual tonsils.   D) pharyngeal tonsils.

Answer: D
Diff: 1   *Page Ref: 701*

35) Which of the following is not found on the right lobe of the lung?

A) middle lobe   B) cardiac notch

C) horizontal fissure   D) oblique fissure

Answer: B
Diff: 1   *Page Ref: 709*

36) Impairments of oxygen transport include:

A) anemic hypoxia, usually caused by congestive heart failure.

B) carbon monoxide poisoning, a form of hypoxemic hypoxia.

C) stagnant hypoxia, due to a functional problem with the lungs.

D) hypoxemic hypoxia, resulting from a decrease in levels of functional red blood cells.

Answer: B
Diff: 1   *Page Ref: 725*

37) Which of the following correctly describes mechanisms of CO_2 transport?

A) 20% of CO_2 is carried dissolved directly into the plasma.

B) 7–8% of CO_2 is carried in the form of carbamino hemoglobin.

C) The chloride shift mechanism enhances CO_2 transport.

D) Carbonic anhydrase is responsible for bonding CO_2 to hemoglobin.

Answer: C
Diff: 1   *Page Ref: 726–728*

38) Factors that influence the rate and depth of breathing include:

A) thalamic control.   B) voluntary cortical control.

C) stretch receptors in the alveoli.   D) composition of alveolar gas.

Answer: B
Diff: 1   *Page Ref: 728–729*

39) Which of the following provide the greatest surface area for gas exchange?

   A) alveolar sacs   B) alveoli

   C) respiratory bronchioles   D) alveolar ducts

   Answer: B
   Diff: 2   Page Ref: 705

40) The respiratory membrane is a combination of:

   A) respiratory bronchioles and alveolar ducts.

   B) alveolar and capillary walls and their fused basal lamina.

   C) atria and alveolar sacs.

   D) respiratory bronchioles and alveolar sacs.

   Answer: B
   Diff: 2   Page Ref: 706

41) Inspiratory capacity is:

   A) the total amount of air that can be inspired after a tidal expiration.

   B) the total amount of exchangeable air.

   C) functional residual capacity.

   D) air inspired after a tidal inhalation.

   Answer: A
   Diff: 2   Page Ref: 716

42) Which of the following factors is most important to hemoglobin saturation?

   A) hydrogen concentration   B) percent of oxygen available

   C) body temperature   D) amount of BPG in the blood

   Answer: C
   Diff: 2   Page Ref: 723–725

43) Which center(s) is (are) located in the pons?

   A) pneumotaxic   B) expiratory

   C) inspiratory   D) Both A and C are correct.

   Answer: A
   Diff: 2   Page Ref: 729

44) Which of the following is a respiratory air movement?

   A) inhaling   B) coughing   C) sneezing   D) yawning

   Answer: A
   Diff: 2   Page Ref: 712

45) The nose serves all the following functions except:

A) as a passageway for air movement.   B) as the initiator of the cough reflex.

C) warming and humidifying the air.   D) cleansing the air.

Answer: B
Diff: 2   Page Ref: 696–699

46) Which statement about alveolar ventilation rate (AVR) is false?

A) AVR in a healthy person should equal about 4200 ml/min.

B) Rapid, shallow breathing decreases AVR.

C) An increase in dead space causes an increase in AVR.

D) If tidal volume approaches zero, AVR drops toward zero.

Answer: C
Diff: 2   Page Ref: 718

47) Select the correct statement about the neural mechanisms of respiratory control.

A) The pons is thought to be instrumental in the smooth transition from inspiration to expiration.

B) The ventral respiratory group (expiratory center) neurons depolarize in a rhythmic way to establish the pattern of breathing.

C) The pneumotaxic center continuously stimulates the medulla to provide inspiratory drive.

D) The dorsal respiratory group (inspiratory center) is contained within the pons.

Answer: A
Diff: 2   Page Ref: 730–731

48) Chemicals in the blood modulate rate and depth of breathing to control CO_2 and O_2 levels in the blood. Select the most correct statement.

A) Major chemical receptors are located in all areas of the body.

B) The main driving force of respiration is changing levels of molecular O_2.

C) Increasing H^+ levels stimulate central chemoreceptors.

D) Hypercapnia causes the pH of the cerebrospinal fluid to increase, thereby stimulating respiratory drive.

Answer: C
Diff: 2   Page Ref: 731

49) Which of the following statements is correct?

A) H^+ acts directly on central chemoreceptors to decrease the rate and depth of breathing.

B) Low arterial pH is the most powerful stimulator of respiration.

C) Arterial pH does not affect central chemoreceptors directly.

D) H^+ has little effect on the blood pH.

Answer: A
Diff: 2   Page Ref: 728

50) If oxygen exerts 159 mm Hg at sea level, then nitrogen exerts _____ mm Hg.

   A) 569   B) 597   C) 620   D) 760

Answer: B
Diff: 2   *Page Ref: 719*

51) Which of these nerve types does not innervate the lungs?

   A) vagus motor   B) sympathetic motor

   C) parasympathetic sensory   D) visceral sensory

Answer: C
Diff: 3   *Page Ref: 710*

52) The factors responsible for holding the lungs to the thorax wall are:

   A) the smooth muscles of the lung.

   B) the diaphragm and the intercostal muscles.

   C) the visceral pleurae and the changing volume of the lungs.

   D) surface tension from pleural fluid, positive pressure, and atmospheric pressure on the thorax.

Answer: D
Diff: 3   *Page Ref: 711-712*

53) The erythrocyte count increases after a while when an individual goes from a low to a high altitude because:

   A) the temperature is lower at higher altitudes.

   B) the basal metabolic rate is higher at high altitudes.

   C) the concentration of oxygen and/or total atmospheric pressure is higher at higher altitudes.

   D) the concentration of oxygen and/or total atmospheric pressure is lower at high altitudes.

Answer: D
Diff: 3   *Page Ref: 733-734*

54) Most inspired particles such as dust fail to reach the lungs because of the:

   A) ciliated mucous lining in the nose.   B) abundant blood supply to nasal mucosa.

   C) porous structure of turbinate bones.   D) action of the epiglottis.

Answer: A
Diff: 3   *Page Ref: 698*

55) In mouth–to–mouth artificial respiration, the rescuer blows air from his or her own respiratory system into that of the victim. Thus:

A) interpleural pressure exceeds intrapulmonary pressure.

B) during inflation of the lungs, the intrapleural pressure decreases.

C) expansion of the victim's lungs is brought about by blowing air in at higher than atmospheric pressure (positive pressure breathing).

D) increasing the CO of the victim's blood.

Answer: C
Diff: 3   *Page Ref: 711*

56) Which of the following is not possible?

A) Gas flow equals pressure gradient over resistance.

B) Pressure gradient equals gas flow over resistance.

C) Resistance equals pressure gradient over gas flow.

D) The amount of gas flowing in and out of the alveoli is directly proportional to the difference in pressure or pressure gradiant between the external atmosphere and the alveoli.

Answer: B
Diff: 3   *Page Ref: 714*

57) Select the correct statement about the physical factors influencing pulmonary ventilation.

A) A decrease in compliance causes an increase in ventilation.

B) A lung that is less elastic will require less muscle action to perform adequate ventilation.

C) As alveolar surface tension increases, additional muscle action will be required.

D) Surfactant helps increase alveolar surface tension.

Answer: C
Diff: 3   *Page Ref: 714–716*

58) Select the correct statement about oxygen transport in blood:

A) During normal activity, a molecule of hemoglobin returning to the lungs contains one molecule of O_2.

B) During conditions of acidosis, hemoglobin is able to carry oxygen more efficiently.

C) Increased 2, 3–BPG levels in the red blood cell enhance oxygen–carrying capacity.

D) A 50% oxygen saturation level of blood returning to the lungs might indicate an activity level higher than normal.

Answer: D
Diff: 3   *Page Ref: 723–724*

Clinical Questions

1) Timothy has been having difficulty breathing since he had pneumonia last month. Recently he had severe pain in his chest and back, and his breathing was extremely irregular. The doctor at the emergency room told him that one of the lobes of his lung had collapsed. How could this happen?

   Answer: Timothy suffered atelectasis, or collapse of his lung, most likely caused by air entering the pleural cavity due to a rupture of the visceral pleura. The rupture could have happened as a result of coughing during his bout with pneumonia.

   Diff: 5   Page Ref: 711–712

2) While having a physical examination, a young male informed his doctor that at age 8 he had lobar pneumonia and pleurisy in his left lung. The physician decided to measure his VC. Describe the apparatus and method used for taking this measurement. Define the following terms used in the description of lung volumes: TV, IRV, ERV, RV, and VC.

   Answer: His vital capacity (VC) was measured using a spirometer. As he breathed into a mouthpiece, a hollow bell, inverted over water, was displaced, giving a graphic recording on a rotating drum. Tidal volume (TV) is the amount of air that moves into and out of the lungs with normal breathing. Inspiratory reserve volume (IRV) is the amount of air that can be forcibly inhaled beyond the tidal volume. The expiratory reserve volume (ERV) is the amount of air that can be evacuated from the lungs over and above a tidal expiration. Residual volume (RV) is the amount of air that remains in the lungs even after the most strenuous expiration. Vital capacity (VC) is the total amount of exchangeable air.

   Diff: 5   Page Ref: 716–717

3) Jane had been suffering through a severe cold and was complaining of a frontal headache and a dull, aching pain at the side of her face. What regions are likely to become sites of secondary infection following nasal infection?

   Answer: Following nasal infection, the paranasal sinuses can become infected.

   Diff: 5   Page Ref: 699

4) A smoker sees his doctor because he has a persistent cough and is short of breath after very little exertion. What diagnosis will the doctor make and what can the person expect if he does not quit smoking?

   Answer: The person is suffering from chronic bronchitis, which causes the dyspnea and coughing. If he does not stop smoking, he can expect frequent pulmonary infections, more coughing, and progressively more severe dyspnea (all symptoms of chronic obstructive pulmonary disease). Ultimately, he can expect to develop hypoxemia, CO_2 retention, and respiratory acidosis. He may develop emphysema or lung cancer.

   Diff: 5   Page Ref: 734–735

CHAPTER 22   The Digestive System

Fill-in-the-Blank/Short Answer Questions

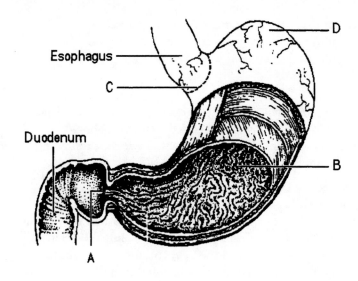

Esophagus

C

Duodenum

A

D

B

Figure 22.1

Using Figure 22.1, identify the following:

1) Fundus.

   Answer: D
   Diff: 1   Page Ref: 756

2) Pyloric sphincter.

   Answer: A
   Diff: 1   Page Ref: 756

3) Gastroesophageal sphincter.

   Answer: C
   Diff: 1   Page Ref: 756

4) Rugae of the stomach.

   Answer: B
   Diff: 1   Page Ref: 756

5) Body region.

   Answer: B
   Diff: 1   Page Ref: 756

6) Cardiac region.

   Answer: C
   Diff: 1   *Page Ref: 756*

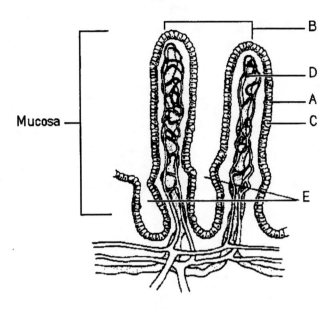

Figure 22.2

Using Figure 22.2, identify the following:

   7) Absorptive cells that line the intestinal tract.

   Answer: A
   Diff: 1   *Page Ref: 765*

   8) Cell type specialized to secrete mucus into the lumen of the intestinal tract.

   Answer: C
   Diff: 2   *Page Ref: 765*

   9) Structures that increase the absorptive area of the small intestine.

   Answer: B
   Diff: 2   *Page Ref: 765*

   10) Structure that absorbs lipids via chylomicrons.

   Answer: A
   Diff: 2   *Page Ref: 765*

   11) Paneth cells are found here.

   Answer: E
   Diff: 2   *Page Ref: 765*

Fill in the blank or provide a short answer:

12) The longest portion of the small intestine is the _____ .

Answer: ileum
Diff: 1   Page Ref: 764

13) The simple columnar epithelial cells that line the villi are called _____ .

Answer: enterocytes
Diff: 1   Page Ref: 766

14) _____ is the principal enzyme for breaking down carbohydrates.

Answer: Amylase
Diff: 1   Page Ref: 783

15) The _____ layer of the intestine is composed of dense irregular connective tissue.

Answer: submucosal
Diff: 2   Page Ref: 744

16) _____ cells of the stomach secrete HCl.

Answer: Parietal
Diff: 2   Page Ref: 758

17) The chief bile pigment is _____ .

Answer: bilirubin
Diff: 2   Page Ref: 772

18) _____ cells are found in the sinusoids of the liver and they remove debris from the blood as it flows past.

Answer: Kupffer
Diff: 2   Page Ref: 770

19) Compare and contrast the structure and function of an incisor and a molar.

Answer: An incisor is chisel–shaped and adapted for cutting. Molars have broad crowns with rounded cusps and are best suited for grinding or cutting.
Diff: 2   Page Ref: 750

20) What are chylomicrons?

Answer: Chylomicrons are tiny fatty droplets composed of triglycerides, small amounts of phospholipids, cholesterol, free fatty acids, and some protein.
Diff: 2   Page Ref: 787

21) _____ peritoneum covers the external surfaces of most digestive organs.

Answer: Visceral
Diff: 3   Page Ref: 742

22) The _____ ligament anchors a tooth in the alveolus of the jaw.

Answer: periodontal
Diff: 3   Page Ref: 751

23) The _____ phase of gastric secretions occurs before food enters the stomach.

Answer: cephalic (or reflex)
Diff: 3   Page Ref: 759

24) Name two regions of the digestive tract where mechanical food breakdown processes are very important. Name two organs that are primarily food conduits. Name the organ where protein digestion is begun. Name the organ where fat digestion begins.

Answer: Mechanical food processes are very important in the mouth (mastication) and stomach (contractions causing mixing of food into chyme). The esophagus and pharynx are primarily food conduits. Protein digestion begins in the stomach. Fat digestion begins in the small intestine.
Diff: 3   Page Ref: 754, 785–786

25) Define constipation and diarrhea. Note possible causes of each.

Answer: Watery stools are called diarrhea. Constipation is a condition in which too much water has been absorbed and the stool becomes hard and difficult to pass. Any condition, such as irritation of the colon by bacteria that rushes food residue through the large intestine before that organ has had sufficient time to absorb the remaining water, is known as diarrhea. Constipation may ensue from the lack of fiber in the diet, improper bowel habits, laxative abuse, or anything that decreases motility.
Diff: 3   Page Ref: 783

26) Assume you have been chewing a piece of bread for 5 or 6 minutes. How would you expect its taste to change during this time? Why?

Answer: The bread will begin to taste sweet as some of the starch is broken down into sugar due to the chemical digestion of carbohydrates by salivary amylase.
Diff: 3   Page Ref: 783

27) What substances are absorbed by the stomach? The large intestine?

Answer: Aspirin and alcohol, as well as some other lipid–soluble drugs, pass easily through the stomach mucosa. The large intestine absorbs vitamin K and some B vitamins, some electrolytes, and water.
Diff: 3   Page Ref: 787–789

28) Name the three pairs of major salivary glands. Describe their relative locations and their microscopic differences.

Answer: The parotid glands lie anterior to the ears between the masseter muscle and the skin. They open into the vestibule next to the second molars of the upper jaw. The submandibular glands lie along the medial aspect of the mandibular body. Their ducts run beneath the mucosa of the oral cavity floor and open at the base of the lingual frenulum. The small sublingual gland lies anterior to the submandibular gland under the tongue. It opens via many ducts into the floor of the mouth. Parotid glands contain only serous cells, submandibular glands have equal numbers of serous and mucous cells, and sublingual are mostly mucous glands.
Diff: 3   Page Ref: 747–748

29) Why is it necessary for the stomach contents to be so acidic? How does the stomach protect itself from digestion?

Answer: The HCl is necessary for the activation and optimal activity of pepsin, and it kills many of the bacteria ingested with food. Mucous cells in the lining of the stomach secrete an alkaline mucus that clings to the stomach wall and helps to shield it from the acid. The epithelial cells of the mucosa are joined together by tight junctions that prevent gastric juice from leaking into underlying tissue layers. Damaged epithelial cells are shed and quickly replaced by cell division.
Diff: 3   Page Ref: 758

30) Identify two ways the small intestine is modified to increase the surface area for digestion and absorption.

Answer: The plicae circulares and villi are modifications of the small intestine for digestion and absorption. The plicae circulares are circular folds of the mucosa and submucosa. They force chyme to move spirally through the lumen. The villi are fingerlike projections of the mucosa. They increase the absorptive surface area. Microvilli are projections of the plasma membrane of the absorptive cells of the mucosa that bear intestinal digestive enzymes. They also enhance absorption.
Diff: 3   Page Ref: 765–766

31) If an older individual had all the wisdom teeth removed, and on each side of the lower jaw one incisor and one molar was missing, what would the dental formula for the lower jaw be?

Answer: 2-0-2-1
Diff: 3   Page Ref: 750

32) How is digestive activity provoked after eating? What activates the secretion of digestive juices into the lumen or hormones into the blood?

Answer: Sensors (mechanoreceptors and chemoreceptors) located in the walls of the gastrointestinal tract respond to stretching by the introduction of food into the lumen. Also, the sensors are able to respond to changes in solute concentration and pH as well as the presence of substrates and end products of digestion.
Diff: 4   Page Ref: 741

33) How is salivation controlled?

    Answer: When we ingest food, chemoreceptors and pressoreceptors in the mouth send signals to the salivatory nuclei in the brain stem. The parasympathetic nervous system activity increases and motor fibers trigger the increase in serous, enzyme–rich saliva.

    Diff: 4   *Page Ref: 749*

34) What is bile and where is it produced? What is its digestive function? Where is it stored and concentrated?

    Answer: Bile is a watery solution containing bile salts, bile pigments, cholesterol, neutral fats, phospholipids, and a variety of electrolytes. It is produced in the liver. Its digestive function is to emulsify fats. It is stored and concentrated in the gallbladder.

    Diff: 4   *Page Ref: 772*

Matching Questions

Match the following:

1) Column 1: Wavelike smooth muscle contractions that move foodstuffs through the alimentary tube.

    Column 2: Peristalsis

    Answer: Peristalsis
    Diff: 1   *Page Ref: 740*

2) Column 1: Chemical or mechanical process of breaking down foodstuffs to substances that can be absorbed.

    Column 2: Digestion

    Answer: Digestion
    Diff: 1   *Page Ref: 740*

3) Column 1: Enzymatic breakdown of any type of food molecule.

    Column 2: Hydrolysis

    Answer: Hydrolysis
    Diff: 1   *Page Ref: 783*

4) Column 1: Process by which the products of digestion pass through the lumen of the gastrointestinal tract into the blood or lymph.

    Column 2: Absorption

    Answer: Absorption
    Diff: 1   *Page Ref: 740*

True/False Questions

1) Food is contained in the gastrointestinal tract from the time of ingestion until it is completely digested and the waste prepared for elimination.

Answer: TRUE
Diff: 1   *Page Ref: 740*

2) As food passes through the digestive tract, it becomes less complex and the nutrients are more readily available to the body.

Answer: TRUE
Diff: 1   *Page Ref: 740–741*

3) Some of the microbes that often invade other organs of the body are rarely found in the stomach. The reason for this is the presence of HCl.

Answer: TRUE
Diff: 1   *Page Ref: 758*

4) Pernicious anemia is a condition brought on by insufficient vitamin B_{12} in the diet.

Answer: TRUE
Diff: 1   *Page Ref: 759*

5) Kupffer cells are found in the liver and are responsible for the phagocytosing bacteria and worn-out cells.

Answer: TRUE
Diff: 1   *Page Ref: 770*

6) The pharyngeal–esophageal phase of swallowing is involuntary and is controlled by the swallowing center in the thalamus and lower pons.

Answer: FALSE
Diff: 1   *Page Ref: 754*

7) The cell type of the wall of the large intestine is very different from that of the small intestine.

Answer: FALSE
Diff: 1   *Page Ref: 781*

8) Pepsinogen is the precursor to the gastric enzyme for protein digestion and is secreted by the parietal cells.

Answer: FALSE
Diff: 1   *Page Ref: 758*

9) Chemical digestion involves processes such as segmentation.

Answer: FALSE
Diff: 1   *Page Ref: 740*

10) The main chemical activity of the stomach is to begin the digestion of proteins.

Answer: TRUE
Diff: 1   *Page Ref: 759*

11) Chemical digestion of lipids is initiated in the mouth.

Answer: FALSE
Diff: 1   *Page Ref: 786*

12) The function of the enzyme salivary amylase is to begin digesting proteins.

Answer: FALSE
Diff: 1   *Page Ref: 783*

13) Rhythmic local constrictions of the intestine are termed *mastication*.

Answer: FALSE
Diff: 1   *Page Ref: 754*

14) The peritoneum is the most extensive serous membrane in the body.

Answer: TRUE
Diff: 1   *Page Ref: 742*

15) Peyer's patches are found in the submucosa of the distal end of the small intestine.

Answer: TRUE
Diff: 1   *Page Ref: 768*

16) The myenteric plexus provides the major nerve supply to the GI tract wall and controls GI motility.

Answer: TRUE
Diff: 1   *Page Ref: 745*

17) The first teeth to appear are the deciduous teeth.

Answer: TRUE
Diff: 1   *Page Ref: 749*

18) Dentin anchors the tooth in place.

Answer: FALSE
Diff: 1   *Page Ref: 751*

19) The digestive function of the liver is to produce bile.

Answer: TRUE
Diff: 1   *Page Ref: 768*

20) The storage and concentration area for bile is at the hepatopancreatic ampulla.

Answer: FALSE
Diff: 1   *Page Ref: 768*

21) The pancreas has both an endocrine and an exocrine function.

Answer: TRUE
Diff: 1   Page Ref: 774

22) Another term for swallowing is deglutition.

Answer: TRUE
Diff: 1   Page Ref: 754

23) The intrinsic ability of visceral smooth muscle to exhibit the stress–relaxation response is termed plasticity.

Answer: TRUE
Diff: 1   Page Ref: 762

24) The stomach's contractile rhythm is set by pacemaker cells found in the spinal cord.

Answer: FALSE
Diff: 1   Page Ref: 763

25) The major stimulus for production of intestinal fluid is distention or irritation of the intestinal mucosa by hypertonic or acidic chyme.

Answer: TRUE
Diff: 1   Page Ref: 768

26) Most nutrients are absorbed through the mucosa of the intestinal villi by active transport.

Answer: TRUE
Diff: 1   Page Ref: 767

27) Ionic iron is actively transported into the mucosal cells, where it binds to the protein ferritin, a phenomenon called the mucosal iron barrier.

Answer: TRUE
Diff: 1   Page Ref: 789

28) The layer of muscle in the intestine directly in contact with the serosa is the circular layer.

Answer: FALSE
Diff: 1   Page Ref: 744

29) Mumps is an inflammation of the parotid glands caused by myxovirus.

Answer: TRUE
Diff: 1   Page Ref: 748

30) The bulk of a tooth is composed of a bonelike material called dentin.

Answer: TRUE
Diff: 1   Page Ref: 751

31) At the junction of the main pancreatic duct and the common bile duct is an enlarged area called the hepatopancreatic ampulla.

Answer: TRUE
Diff: 1   Page Ref: 764

32) The mucosa membrane is found only in the jejunum because this is the only part of the small intestine in need of mucus.

Answer: FALSE
Diff: 2   Page Ref: 765

33) Food that is stored in the fundus of the stomach often remains in storage for up to 5 hours before being mixed with the powerful gastric juices secreted by the cells of the stomach.

Answer: FALSE
Diff: 2   Page Ref: 763

34) Fats significantly delay the emptying of the stomach.

Answer: TRUE
Diff: 2   Page Ref: 763

35) The soft palate rises reflexively to open the nasopharynx when we swallow food.

Answer: FALSE
Diff: 2   Page Ref: 754

36) *Haustral contractions* is another term for *peristalsis*.

Answer: TRUE
Diff: 2   Page Ref: 782

37) The only difference between a molar and a premolar is the number of cusps on the crown.

Answer: FALSE
Diff: 2   Page Ref: 750

Multiple-Choice Questions

1) The mechanical and chemical receptors that control digestive activity are located:
   A) in the glandular tissue that lines the organ lumen.
   B) in the walls of the tract organs.
   C) in the pons and medulla.
   D) only in the esophagus because this is the only part of the tract that needs to change to accommodate food passage.

Answer: B
Diff: 1   Page Ref: 741

2) Defensins are _____ compounds that protect against oral microorganisms.

    A) arsenic   B) cyanide   C) nitric oxide   D) mucin

Answer: B
Diff: 3   Page Ref: 749

3) The function of the hepatic portal circulation is to:

    A) carry toxins to the venous system for disposal through the urinary tract.

    B) collect absorbed nutrients for metabolic processing or storage before releasing them to the circulation for cellular use.

    C) distribute hormones.

    D) return glucose to the general circulation when blood sugar is low.

Answer: B
Diff: 1   Page Ref: 768

4) The chemical and mechanical processes of food breakdown are called:

    A) digestion.   B) absorption.   C) ingestion.   D) secretion.

Answer: A
Diff: 1   Page Ref: 740

5) When we ingest large molecules such as lipids, carbohydrates, and proteins, they must undergo catabolic reactions whereby enzymes split these molecules. This series of reactions is called:

    A) absorption.   B) secretion.

    C) chemical digestion.   D) mechanical digestion.

Answer: C
Diff: 1   Page Ref: 740

6) The sheets of peritoneal membrane that hold the digestive tract in place are called:

    A) mesenteries.   B) lamina propria.   C) serosal lining.   D) mucosal lining.

Answer: A
Diff: 1   Page Ref: 742

7) From the esophagus to the anal canal, the walls of every organ of the alimentary canal are made up of the same four basic layers. Arrange them in order from the lumen.

    A) muscularis externa, serosa, mucosa, and submucosa

    B) serosa, mucosa, submucosa, and muscularis externa

    C) submucosa, serosa, muscularis externa, and mucosa

    D) mucosa, submucosa, muscularis externa, and serosa

Answer: D
Diff: 1   Page Ref: 743-744

8) The structure known as the fauces is the:

   A) submaxillary gland.

   B) epiglottis.

   C) thyroid gland.

   D) passageway between the oral cavity and the pharynx.

   Answer: D
   Diff: 1   Page Ref: 746

9) The epithelial membrane called the mucosa:

   A) absorbs mucus, digestive enzymes, and hormones.

   B) absorbs the end products of digestion into the lymphatic system.

   C) fights infectious disease.

   D) contains the lamina propria.

   Answer: D
   Diff: 1   Page Ref: 743

10) The capillaries that nourish the epithelium and absorb digested nutrients lie in the:

   A) muscularis mucosae.   B) serosa.

   C) adventitia.   D) lamina propria.

   Answer: D
   Diff: 1   Page Ref: 743

11) The fusion of the common bile duct and the pancreatic duct form the:

   A) jejunum.   B) pyloric sphincter.

   C) hepatopancreatic ampulla.   D) fundus of the stomach.

   Answer: C
   Diff: 1   Page Ref: 764

12) The plicae circulares and intestinal villi are found in which of the four layers of the alimentary tube wall?

   A) mucosa   B) serosa   C) adventitia   D) lamina propria

   Answer: A
   Diff: 1   Page Ref: 765–766

13) The structures that produce new cells for the mucosa of the small intestine are the:

   A) lacteals.   B) cilium.

   C) intestinal crypts.   D) microvilli.

   Answer: C
   Diff: 1   Page Ref: 766

14) The absorptive effectiveness of the small intestine is enhanced by increasing the surface area of the mucosal lining. Which of the following accomplish this task?

A) plicae circularis and intestinal villi

B) the vast array of digestive enzymes

C) Brunner glands

D) the rugae

Answer: A
Diff: 1   Page Ref: 765–766

15) Select the statement that is true concerning primary teeth.

A) There are 27 primary teeth, and the molars are permanent.

B) There are 24 primary teeth, and no new primary teeth appear after 13 months.

C) There are 20 primary teeth, and by 24 months of age most children have all 20.

D) There are 32 primary teeth, and most children lose these teeth due to decay because they are never very strong.

Answer: C
Diff: 1   Page Ref: 750

16) Which of the following is true concerning the number and type of permanent teeth?

A) There are 32 permanent teeth, and the wisdom teeth are the last to emerge.

B) There are 27 permanent teeth, and the first molars are usually the last to emerge.

C) The number of permanent teeth is always equal to the number of primary teeth.

D) The number of upper permanent teeth is not equal to the number of lower permanent teeth.

Answer: A
Diff: 1   Page Ref: 750

17) Which of the following is not true of saliva?

A) cleanses the mouth

B) contains enzymes that begin the breakdown of proteins

C) moistens food and aids in compacting of the bolus

D) dissolves food chemicals so they can be tasted

Answer: B
Diff: 1   Page Ref: 749

18) The salivary glands are composed of which two types of secretory cells?

A) goblet cells and squamous epithelial cells

B) parietal cells and glial cells

C) serous cells and mucous cells

D) cuboidal epithelium and ciliated columnar cells

Answer: C
Diff: 1   Page Ref: 748

19) The solutes contained in saliva include:

 A) only salts and minerals.

 B) only proteases and amylase.

 C) mucin, lysozyme, electrolytes, salts, and minerals.

 D) electrolytes, digestive enzyme, mucin, lysozyme, wastes, and IgA.

Answer: D
Diff: 1   Page Ref: 749

20) In addition to storage and mechanical breakdown of food, the stomach:

 A) initiates protein digestion and denatures proteins.

 B) is the first site where absorption takes place.

 C) is the only place where fats are completely digested.

 D) is the first site where chemical digestion of starch takes place.

Answer: A
Diff: 1   Page Ref: 759

21) Chyme is created in the:

 A) mouth.   B) stomach.   C) esophagus.   D) small intestine.

Answer: B
Diff: 1   Page Ref: 754

22) Hydrochloric acid is secreted by which of the secretory cells of the stomach?

 A) chief cells   B) parietal cells

 C) serous cells   D) mucous neck cells

Answer: B
Diff: 1   Page Ref: 759

23) Gastrin, histamine, endorphins, serotonin, cholecystokinin, and somatostatin are hormones that are released directly into the lamina propria. Which of the following cell types synthesize and secrete these products?

 A) enteroendocrine cells   B) parietal cells

 C) zymogenic cells   D) mucous neck cells

Answer: A
Diff: 1   Page Ref: 758

24) There are three phases of gastric secretion. The cephalic phase occurs:

 A) before food enters the stomach and is triggered by aroma, sight, or thought.

 B) immediately after food enters the stomach, preparing the small intestine for the influx of a variety of nutrients.

 C) at the end of a large meal, and the juices secreted are powerful and remain in the GI tract for a long period of time.

 D) when the meal is excessively high in acids and neutralization is required.

Answer: A
Diff: 1   Page Ref: 759

25) Peristaltic waves are:

   A) segmental regions of the gastrointestinal tract.

   B) churning movements of the gastrointestinal tract.

   C) pendular movements of the gastrointestinal tract.

   D) waves of muscular contractions that propel contents from one point to another.

   Answer: D
   Diff: 1   Page Ref: 740

26) Gastrin is a digestive hormone that is responsible for the stimulation of acid secretions in the stomach. These secretions are stimulated by the presence of:

   A) starches and complex carbohydrates.   B) protein and peptide fragments.

   C) simple carbohydrates and alcohols.   D) fatty acids.

   Answer: B
   Diff: 1   Page Ref: 761

27) Pepsinogen, a digestive enzyme, is secreted by the:

   A) chief cells of the stomach.   B) parietal cells of the duodenum.

   C) Brunner glands.   D) goblet cells of the small intestine.

   Answer: A
   Diff: 1   Page Ref: 758

28) You have just eaten a meal high in complex carbohydrates. Which of the following enzymes will help to digest the meal?

   A) gastrin   B) amylase   C) cholecystokinin   D) trypsin

   Answer: B
   Diff: 1   Page Ref: 783

29) The ducts that deliver bile and pancreatic juice from the liver and pancreas, respectively, unite to form the:

   A) portal vein.   B) pancreatic acini.

   C) bile canaliculus.   D) hepatopancreatic ampulla.

   Answer: D
   Diff: 1   Page Ref: 764

30) The enzymatic breakdown of any type of food molecule is called _____.

   A) diffusion.   B) active transport.   C) hydrolysis.   D) denatured.

   Answer: C
   Diff: 1   Page Ref: 783

31) Secretin is an enzyme that is liberated by the small intestinal mucosa in response to:

A) acidic chyme entering the small intestine.

B) irritation in the lining of the stomach.

C) distention of the stomach.

D) the enterogastric reflex.

Answer: A
Diff: 1   Page Ref: 762

32) Short-chain triglycerides found in foods such as butterfat molecules in milk are split by a specific enzyme in preparation for absorption. Which of the following enzymes is responsible?

A) rennin   B) pepsin   C) lipase   D) cholecystokinin

Answer: C
Diff: 1   Page Ref: 786

33) Parietal cells of the stomach produce:

A) mucin.   B) pepsinogen.

C) hydrochloric acid.   D) rennin.

Answer: C
Diff: 1   Page Ref: 758

34) Hepatocytes do not:

A) produce digestive enzymes.   B) process nutrients.

C) store fat-soluble vitamins.   D) detoxify.

Answer: A
Diff: 1   Page Ref: 770

35) Which of the following is not a phase of gastric secretion?

A) cephalic   B) gastric   C) intestinal   D) enterogastric

Answer: D
Diff: 1   Page Ref: 759–760

36) Which vitamin requires intrinsic factor in order to be absorbed?

A) B_{12} B) K   C) A   D) C

Answer: A
Diff: 1   Page Ref: 759

37) Zymogenic cells:

A) occur in the intestine.

B) produce HCl.

C) are found in the basalar regions of the gastric glands.

D) produce mucin.

Answer: C
Diff: 1   Page Ref: 758

38) Due to hepatic action, a comparison of blood entering and leaving the liver shows that:

A) blood leaving the liver contains more glucose.

B) blood leaving the liver contains more amino acids.

C) blood leaving the liver usually has more ingested toxic substances.

D) blood leaving the liver via the hepatic vein contains fewer nutrients and waste material than the blood that entered it.

Answer: D
Diff: 1   *Page Ref: 770*

39) The _____ contains lobules with sinusoids (lined with macrophages) that lead to a central venous structure.

A) liver   B) spleen   C) pancreas   D) stomach

Answer: A
Diff: 1   *Page Ref: 770*

40) If an incision has to be made in the small intestine to remove an obstruction, the first layer of tissue to be cut is the:

A) serosa.   B) mucosa.

C) muscularis externa.   D) submucosa.

Answer: A
Diff: 1   *Page Ref: 744*

41) The terminal portion of the small intestine is known as the:

A) duodenum.   B) ileum.

C) jejunum.   D) pyloric sphincter.

Answer: B
Diff: 1   *Page Ref: 764*

42) The dental formula for an adult is 2–1–2–3. What does the 1 stand for?

A) incisor tooth   B) molar tooth   C) premolar tooth   D) canine tooth

Answer: D
Diff: 1   *Page Ref: 750*

43) Digestion of which of the following would be affected the most if the liver were severely damaged?

A) lipids   B) carbohydrates   C) proteins   D) starches

Answer: A
Diff: 1   *Page Ref: 784*

44) _____ is locally regulated in the blood by the active form of vitamin D, which acts as a cofactor.

A) Iron   B) Sodium   C) Phosphorus   D) Calcium

Answer: D
Diff: 1   *Page Ref: 789*

45) As the food in the stomach is repeatedly squeezed and mixed with gastric juice, it is converted into a creamy paste called:

    A) a bolus.   B) chyme.   C) bile.   D) feces.

Answer: B
Diff: 1   *Page Ref: 754*

46) Chemical digestion involves:

    A) enzymatic assembly of monosaccharides into carbohydrates.

    B) anabolic processes.

    C) the addition of water to molecular bonds.

    D) mainly the large intestine.

Answer: C
Diff: 1   *Page Ref: 783*

47) The mechanical process of digestion does not include:

    A) mixing food.   B) segmentation.   C) peristalsis.   D) churning food.

Answer: C
Diff: 1   *Page Ref: 740*

48) Important peritoneal folds do not include the:

    A) omenta.   B) peritoneum.   C) mesentery.   D) round ligament.

Answer: D
Diff: 1   *Page Ref: 742*

49) The lamina propria is composed of:

    A) loose connective tissue.   B) dense irregular connective tissue.

    C) dense regular connective tissue.   D) reticular connective tissue.

Answer: A
Diff: 1   *Page Ref: 743*

50) _____ is/are not important as a stimulus in the gastric phase of gastric secretion.

    A) Distension   B) Carbohydrates   C) Peptides   D) Low acidity

Answer: B
Diff: 1   *Page Ref: 760–761*

51) Pancreatic amylase does not get to the small intestine via the:

    A) accessory pancreatic duct.   B) main pancreatic duct.

    C) cystic duct.   D) hepatopancreatic ampulla.

Answer: C
Diff: 1   *Page Ref: 775*

52) The function of the goblet cells is to:

A) absorb nutrients from digested food and store them for future use.

B) produce mucus that protects parts of the digestive organs from the effects of powerful enzymes needed for food digestion.

C) secrete buffers in order to keep the pH of the digestive tract close to neutral.

D) provide protection against invading bacteria and other disease-causing organisms that enter the digestive tract in food.

Answer: B
Diff: 2   Page Ref: 757

53) Under normal conditions, the gastric mucosa pours out as much as:

A) 10 liters of gastric juice per hour.

B) 1 pint of gastric juice following each meal.

C) 2 to 3 liters of gastric juice per day.

D) 6 liters of gastric juice when the meal is unusually heavy in fats.

Answer: C
Diff: 2   Page Ref: 759

54) Nervous control of gastric secretion is provided by:

A) somatic neurons in the spinal cord.

B) the vagus nerve and enteric plexus.

C) the rubrospinal tracts.

D) the reticulospinal and vestibulospinal tracts.

Answer: B
Diff: 2   Page Ref: 759

55) Which of the following are types of papillae on the tongue that contain taste buds?

A) fungiform and circumvallate   B) palatine and circumvallate
C) circumvallate and filiform   D) fungiform, circumvallate, and filiform

Answer: A
Diff: 2   Page Ref: 747

56) Which of the following produce intrinsic factor?

A) parietal cells   B) zymogenic cells
C) mucous neck cells   D) enteroendocrine cells

Answer: A
Diff: 2   Page Ref: 758

57) Which of the following enzymes is specific for proteins?

A) dextrinase   B) amylase   C) trypsin   D) lipase

Answer: C
Diff: 2   Page Ref: 785

58) Which of the following apply to the small intestine?

    A) Carbohydrates and proteins but not fats are digested.

    B) Most of the water absorption from the digestive tract occurs here.

    C) Foods are acted on for the first time in this organ by protein–splitting enzymes.

    D) It has epiploic appendages attached.

Answer: B
Diff: 2   Page Ref: 764

59) Surgical cutting of the lingual frenulum would occur in which part of the body?

    A) tongue   B) esophagus   C) nasal cavity   D) salivary glands

Answer: A
Diff: 2   Page Ref: 747

60) The site of production of secretin and cholecystokinin is the:

    A) stomach.   B) pancreas.   C) small intestine.   D) large intestine.

Answer: C
Diff: 2   Page Ref: 776

61) A fluid secreted into the small intestine during digestion that contains cholesterol, emulsification agents, and phospholipids is:

    A) bile.   B) pancreatic juice.   C) intestinal juice.   D) gastric juice.

Answer: A
Diff: 2   Page Ref: 772

62) The layer of the digestive tube that contains blood vessels, lymphatic nodes, and a rich supply of elastic fibers is the:

    A) mucosa.   B) submucosa.

    C) muscularis externa.   D) serosa.

Answer: B
Diff: 2   Page Ref: 744

63) When the acid contents of the stomach enter the normally alkaline duodenum, a hormone is released that causes the pancreas to secrete a bicarbonate–rich juice. This hormone is:

    A) gastrin.   B) enterokinase.   C) secretin.   D) cholecystokinin.

Answer: C
Diff: 2   Page Ref: 764

64) Which of the following is not characteristic of the large intestine? It:

    A) does not contain villi.

    B) exhibits external muscular bands called teniae coli.

    C) is longer than the small intestine.

    D) has haustra.

Answer: C
Diff: 2   Page Ref: 778

65) Tooth structure includes:

A) the dentin, which is the hardest substance in the body.

B) a root covered with enamel.

C) a thin periodontal ligament that holds the tooth in place.

D) pulp, an avascular connective tissue filling the hollow cavity of the tooth.

Answer: C
Diff: 2   Page Ref: 750–751

66) The propulsion of food down the gastrointestinal tract includes:

A) The pharyngeal–esophageal phase, an involuntary process.

B) Deglutition, which is the elimination of undigested materials.

C) The buccal phase, an involuntary phase controlled by swallowing centers in the medulla and pons.

D) The gastric phase, activated by distension of the stomach receptors.

Answer: A
Diff: 2   Page Ref: 754

67) Select the correct statement about the regulation of gastric secretion.

A) Vagus stimulation of the stomach results in decreased secretion of gastric juice.

B) The presence of food in the stomach prevents hormonal control of gastric secretion.

C) Gastric secretion can be stimulated before food has entered the mouth.

D) Gastric secretion is enhanced by very low pH (below pH 2).

Answer: C
Diff: 2   Page Ref: 759

68) Select the correct statement about digestive processes.

A) Enterogastrone is a hormone that helps increase gastric motility.

B) Pepsin is an enzyme produced by the stomach for the purpose of starch digestion.

C) Chyme entering the duodenum can decrease gastric motility via the enterogastric reflex.

D) All commonly ingested substances are significantly absorbed by the mucosa of the stomach.

Answer: C
Diff: 2   Page Ref: 761

69) Chemical digestion in the small intestine involves:

A) a significant amount of enzyme secretion by the intestinal mucosa.

B) cholecystokinin (CCK), an intestinal hormone responsible for gallbladder contraction.

C) secretions from the spleen that contain all enzymes necessary for complete digestion.

D) bile salts that help emulsify carbohydrates so that they can be easily digested by enzymatic action.

Answer: B
Diff: 2   Page Ref: 776

70) Select the correct enzyme/substrate combination:

   A) amylase: starches

   B) chymotrypsin: neutral fats

   C) nucleases: proteins

   D) amylase: starches and nucleases: proteins

   Answer: A
   Diff: 2   Page Ref: 783

71) Select the correct statement about absorption:

   A) Eighty percent of ingested materials have been absorbed by the end of the large intestine.

   B) Carbohydrates diffuse across the villus epithelium and are then actively transported into blood capillaries.

   C) If intact proteins are transported across the villus epithelium, an immune response may be generated.

   D) Amino acid transport is linked to chloride transport.

   Answer: C
   Diff: 2   Page Ref: 786–787

72) Select the correct statement about electrolyte absorption:

   A) Chlorine ion absorption is coupled to glucose and amino acid transport.

   B) Potassium moves across the epithelium by active transport.

   C) If vitamin B is not present, calcium is not absorbed.

   D) Iron and calcium is absorbed mostly by the duodenum.

   Answer: D
   Diff: 2   Page Ref: 788

73) You have just eaten french fries, buttered toast, ice cream, and whole milk. Which of the following glands would be active in helping you to digest this food?

   A) the pancreas   B) the buccal glands

   C) the thyroid gland   D) the parotid glands

   Answer: A
   Diff: 3   Page Ref: 775

74) The ingestion of a meal high in fat content would cause which of the following to occur?

   A) Severe indigestion would occur, caused by the lack of sufficient digestive enzymes.

   B) This type of food would cause secretion of gastrin to cease, causing digestive upset.

   C) Bile would be released from the gallbladder to emulsify the fat in the duodenum.

   D) The acid secretions from the stomach would be sufficient to digest this food.

   Answer: C
   Diff: 3   Page Ref: 776

75) The entry of bile and pancreatic juice into the duodenum is controlled by:

   A) sinusoids of the liver.   B) the common pancreatic duct.

   C) the central vein.   D) the sphincter of Oddi.

   Answer: D
   Diff: 3   Page Ref: 764

76) Specific digested foods are able to pass through the cells of the digestive tract and into the bloodstream and the lymphatic system. Accordingly, which of the following molecules are absorbed?

   A) glycerol, glycerides, monosaccharides, amino acids, and fatty acids

   B) peptides, monosaccharides, amino acids, and glycerol

   C) glycerol, glycerides, and fatty acids

   D) monosaccharides, disaccharides, fatty acids, amino acids, glycerides, and dipeptides

   Answer: D
   Diff: 3   Page Ref: 786–788

77) A baby is admitted to the hospital with a history of projectile vomiting after each feeding. On examination, it is found that the sphincter controlling food passage from the stomach to the duodenum is thickened and does not open readily. Because of the baby's loss of gastric juice, his blood probably indicates:

   A) acidosis.   B) ketosis.   C) alkalosis.   D) dysphagia.

   Answer: C
   Diff: 3   Page Ref: 764

78) Nervous control of digestion involves:

   A) the submucosal plexus.   B) the mucosal plexus.

   C) the myenteric plexus.   D) Both A and C are correct.

   Answer: D
   Diff: 3   Page Ref: 741–742

79) Hormones that inhibit gastric secretion include:

   A) seretion.   B) secretin.   C) gastrin.   D) histamine.

   Answer: B
   Diff: 3   Page Ref: 759

Clinical Questions

1) Mrs. Wong goes to the emergency room with the following symptoms: severe pain in the umbilical region, loss of appetite, nausea, and vomiting. While she was waiting to see a doctor, the pain moved to the lower right abdominal quadrant. What is the diagnosis and treatment?

   Answer: The diagnosis is appendicitis. The accepted treatment is immediate surgical removal of the appendix.
   Diff: 4   Page Ref: 778

2) Sami has been hospitalized with acute gastritis. Her symptoms were epigastric pressure (just above the stomach), headache, nausea, and, vomiting. She revealed that she had been suffering back pain and drank four shots of gin and took three aspirin to "kill the pain." What led the physician to make this diagnosis, and what may have caused the sudden attack?

Answer: Gastritis is an inflammation of the mucosal lining of the stomach. The probable reason for the abrupt onset of symptoms is due to rapid and heavy ingestion of alcohol and aspirin. Acute gastritis is often due to chemical irritants, particularly alcohol or salicylate.

Diff: 5   *Page Ref: 758*

3) A woman is brought to an emergency room complaining of severe pain in her left iliac region. She claims previous episodes and says that the condition is worse when she is constipated, and is relieved by defecation. A large, tender mass is palpated in the left iliac fossa and a barium study reveals a large number of diverticula in her descending and sigmoid colon. What are diverticula, and what is believed to promote their formation? Does this woman have diverticulitis or diverticulosis? Explain.

Answer: Diverticula are small herniations of the mucosa through the colon walls, a condition called diverticulosis. They are believed to form when the diet lacks bulk and the volume of residue in the colon is small. The colon narrows contractions of its circular muscles and they become more powerful, increasing the pressure on its walls. Diverticulitis is a condition in which the diverticula become inflamed. This woman has diverticulitis due to the inflammation of her diverticula.

Diff: 5   *Page Ref: 782*

CHAPTER 23   Nutrition, Metabolism, and Body Temperature Regulation

Fill-in-the-Blank/Short Answer Questions

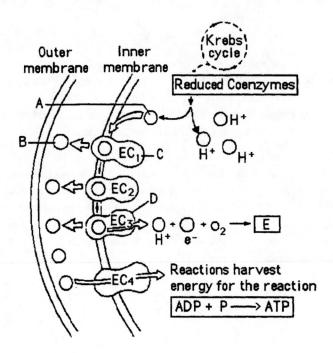

Figure 23.1

Using Figure 23.1, identify the following:

1) H+ ions.

    Answer: B
    Diff: 2   Page Ref: 812

2) Cytochrome oxidase complex.

    Answer: D
    Diff: 2   Page Ref: 812

3) Electron (e−).

    Answer: A
    Diff: 2   Page Ref: 812

4) NADH dehydrogenase complex.

Answer: C
Diff: 2   Page Ref: 812

5) Water.

Answer: E
Diff: 2   Page Ref: 812

Fill in the blank or provide a short answer:

6) The Krebs cycle produces _____ ATP molecules per glucose molecule.

Answer: two
Diff: 1   Page Ref: 810

7) _____ is a urea derivative containing sulfur. It functions as coenzymes for a number of enzymes that catalyze carboxylation/decarboxylation deamination reactions.

Answer: Biotin
Diff: 2   Page Ref: 800

8) Abnormal storage of _____ will cause Wilson's disease.

Answer: copper
Diff: 2   Page Ref: 803

9) Fat burning causes an accumulation of acetyl CoA, which the liver converts to _____.

Answer: ketones
Diff: 2   Page Ref: 817

10) _____ is controlled hyperthermia.

Answer: Fever
Diff: 2   Page Ref: 837

11) _____ cannot be stored; those not used immediately to build proteins are oxidized for energy or converted to carbohydrates or fats.

Answer: Essential amino acids
Diff: 2   Page Ref: 794-795

12) The enzymes that catalyze oxidation-reduction reactions by removing hydrogen are specifically called _____.

Answer: dehydrogenases
Diff: 2   Page Ref: 806

13) The process of splitting glucose through a series of steps that produces two pyruvic acid molecules is called _____.

Answer: glycolysis
Diff: 2   Page Ref: 809

14) In the Krebs cycle, citric acid is followed by _____ acid.

   Answer: isocitric
   Diff: 2   *Page Ref: 811*

15) What are essential amino acids?

   Answer: Essential amino acids are amino acids that cannot be made in the body and must be
           provided by the diet.
   Diff: 2   *Page Ref: 794–795*

16) Where is urea formed, and how is it excreted?

   Answer: Urea is formed in the liver only, but the kidneys are responsible for its excretion.
   Diff: 3   *Page Ref: 827*

17) What are the four mechanisms of heat exchange and how are they defined?

   Answer: (1) Radiation is the loss of heat as thermal energy. (2) Conduction is the transfer of heat
           between objects that are in direct contact with each other. (3) Convection is the process
           of replacing the warm air around the body with cooler air and thus removing body heat.
           (4) Evaporation cools by removing large amounts of heat as water changes state from
           liquid to gas.
   Diff: 3   *Page Ref: 834–835*

18) Define *amino acid pool* and explain how the pool is maintained even though we excrete amino
   acids daily.

   Answer: The amino acid pool consists of the body's total supply of free amino acids needed to
           resynthesize body proteins. Even though a small amount of amino acids and proteins is
           lost daily in urine, these are replaced through diet. If they are not replaced, the amino
           acids resulting from tissue breakdown become a part of the pool.
   Diff: 4   *Page Ref: 820*

19) Hypervitaminosis may have serious consequences. Which vitamin group, water or fat soluble,
   is most likely to be involved in such cases and why?

   Answer: Fat–soluble vitamins are most likely involved in hypervitaminosis, because they are
           stored in the body and excesses are not removed.
   Diff: 4   *Page Ref: 797*

20) How is the postabsorptive state controlled and initiated?

   Answer: The postabsorptive state is controlled by the interaction of the sympathetic nervous
           system and several hormones. The trigger for initiating postabsorptive events is
           damping of insulin release, which occurs as blood glucose levels begin to drop. Insulin
           levels decline, and the insulin–induced cellular responses are inhibited.
   Diff: 5   *Page Ref: 823–827*

21) What is the significance of the fact that monosaccharides are phosphorylated immediately upon entry into cells?

Answer: Monosaccharides are phosphorylated immediately upon entry into cells, so that entry into metabolic pathways is possible. Additionally, phosphorylation, to change the structure of glucose, allows the maintenance of a diffusion gradient for simple glucose. Phosphorylation also prevents glucose from leaving the cell.
Diff: 5   *Page Ref: 805*

22) Explain what happens to pyruvic acid if oxygen is not present in sufficient quantities to support the electron transport system.

Answer: When oxygen is not present in sufficient amounts, the $NADH + H^+$ produced during glycolysis begins to unload its hydrogen "baggage" back onto pyruvic acid, reducing it. This addition of three hydrogen atoms to pyruvic acid results in the production of lactic acid.
Diff: 5   *Page Ref: 810*

23) Define *nitrogen balance*. List three factors that might lead to negative nitrogen balance and three that might result in positive nitrogen balance.

Answer: Nitrogen balance is a state when the amount of nitrogen ingested in proteins equals the amount of nitrogen excreted in urine and feces. Factors leading to negative nitrogen balance, when protein breakdown exceeds the use of protein for building structural or functional molecules, include physical and emotional stress, poor–quality dietary protein, and starvation. Factors leading to positive nitrogen balance, when the rate of protein synthesis is higher than the rate of its breakdown and loss, include the normal condition in growing children and pregnant women, periods of rebuilding or repair following illness, and site-specific regeneration following injury.
Diff: 5   *Page Ref: 794–795*

Matching Questions

Match the following:

1) Column 1: Glucose serves as the initial reactant.

Column 2: Glycolysis

Answer: Glycolysis
Diff: 1   *Page Ref: 815*

2) Column 1: Involves the formation of a 6–carbon molecule and its successive degradation to a 4–carbon pickup molecule.

Column 2: Krebs cycle

Answer: Krebs cycle
Diff: 1   *Page Ref: 810–815*

3) Column 1: Occurs in the cytoplasm of a cell.

   Column 2: Glycolysis

   Answer: Glycolysis
   Diff: 1   *Page Ref: 815*

4) Column 1: Produces ATP.

   Column 2: Glycolysis, Krebs cycle, and electron transport chain

   Foil: Electron transport chain

   Answer: Glycolysis, Krebs cycle, and electron transport chain
   Diff: 1   *Page Ref: 810-815*

5) Column 1: Involves the removal and/or transfer of hydrogen (or electrons) from the substrate molecule.

   Column 2: Glycolysis, Krebs cycle, and electron transport chain

   Answer: Glycolysis, Krebs cycle, and electron transport chain
   Diff: 3   *Page Ref: 810-815*

Match the following:

6) Column 1: A deficiency in iodine would result in _____.

   Column 2: Hypothyroidism

   Answer: Hypothyroidism
   Diff: 1   *Page Ref: 804*

7) Column 1: Inability to excrete excess sodium and/or excessive ingestion of sodium may result in _____.

   Column 2: Hypertension

   Answer: Hypertension
   Diff: 1   *Page Ref: 802*

8) Column 1: A person showing signs of anemia could have a diet low in _____.

   Column 2: Iron

   Answer: Iron
   Diff: 1   *Page Ref: 804*

9) Column 1: A calcium deficiency would result in _____.

Column 2: Osteomalacia, rickets

Answer: Osteomalacia, rickets
Diff: 2   Page Ref: 801

Match the following:

10) Column 1: Night blindness can often be caused by a deficiency in

_____.

Column 2: Vitamin A

Answer: Vitamin A
Diff: 1   Page Ref: 798

11) Column 1: Found abundant in lean meats, liver, fish, leafy green vegetables, and legumes.

Column 2: Vitamin B_1

Answer: Vitamin B_1
Diff: 1   Page Ref: 799

12) Column 1: A condition known as beriberi can result from a deficiency in

_____.

Column 2: Vitamin B_1

Answer: Vitamin B_1
Diff: 2   Page Ref: 799

13) Column 1: A person who required a prolonged clotting time would most likely be deficient in

_____.

Column 2: Vitamin K

Answer: Vitamin K
Diff: 2   Page Ref: 798

14) Column 1: Dermatitis is often a result of a deficiency in _____.

Column 2: Vitamin B_2

Answer: Vitamin B_2
Diff: 2   Page Ref: 799

True/False Questions

1) Beta oxidation is the initial phase of fatty acid oxidation, and it occurs in the cytoplasm.

Answer: FALSE
Diff: 2   Page Ref: 816

2) The increased use of noncarbohydrate molecules to conserve glucose is called glucose sparing.

Answer: TRUE
Diff: 1   Page Ref: 825

3) Except for lactose and some glycogen, the carbohydrates we ingest are mainly from animals.

Answer: FALSE
Diff: 1   Page Ref: 793

4) There are no minimum daily requirements for the ingestion of carbohydrates in order to maintain adequate blood glucose levels.

Answer: FALSE
Diff: 1   Page Ref: 793

5) The term *essential nutrient* refers to the chemicals that can be interconverted in the liver so that the body can maintain life and good health.

Answer: FALSE
Diff: 1   Page Ref: 792

6) It is not possible for the body to convert amino acids so that they can be used as ATP when necessary.

Answer: FALSE
Diff: 1   Page Ref: 819

7) The most abundant dietary lipids in the diets of most Americans are triglycerides.

Answer: TRUE
Diff: 1   Page Ref: 793

8) There are no complete proteins. All animal products should be eaten with plant material to make a complete protein.

Answer: FALSE
Diff: 1   Page Ref: 794

9) The body is considered to be in nitrogen balance when the amount of nitrogen ingested in lipids equals the amount excreted in urine.

Answer: FALSE
Diff: 2   Page Ref: 794

10) The amount of protein needed by each person is determined by the age, size, and metabolic rate of the person.

Answer: TRUE
Diff: 1   Page Ref: 795

11) Vitamins are inorganic compounds that are essential for growth and good health.

Answer: FALSE
Diff: 1   Page Ref: 796

12) Cellular respiration is an anabolic process.

Answer: FALSE
Diff: 1   Page Ref: 805

13) Glycolysis is a series of six chemical steps, all of which take place in the mitochondria.

Answer: FALSE
Diff: 1   Page Ref: 809

14) Glycogenesis begins when glucose entering cells is phosphorylated to glucose-6-phosphate and converted to its isomer, glucose-1-phosphate.

Answer: TRUE
Diff: 1   Page Ref: 815

15) Athletes require diets high in protein and calories in order to perform and to maintain their muscle mass.

Answer: TRUE
Diff: 1   Page Ref: 815

16) In order for amino acids to be oxidized for energy, the amine group (NH_2) must be removed.

Answer: TRUE
Diff: 2   Page Ref: 819

17) The cell gains 34 ATP molecules from aerobic metabolism of one glucose molecule.

Answer: FALSE
Diff: 1   Page Ref: 808

18) The current recommendation is to consume 125 to 175 grams of carbohydrate per day with the emphasis on complex carbohydrates.

Answer: TRUE
Diff: 1   Page Ref: 793

19) Plant products contain the highest quality protein.

Answer: FALSE
Diff: 1   Page Ref: 794

20) The body requires adequate supplies of only three minerals (calcium, sodium, chloride) and trace amounts of all others.

Answer: FALSE
Diff: 1   Page Ref: 797

21) Processes that break down complex molecules into simpler ones are anabolic.

Answer: FALSE
Diff: 1   Page Ref: 805

22) NAD and FAD are two important coenzymes.

Answer: TRUE
Diff: 1   Page Ref: 807

23) All food carbohydrates are eventually transformed to glucose.

Answer: TRUE
Diff: 1   Page Ref: 808

24) Triglycerides and cholesterol do not circulate free in the bloodstream.

Answer: TRUE
Diff: 1   Page Ref: 793

25) The pancreas is the primary source of VLDLs.

Answer: FALSE
Diff: 1   Page Ref: 828

26) Normal body temperature range is 98.6–100 °F, regardless of external temperature.

Answer: FALSE
Diff: 1   Page Ref: 833

27) A deficit of potassium can cause rickets.

Answer: FALSE
Diff: 1   Page Ref: 802

28) Eating a candy bar before an athletic event does more harm than good.

Answer: TRUE
Diff: 1   Page Ref: 815

29) A respirometer is a machine used in hospitals for patients with lower respiratory problems.

Answer: FALSE
Diff: 1   Page Ref: 831

30) It would not be healthy to eliminate all fats from your diet because they serve a useful purpose in maintaining the body.

Answer: TRUE
Diff: 2   Page Ref: 793–794

31) One reason why some lipids are necessary in the diet is that fat–soluble vitamins bind to ingested lipids and are absorbed with other nutrients.

Answer: TRUE
Diff: 2   Page Ref: 797

32) There are 686 kilocalories of energy present in one mole of glucose, and 278 kilocalories of it is captured in the bonds of ATP molecules.

Answer: TRUE
Diff: 2   Page Ref: 814

33) The body's thermoregulatory centers are located in the thalamus.

Answer: FALSE
Diff: 2   Page Ref: 835

34) The greatest amount of ATP energy is generated during the Krebs cycle.

Answer: FALSE
Diff: 2   Page Ref: 814

35) Carbohydrate and fat pools are oxidized directly to produce cellular energy, but amino acid pools must first be converted to a carbohydrate intermediate before being sent through cellular respiration pathways.

Answer: TRUE
Diff: 2   Page Ref: 821

36) High levels of HDLs are considered good.

Answer: TRUE
Diff: 2   Page Ref: 828

37) Diets high in cholesterol and saturated fats tend to have high HDL concentrations.

Answer: FALSE
Diff: 3   Page Ref: 828–829

38) The body's appetite control center is located in several brain areas.

Answer: TRUE
Diff: 3   Page Ref: 830–831

39) In a hot, dry climate, under ordinary conditions, the greatest loss of body heat occurs through evaporation.

Answer: TRUE
Diff: 3   Page Ref: 834

40) The electron transport system includes cytochrome A, FAD, urochrome, and ubiquinine.

Answer: FALSE
Diff: 3   Page Ref: 812–813

Multiple-Choice Questions

1) The molecule that serves as the major source of readily available body fuel is:

A) fat.   B) glucose.   C) acetyl CoA.   D) cellulose.

Answer: B
Diff: 1   Page Ref: 793

2) The peptides, orexins:

A) serve as indicators of the body's total energy stores.

B) are the "set points" which maintain total energy content.

C) are intestinal hormones secreted during food digestion.

D) are powerful appetite enhancers.

Answer: D
Diff: 3   Page Ref: 830

3) Dietary fats are important because:

A) they keep blood pressure normal.

B) they help the body absorb fat-soluble vitamins.

C) they contribute significantly to the health of the skin.

D) they help prevent the common cold.

Answer: B
Diff: 1   Page Ref: 797

4) Cholesterol, while it is not an energy molecule, has importance in the body because:

A) it is a stabilizing component of the plasma membranes and is the parent molecule of steroid hormones.

B) it helps provide essential nutrients to the brain and lungs.

C) it helps mobilize fats during periods of starvation.

D) it enters the glycolytic pathway without being altered.

Answer: A
Diff: 1   Page Ref: 794

5) Which of the following statements best describes *complete protein*?

A) derived from meat and fish only

B) meets all the minimum daily requirements for a sound diet

C) derived from legumes and other plant material

D) must meet all the body's amino acid requirements for maintenance and growth

Answer: D
Diff: 1   Page Ref: 794

6) The term *metabolism* is best defined as:

    A) the length of time it takes to digest and absorb fats.

    B) a measure of carbohydrate utilization.

    C) the number of calories it takes to keep from shivering on a cold day.

    D) the sum of energy produced by all the chemical reactions and mechanical work of the body.

Answer: D
Diff: 1   *Page Ref: 830–831*

7) The term *energy output* includes:

    A) the energy lost as heat.   B) the loss of organic molecules in urine.

    C) the loss of organic molecules in feces.   D) the loss of energy to perspiration.

Answer: A
Diff: 1   *Page Ref: 830*

8) When proteins undergo deamination, a substance found in the urine is:

    A) steroids.   B) ammonia.   C) acetyl CoA.   D) ketone bodies.

Answer: B
Diff: 1   *Page Ref: 819*

9) It is important to ensure that your diet is adequately rich in vitamins because:

    A) vitamins provide protection against the common cold.

    B) very few foods contain vitamins.

    C) most vitamins are coenzymes needed to help the body utilize essential nutrients.

    D) all vitamins are water-soluble and pass out of the body too quickly to ensure utilization.

Answer: C
Diff: 1   *Page Ref: 796*

10) Oxidation-reduction reactions are catalyzed by which of the following enzymes?

    A) dehydrogenases and oxidases   B) kinases and phosphorylases

    C) phosphatases and kinases   D) synthetases and lipases

Answer: A
Diff: 1   *Page Ref: 806*

11) Of all the minerals required by the human body, _____ and _____ account for three-quarters of the total.

    A) zinc; selenium   B) potassium; sodium

    C) sulfur; chlorine   D) calcium; phosphorus

Answer: D
Diff: 1   *Page Ref: 796*

12) A diet rich in minerals would include which of the following foods?

A) fats, sugars, and apples

B) refined cereals, grains, and rye bread

C) legumes, milk, and pork

D) eggs, bacon, and pizza

Answer: C
Diff: 1   *Page Ref: 796*

13) Anabolism includes reactions in which:

A) carbohydrate utilization increases.

B) larger molecules or structures are built from smaller ones.

C) structural proteins are used as a potential energy source.

D) ketone bodies are formed.

Answer: B
Diff: 1   *Page Ref: 805*

14) Catabolism involves processes that:

A) cause a decline in circulating ketone bodies.

B) mobilize fat during the postabsorptive state.

C) break down complex structures to simpler ones.

D) elevate glucagon levels.

Answer: C
Diff: 1   *Page Ref: 805*

15) The primary function of cellular respiration is to:

A) determine the amount of heat needed by the human body.

B) provide the body with adequate amounts of vitamins and minerals.

C) efficiently monitor the energy needs of the body.

D) generate ATP, which traps some of the chemical energy of food molecules in its high–energy bonds.

Answer: D
Diff: 1   *Page Ref: 805*

16) The process of breaking triglycerides down into glycerol and fatty acids is known as:

A) gluconeogenesis.

B) fat utilization.

C) carbohydrate utilization.

D) lipolysis.

Answer: D
Diff: 1   *Page Ref: 817*

17) Which of the following mechanisms yields the most energy that is captured in ATP bonds during cellular respiration?

A) oxidative phosphorylation

B) substrate–level phosphorylation

C) oxidation–reduction reactions

D) oxidation reactions

Answer: A
Diff: 1   *Page Ref: 814*

18) Lipogenesis occurs when:
    A) there is a shortage of fatty acids.
    B) glucose levels drop slightly.
    C) excess proteins are transported through the cell membrane.
    D) cellular ATP and glucose levels are high.

    Answer: D
    Diff: 1   Page Ref: 817

19) Oxidative deamination takes place in the:
    A) liver.   B) muscles.   C) kidneys.   D) blood.

    Answer: A
    Diff: 1   Page Ref: 819

20) Transamination is the process whereby the amine group of an amino acid is:
    A) transferred to acetyl CoA.   B) converted to urea.
    C) transferred to a keto acid.   D) converted to ammonia.

    Answer: C
    Diff: 1   Page Ref: 819

21) Glycogen is formed in the liver during the:
    A) postabsorptive state.   B) absorptive state.
    C) starvation period.   D) period when the metabolic rate is lowest.

    Answer: B
    Diff: 1   Page Ref: 822

22) Which of the following is a normal consequence of the activation of the heat-promoting center?
    A) release of epinephrine   B) shivering
    C) increase in ADH production   D) vasodilation of cutaneous blood vessels

    Answer: B
    Diff: 1   Page Ref: 835

23) Gluconeogenesis is the process in which:
    A) glycogen is broken down to release glucose.
    B) glucose is formed from noncarbohydrate precursors.
    C) glycogen is formed.
    D) glucose is converted into carbon dioxide and water.

    Answer: B
    Diff: 1   Page Ref: 816

24) Deamination is a chemical process in which:

   A) protein is synthesized.

   B) amino acids are buffered in the kidney.

   C) the amine group is removed from the amino acid.

   D) amino acids are broken down for energy.

   Answer: C
   Diff: 1   *Page Ref: 819*

25) Glycolysis is best defined as the:

   A) conversion of glucose into carbon dioxide and water.

   B) conversion of glucose into two molecules of pyruvic acid.

   C) conversion of pyruvic acid into carbon dioxide and water.

   D) formation of sugar.

   Answer: B
   Diff: 1   *Page Ref: 809*

26) Among the conditions required for measuring the basal metabolic rate is:

   A) being in an absorptive state.

   B) remaining in an upright position.

   C) keeping the room temperature between 20 and 25 degrees C.

   D) sleeping.

   Answer: C
   Diff: 1   *Page Ref: 831–832*

27) The primary function of carbohydrates is to:

   A) contribute to cell structure.

   B) maintain a large storehouse of glycogen.

   C) maintain energy production within the cells.

   D) form functional molecules like hemoglobin and cytochromes.

   Answer: C
   Diff: 1   *Page Ref: 793*

28) During normal conditions, proteins are essential to the body for all of the following except:

   A) production of energy.

   B) production of some hormones.

   C) production of enzymes, clotting factors, and antibodies.

   D) formation of functional molecules like hemoglobin and cytochromes.

   Answer: A
   Diff: 1   *Page Ref: 794*

29) During aerobic respiration, electrons are passed down the electron transport chain and
_____ is formed.

A) water   B) oxygen   C) glycogen   D) NADH$_2$

Answer: A
Diff: 1   Page Ref: 812–813

30) If oxygen is lacking, how many net ATP are produced by the catabolism of one molecule of
glucose?

A) 83   B) 28   C) 42   D) 38

Answer: B
Diff: 1   Page Ref: 810–815

31) The most abundant dietary lipids are:

A) cholesterol.   B) phospholipids.   C) fatty acids.   D) neutral fats.

Answer: D
Diff: 1   Page Ref: 793

32) Loss of heat in the form of infrared waves is termed:

A) radiation.   B) convection.   C) conduction.   D) evaporation.

Answer: A
Diff: 1   Page Ref: 834

33) In carbohydrate metabolism, the carbohydrates:

A) are converted into fat if present in excess.

B) such as the monomer galactose are normally used to make ATP.

C) are converted into fructose by the liver before they enter into general circulation.

D) that are highly refined offer many valuable nutrients in addition to calories.

Answer: A
Diff: 1   Page Ref: 815

34) Vitamins are organic compounds. They:

A) are classified as water–soluble or protein–soluble classes.

B) are also called provitamins if used in catalytic reactions.

C) often function as coenzymes to assist in catalysis.

D) may serve as building blocks.

Answer: C
Diff: 1   Page Ref: 796

35) Minerals are substances that cannot be used for fuel. They:

   A) include substances like carbon, hydrogen, and nitrogen.

   B) are the major electrolytes in the blood.

   C) help maintain body heat balance.

   D) help to regulate liver by-products.

Answer: B
Diff: 1   Page Ref: 797

36) As the body progresses from the absorptive to the postabsorptive state, only the _____ continues to burn glucose while every other organ in the body switches to fatty acids.

   A) liver   B) brain   C) pancreas   D) spleen

Answer: B
Diff: 1   Page Ref: 823

37) In gluconeogenesis, amino acids and _____ are converted to glucose.

   A) glycerol   B) glycogen   C) glyceraldehyde   D) glucagon

Answer: A
Diff: 1   Page Ref: 816

38) In the liver, the amine group of glutamic acid is removed as _____ in the oxidative state.

   A) glyceraldehyde   B) pyruvic acid   C) ammonia   D) oxaloacetic acid

Answer: C
Diff: 1   Page Ref: 827

39) Only the _____ forms urea.

   A) kidney   B) pancreas   C) spleen   D) liver

Answer: D
Diff: 1   Page Ref: 827

40) Which of the following is most correct?

   A) Saturated fats stimulate the liver to synthesize cholesterol.

   B) Unsaturated fats are easily oxidized but decrease cholesterol excretion.

   C) Smoking has been implicated in enhanced HDL synthesis.

   D) Excess intracellular cholesterol stimulates cellular production of LDL receptors.

Answer: A
Diff: 1   Page Ref: 828

41) Heat–loss mechanisms do not include:

 A) direct loss by touching a cooler object.

 B) the evaporation of water.

 C) cool air circulating around the body.

 D) vasoconstriction of peripheral blood vessels.

Answer: D
Diff: 1   Page Ref: 836–837

42) The amount of _____ produced is probably the most important factor in determining BMR.

 A) norepinephrine   B) thyroxine   C) prolactin   D) ADH

Answer: B
Diff: 1   Page Ref: 832

43) When ketone bodies are present in the blood and urine in large amounts, it indicates increased metabolism of:

 A) amino acids.   B) fatty acids.   C) glycogen.   D) lactic acid.

Answer: B
Diff: 1   Page Ref: 817

44) Which cells of the body would suffer most if blood glucose levels were to drop drastically?

 A) liver and spleen   B) intestinal and pancreatic

 C) heart and lung   D) brain neurons and red blood cells

Answer: D
Diff: 2   Page Ref: 823

45) Many factors influence BMR. What is the most critical factor?

 A) The way an individual metabolizes fat.

 B) The way skeletal muscles break down glycogen.

 C) The ratio of surface area to volume (weight) of the body.

 D) An individual's body weight.

Answer: C
Diff: 2   Page Ref: 831–832

46) While the amount of protein required in the diet varies depending on age, size, and needs, the daily recommendation is approximately:

 A) 0.4 g/kg body weight.   B) 0.8 g/kg body weight.

 C) 10 g/kg body weight.   D) 13 g/kg body weight.

Answer: B
Diff: 2   Page Ref: 795

47) Which of the following does not occur in the mitochondria?

    A) electron transport

    B) glycolysis

    C) Krebs cycle

    D) formation of malic acid from fumaric acid

Answer: B
Diff: 2   Page Ref: 809

48) Which of the following is not true of beta oxidation?

    A) It occurs in the mitochondrion.

    B) Cleavage occurs at every second carbon.

    C) It involves the anabolism of fats.

    D) It yields acetic acid.

Answer: C
Diff: 2   Page Ref: 816–817

49) Select the correct statement about proteins.

    A) Strict vegetarians need not worry about adequate protein intake, as all vegetables are almost perfect sources of amino acids.

    B) Proteins can be synthesized in the body if most of the amino acids are present.

    C) Proteins will be used for ATP synthesis if insufficient calories are ingested.

    D) Catabolic steroids (hormones) accelerate the rate of protein synthesis.

Answer: C
Diff: 2   Page Ref: 794–796

50) Oxidation reduction reactions:

    A) utilize hydrogenases.

    B) require oxidases.

    C) are rarely coupled together.

    D) occur via the gain of hydrogen or the loss of oxygen.

Answer: B
Diff: 2   Page Ref: 806

51) Vitamin _____ is present in the body as coenzyme FAD and FMN and is a component of amino acid oxidase.

    A) A

    B) D

    C) B_1

    D) B_2

Answer: D
Diff: 2   Page Ref: 799

52) The pickup molecule for the Krebs cycle is _____ acid.

    A) isocitric

    B) fumaric

    C) oxaloacetic

    D) malic

Answer: C
Diff: 2   Page Ref: 810

53) Which of the following is most correct?

   A) Most of the ATP are produced by substrate-level phosphorylation.

   B) Oxidation of FADH$_2$ yields four ATP via oxidative phosphorylation.

   C) Glycolysis relies on substrate-level phosphorylation for the four ATP produced in this pathway.

   D) Most of the ATP are produced directly in the Krebs cycle.

   Answer: B
   Diff: 2   Page Ref: 814

54) Which of the following is most correct?

   A) A 24-carbon fatty acid yields six acetyl CoA molecules.

   B) The total yield from the complete oxidation of a 10-carbon fatty acid would be 60 ATP.

   C) Lipogenesis is triglyceride synthesis.

   D) Lipolysis results in the formation of triglycerides.

   Answer: C
   Diff: 2   Page Ref: 817

55) The term *essential amino acid* refers to those amino acids that:

   A) the body cannot synthesize.   B) contribute to structural proteins.

   C) become part of the metabolic reserves.   D) are stored.

   Answer: A
   Diff: 3   Page Ref: 795

56) Which of the following food groups may be considered complete proteins?

   A) corn, cottonseed oil, soy oil, and wheat germ

   B) lima beans, kidney beans, nuts, and cereals

   C) egg yolk, fish roe, and grains

   D) eggs, milk, yogurt, meat, and fish

   Answer: D
   Diff: 3   Page Ref: 794

57) Conditions that promote the oxidative deamination of amino acids include:

   A) adequate essential amino acids.

   B) adequate fat calories to provide adequate ATP formation.

   C) excessive amounts of protein in the diet.

   D) ammonia combining with oxygen to form urea.

   Answer: C
   Diff: 3   Page Ref: 819

58) When a person's hypothalamic thermostat is set to a higher level and the actual body temperature is below that level, the person may:

A) pant.   B) exhibit vasodilation.

C) perspire heavily.   D) shiver.

Answer: D
Diff: 3   Page Ref: 835

59) Select the correct statement.

A) Anabolism is the process of breaking down large substances into smaller ones.

B) Cellular respiration is a catabolic process.

C) During oxidation reactions, substances gain electrons.

D) During reduction reactions, substances lose electrons.

Answer: B
Diff: 3   Page Ref: 805

60) The liver synthesizes lipoproteins for cholesterol transport. Select the other function(s) of the liver.

A) synthesizes a component essential for blood clotting

B) synthesizes phospholipids

C) uses phospholipids to make bile components

D) synthesizes some vitamins

Answer: A
Diff: 3   Page Ref: 827

61) Insulin is synthesized in the pancreas, and it:

A) inactivates carrier-mediated diffusion of glucose into cells.

B) decreases glucose oxidation so that energy reserves are spared.

C) stimulates the catabolism of fat.

D) stimulates glycogen formation.

Answer: D
Diff: 3   Page Ref: 822–823

62) Glucose can be obtained from:

A) glycogenolysis.   B) fatty acid hydrolysis.

C) protein anabolism.   D) ketogenesis.

Answer: A
Diff: 3   Page Ref: 815

63) Which is not a function of LDLs?

A) transport cholesterol from the peripheral tissues

B) regulate cholesterol synthesis in tissue cells

C) make cholesterol available to tissue cells for membrane or hormone synthesis

D) one form promotes plaque formation in blood vessels

Answer: A
Diff: 3   *Page Ref: 828–829*

64) Which of the following best defines *negative nitrogen balance*?

A) Protein breakdown exceeds protein synthesis.

B) It is a condition caused by having a diet low in fish and meat.

C) A negative nitrogen balance is normal and is a way of maintaining homeostasis.

D) It occurs when amino acids are broken down by liver enzymes and carried to the bloodstream.

Answer: A
Diff: 2   *Page Ref: 795*

Clinical Questions

1) After chopping wood for about 2 hours, on a hot but breezy afternoon, John stumbled into the house and immediately fainted. His T-shirt was wringing wet with perspiration, and his pulse was faint and rapid. Was he suffering from heat stroke or heat exhaustion? Explain your reasoning and note what you should do to help John's recovery.

Answer: John was suffering from heat exhaustion due to excessive loss of body fluids (indicated by his wet T-shirt); his low blood pressure; and cool, clammy skin. To help his recovery, he should be given fluid and electrolyte replacement therapy and should be cooled down.
Diff: 4   *Page Ref: 837*

2) Harry is hospitalized with bacterial pneumonia. When you visit him, his teeth are chattering, his skin is cool and clammy to the touch, and he complains of feeling cold, even though the room is quite warm. Explain his symptoms.

Answer: Harry's symptoms indicate a fever caused by his bacterial pneumonia. The white cells battling the pneumonia release pyrogens that act directly on the hypothalamus, causing its neurons to release prostaglandins. The prostaglandins reset the hypothalamic thermostat to a higher temperature, causing the body to initiate heat-promoting mechanisms. Vasoconstriction causes a decline of heat loss from the body surface, cooling of the skin, and shivering.
Diff: 4   *Page Ref: 837*

3) Hank, a 17–year–old high school student, suffered a heart attack during a recreational swim. An autopsy revealed that he had had atherosclerosis and that his death had been caused by coronary artery disease. What might have been the cause of this disease that usually strikes a person much older than Hank?

Answer: Hank suffered from a genetic disorder known a "familial hypercholesterolemia," a condition in which the LDL receptors are absent or abnormal, the uptake of cholesterol by tissue cells is blocked, and the total concentration of cholesterol and LDLs in the blood is enormously elevated. The victims of the disease usually die in adolescence of coronary artery disease.

Diff: 5   *Page Ref: 828–829*

4) A young athlete on a stringent vitamin regimen is admitted to the hospital with diarrhea, vomiting, bone and joint pain, hyperglycemia and tingling sensations. What is the problem?

Answer: When asked what he had been taking, the athlete confessed that he was taking megadoses of vitamins to "help his body get stronger." Overdoses of vitamins A, D, E, C, B_6, and niacin can have catastrophic and sometimes irreversible consequences.

Diff: 5   *Page Ref: 797*

CHAPTER 24   The Urinary System

Fill–in–the–Blank/Short Answer Questions

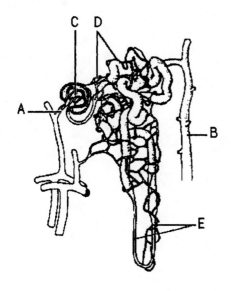

Figure 24.1

Using Figure 24.1, identify the following:

1) Glomerulus.

   Answer: C
   Diff: 1   Page Ref: 846

2) Afferent arteriole.

   Answer: A
   Diff: 1   Page Ref: 846

3) Collecting tubule.

   Answer: B
   Diff: 1   Page Ref: 846

4) Loop of Henle.

   Answer: E
   Diff: 1   Page Ref: 846

5) Peritubular capillary.

   Answer: D
   Diff: 1   Page Ref: 846

6) Site where juxtaglomerular cells are found.

> Answer: A
> *Diff: 1*   *Page Ref: 846*

7) Medulla of the kidney.

> Answer: E
> *Diff: 1*   *Page Ref: 846*

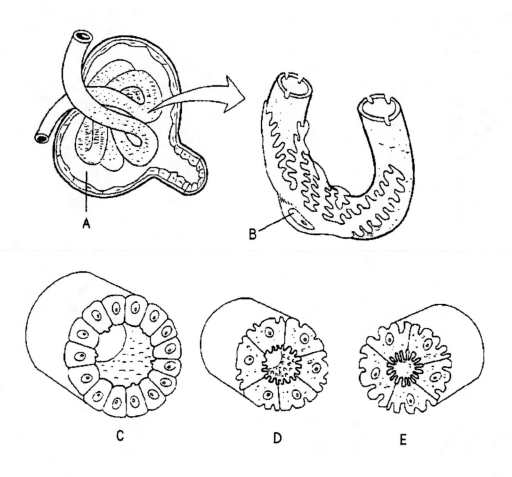

Figure 24.2

Using Figure 24.2, identify the following:

8) Podocyte.

> Answer: B
> *Diff: 1*   *Page Ref: 848*

9) Is composed of simple squamous epithelium.

> Answer: A
> *Diff: 1*   *Page Ref: 844*

10) Collecting duct.

Answer: C
Diff: 1   *Page Ref: 844*

11) Proximal convoluted tubule.

Answer: E
Diff: 1   *Page Ref: 844*

12) Filtrate in this tube is about the same osmolarity as blood plasma.

Answer: E
Diff: 2   *Page Ref: 844*

13) Tube that is the most active in reabsorbing the filtrate.

Answer: E
Diff: 2   *Page Ref: 844*

14) Tube that reabsorbs virtually all the nutrients.

Answer: E
Diff: 2   *Page Ref: 844*

15) Duct that is most affected by ADH.

Answer: C
Diff: 3   *Page Ref: 844*

16) Almost no water is absorbed in this tube.

Answer: D
Diff: 3   *Page Ref: 844*

Fill in the blank or provide a short answer:

17) The capillary bed that surrounds the descending and ascending loop of Henle is called the
_____.

Answer: vasa recta
Diff: 1   *Page Ref: 874*

18) Abnormally low output of urine is called _____.

Answer: anuria
Diff: 1   *Page Ref: 853*

19) Urine crystals in the renal pelvis are called _____.

Answer: renal calculi
Diff: 1   *Page Ref: 865*

20) The areas on either side of the renal pyramids are called the renal _____.

Answer: columns
Diff: 1   Page Ref: 842

21) The area between the ureters and urethra is called the _____ in a bladder.

Answer: trigone
Diff: 1   Page Ref: 865

22) The _____ mechanism is the general tendency of vascular smooth muscle to contract when stretched.

Answer: myogenic
Diff: 2   Page Ref: 851

23) The renal clearance rate equation is RC = _____.

Answer: UV/P
Diff: 2   Page Ref: 863

24) The presence of pus in the urine is a condition called _____.

Answer: pyuria
Diff: 2   Page Ref: 864

25) Sodium–linked water flow across a membrane is called _____ water reabsorption.

Answer: obligatory
Diff: 3   Page Ref: 855

26) Explain the path of the blood vessels in the kidney.

Answer: The renal artery divides into smaller segmental arteries, which in turn branch into lobar arteries. Lobar arteries branch and enter the columns as interlobar, then turn and follow the cortex–medulla boundary as arcuate arteries. Interlubolular arteries travel up into the cortex and branch into afferent arterioles, which enter the Bowman's capsule as glomerular capillaries and exit as efferent arterioles branching further into peritubular capillaries and the vasa recta. These capillaries return via the interlobular, arcuate, interlobar, lobar, segmental, and renal veins.
Diff: 3   Page Ref: 843

27) Explain how filtration works in the glomerular capillaries.

Answer: The glomerular capillaries are fenestrated, allowing fairly large molecules to pass through. The substances must pass through the basement membrane, where they are further selected for size by the filtration slits of the podocytes.
Diff: 3   Page Ref: 849

28) List three substances that are abnormal urinary constituents and provide the proper clinical term for such abnormalities.

Answer: Abnormal urinary constituents include the following (the clinical term for each is listed in parentheses): glucose (glycosuria), proteins (proteinuria or albuminuria), ketone bodies (ketonuria), hemoglobin (hemoglobinuria), bile pigments (bilirubinuria), erythrocytes (hematuria), and leukocytes (pyuria).

Diff: 4   *Page Ref: 864*

29) Explain the role of aldosterone in sodium and water balance.

Answer: Aldosterone targets the distal tubule and collecting duct and enhances sodium-ion reabsorption so that very little leaves the body in urine. Aldosterone also causes increased water reabsorption because, as sodium is reabsorbed, water follows it back into the blood.

Diff: 4   *Page Ref: 857–858*

30) Explain what is meant by the terms *cotransport process* and *transport maximum*.

Answer: Cotransport process refers to the active transport of one solute coupled to the active movement of another during tubular reabsorption. Transport maximum reflects the number of carriers in the renal tubules available to "ferry" a particular substance.

Diff: 4   *Page Ref: 855*

31) Humans can survive for a period of time without water thanks to the ability of the kidneys to produce concentrated urine. Briefly explain what factors allow this to happen.

Answer: Facultative water reabsorption depends on the presence of antidiuretic hormone. In the presence of ADH, the pores of the collecting tubule enlarge and the filtrate loses water by osmosis as it passes through the medullary regions of increasing osmolarity. Consequently, water is conserved and urine becomes concentrated. The water that passes through these regions is reabsorbed by the body in order to prevent dehydration.

Diff: 4   *Page Ref: 861–863*

32) List and describe three pressures operating at the filtration membrane, and explain how each influences net filtration pressure.

Answer: Glomerular hydrostatic pressure (GHP) is the chief force pushing water and solutes across the filtration membrane. The higher the GHP, the more filtrate is pushed across the membrane. Glomerular osmotic pressure of plasma proteins in the glomerular blood, and capsular hydrostatic pressure exerted by fluids in the glomerular capsule, drive fluids back into the glomerular capillaries. The net filtration pressure equals glomerular hydrostatic pressure minus (glomerular osmotic pressure plus capsular hydrostatic pressure).

Diff: 5   *Page Ref: 850*

33) In addition to the renin–angiotensin mechanism, the renal cells produce other chemicals. Name five, and briefly give the main function of each.

Answer: Renal cells also produce chemicals, some of which act locally as signaling molecules. These chemicals include prostaglandins (vasodilators and vasoconstrictors), which probably regulate GFR; endothelium–derived relaxing factor, a potent vasodilator; kallikrein, also a potent vasodilator; adenosine, which constricts renal vasculature; and endothelin, a vasoconstrictor that inhibits renin release.
Diff: 5   Page Ref: 853

Matching Questions

Match the following:

1) Column 1: Proximal convoluted tubule.

Column 2: Site at which most of the tubular reabsorption occurs.

Answer: Site at which most of the tubular reabsorption occurs.
Diff: 1   Page Ref: 845

2) Column 1: Glomerulus.

Column 2: Site of filtrate formation.

Answer: Site of filtrate formation.
Diff: 1   Page Ref: 843

3) Column 1: Peritubular capillaries.

Column 2: Blood supply that directly receives substances from the tubular cells.

Answer: Blood supply that directly receives substances from the tubular cells.
Diff: 2   Page Ref: 845

4) Column 1: Collecting duct.

Column 2: Site that drains the distal convoluted tubule.

Answer: Site that drains the distal convoluted tubule.
Diff: 2   Page Ref: 845

5) Column 1: Arcuate vein.

Column 2: Receives venous blood from the interlobular veins.

Answer: Receives venous blood from the interlobular veins.
Diff: 2   Page Ref: 843

True/False Questions

1) The glomerular filtration rate is approximately 350 ml/min.

Answer: FALSE
Diff: 1   *Page Ref: 850*

2) The outermost portion of the kidney parenchyma is the cortex.

Answer: TRUE
Diff: 1   *Page Ref: 842*

3) The functional unit of the kidney is the renal column.

Answer: FALSE
Diff: 1   *Page Ref: 842*

4) The ureter transports urine from the kidney to the urinary bladder.

Answer: TRUE
Diff: 1   *Page Ref: 864*

5) The terminal portion of the urinary system is the urethra.

Answer: TRUE
Diff: 1   *Page Ref: 867*

6) The position of the kidneys behind the peritoneal lining of the abdominal cavity is described by the term *retroperitoneal*.

Answer: TRUE
Diff: 1   *Page Ref: 840*

7) The entire responsibility for urine formation lies with the nephron.

Answer: TRUE
Diff: 1   *Page Ref: 843*

8) Urine is 95% water by volume.

Answer: TRUE
Diff: 1   *Page Ref: 864*

9) The act of emptying the bladder is called voiding.

Answer: TRUE
Diff: 1   *Page Ref: 867*

10) Glomerular filtration is an ATP–driven process.

Answer: FALSE
Diff: 1   *Page Ref: 850*

11) In the absence of hormones, the distal tubule and collecting ducts are relatively impermeable to water.

Answer: TRUE
Diff: 1   Page Ref: 857

12) The collecting duct is impermeable to water in the presence of ADH.

Answer: FALSE
Diff: 1   Page Ref: 857–858

13) The urethra contains an internal sphincter of smooth muscle.

Answer: TRUE
Diff: 1   Page Ref: 867

14) Angiotensin II is a substance made by the body to lower blood pressure during stress.

Answer: FALSE
Diff: 1   Page Ref: 853

15) Aldosterone is a hormone that causes the renal tubules to reclaim sodium ions from the filtrate.

Answer: TRUE
Diff: 1   Page Ref: 857

16) Blood pressure in the renal glomerulus is lower than in most parts of the body in order to conserve body water.

Answer: FALSE
Diff: 1   Page Ref: 850

17) The proximal convoluted tubule is the portion of the nephron that attaches to the collecting duct.

Answer: FALSE
Diff: 1   Page Ref: 845

18) Major calyces are large branches of the renal column.

Answer: FALSE
Diff: 1   Page Ref: 842–843

19) Urea is reabsorbed in the loop of Henle.

Answer: FALSE
Diff: 1   Page Ref: 855

20) Ureters, like the urethra, are lined with transitional epithelium.

Answer: FALSE
Diff: 1   Page Ref: 865

21) Incontinence is the inability to control voluntary micturition.

Answer: TRUE
Diff: 1   *Page Ref: 869*

22) The myogenic mechanism reflects the tendency of vascular smooth muscle to stretch.

Answer: FALSE
Diff: 2   *Page Ref: 851*

23) An excessive urine output is called anuria.

Answer: FALSE
Diff: 2   *Page Ref: 853*

24) Tubular secretion is effective in controlling blood pH.

Answer: TRUE
Diff: 2   *Page Ref: 858*

25) The main activity in the proximal tubule is secretion.

Answer: FALSE
Diff: 2   *Page Ref: 855*

26) The trigone is so named because of the shape of the urinary bladder.

Answer: FALSE
Diff: 2   *Page Ref: 865*

27) Atrial naturetic factor inhibits sodium reabsorption.

Answer: TRUE
Diff: 2   *Page Ref: 858*

28) Particles smaller than three nanometers are passed into the filtrate.

Answer: TRUE
Diff: 2   *Page Ref: 850*

29) During the micturition reflex, there is increased activity of the sympathetic neurons that control the smooth muscle of the bladder.

Answer: FALSE
Diff: 2   *Page Ref: 867–868*

30) The highest osmotic pressure in the kidney is found in the medulla.

Answer: TRUE
Diff: 2   *Page Ref: 859*

31) Obligatory water reabsorption involves the movement of water along an osmotic gradient.

Answer: TRUE
Diff: 3   *Page Ref: 855*

32) Having a kinked ureter is called ptosis.

Answer: FALSE
Diff: 3   Page Ref: 841

Multiple–Choice Questions

1) Which of the following regions of the nephron is most likely to be found in the renal medulla?
   A) loop of Henle   B) proximal convoluted tubule
   C) distal convoluted tubule   D) glomerulus

   Answer: A
   Diff: 1   Page Ref: 845

2) The mechanism that establishes the medullary osmotic gradient depends most on the permeability properties of the:
   A) loop of Henle.   B) glomerular filtration membrane.
   C) proximal convoluted tubule.   D) distal convoluted tubule.

   Answer: A
   Diff: 1   Page Ref: 859

3) Urine passes through the:
   A) kidney hilus to the bladder to the ureter.
   B) pelvis of the kidney to ureter to bladder to urethra.
   C) glomerulus to ureter to renal tubule.
   D) hilus to urethra to bladder.

   Answer: B
   Diff: 1   Page Ref: 842

4) A Bowman's capsule does not contain:
   A) a podocyte.   B) a vasa recta.
   C) a fenestrated capillary.   D) an efferent arteriole.

   Answer: B
   Diff: 1   Page Ref: 843

5) An increase in the permeability of the cells of the collecting tubule to water is due to:
   A) a decrease in the production of ADH.
   B) an increase in the production of ADH.
   C) an increase in the production of aldosterone.
   D) a decrease in the concentration of the blood plasma.

   Answer: B
   Diff: 1   Page Ref: 856

6) The urinary bladder is composed of _____ epithelium.

A) transitional

B) simple squamous

C) stratified squamous

D) pseudostratified columnar

Answer: A
Diff: 1   Page Ref: 865

7) The kidneys are stimulated to produce renin:

A) when the peritubular capillaries are dilated.

B) when the pH of the urine decreases.

C) by a decrease in the blood pressure.

D) when the specific gravity of urine rises above 1.10.

Answer: C
Diff: 1   Page Ref: 853

8) Blood vessels of the renal columns are called:

A) lobar.   B) segmental.   C) interlobar.   D) interlobular.

Answer: C
Diff: 1   Page Ref: 843

9) Which gland sits atop each kidney?

A) adrenal   B) thymus   C) pituitary   D) pancreas

Answer: A
Diff: 1   Page Ref: 841

10) The _____ artery lies on the boundary between the cortex and medulla of the kidney.

A) lobar   B) arcuate   C) interlobar   D) interlobular

Answer: B
Diff: 1   Page Ref: 843

11) The glomerulus differs from other capillaries in the body in that it:

A) has a basement membrane.

B) is impermeable to most substances.

C) is drained by an efferent arteriole.

D) has a blood pressure much lower than other organ systems.

Answer: C
Diff: 1   Page Ref: 845

12) The descending limb of the loop of Henle:

    A) is not permeable to water.

    B) is freely permeable to sodium and urea.

    C) pulls water by osmosis into the lumen of the tubule.

    D) contains fluid that becomes more concentrated as it moves down into the medulla.

    Answer: D
    Diff: 1   Page Ref: 857

13) Select the correct statement about the ureters.

    A) Ureters contain sphincters at the entrance to the bladder to prevent the backflow of urine.

    B) The epithelium is stratified squamous like the skin, which allows a great deal of stretch.

    C) The ureters are capable of peristalsis like that of the gastrointestinal tract.

    D) The ureter is innervated by parasymphathetic nerve endings only.

    Answer: C
    Diff: 1   Page Ref: 864–865

14) The fatty tissue surrounding the kidneys is important because:

    A) it ensures adequate energy for the adrenal glands to operate efficiently.

    B) it stabilizes the position of the kidneys by holding them in their normal position.

    C) it is necessary as a barrier between the adrenal glands and kidneys.

    D) Actually, it is not important and in fact can be a detriment to the kidneys.

    Answer: B
    Diff: 1   Page Ref: 841

15) The renal corpuscle is made up of:

    A) Bowman's capsule and glomerulus.   B) the descending loop of Henle.

    C) the renal pyramid.   D) the renal papilla.

    Answer: A
    Diff: 1   Page Ref: 843

16) The functional and structural unit of the kidneys is:

    A) the nephron.

    B) the loop of Henle.

    C) Bowman's capsule.

    D) the basement membrane of the capillaries.

    Answer: A
    Diff: 1   Page Ref: 843

17) The juxtaglomerular apparatus is responsible for:

A) the secretion of drugs.

B) the secretion of acids and ammonia.

C) reabsorption of organic molecules, vitamins, and water.

D) regulating the rate of filtrate formation and controlling systemic blood pressure.

Answer: D
Diff: 1   Page Ref: 847–849

18) The chief force pushing water and solutes out of the blood across the filtration membrane is:

A) the design and size of the podocytes.

B) the thickness of the capillary endothelium.

C) glomerular hydrostatic pressure (glomerular blood pressure).

D) the size of the pores in the basement membrane of the capillaries.

Answer: C
Diff: 1   Page Ref: 850

19) Which of the following statements describes the histology of the ureters?

A) They are trilayered (mucosa, muscularis, and adventitia).

B) They are actually an extension of the visceral peritoneum.

C) They are made up of several layers of endothelium.

D) They are made up entirely of muscle tissue because they need to contract in order to transport urine efficiently.

Answer: A
Diff: 1   Page Ref: 865

20) The first major branch of the renal artery is:

A) arcuate.   B) interlobular.   C) segmental.   D) lobular.

Answer: C
Diff: 1   Page Ref: 843

21) Which of the following statements is true regarding the structural differences between the urethras of males and females?

A) The female has a longer urethra.

B) There are no differences; the length of the urethra is always the same in a particular species.

C) The male urethra is about 20 cm long, while the female urethra is 3–4 cm long.

D) The length of the urethra varies among humans; gender makes no difference.

Answer: C
Diff: 1   Page Ref: 867

22) Which of the following acts as the trigger for the initiation of micturition (voiding)?

A) The stretching of the bladder wall serves as the trigger.

B) Motor neurons control micturition.

C) The pressure of the fluid in the bladder opens a sphincter and allows the urine to flow by gravity down the urethra.

D) The sympathetic efferents are the predominant system controlling micturition.

Answer: A
Diff: 1   *Page Ref: 867*

23) The filtration membrane includes all but:

A) glomerular endothelium.   B) podocytes.

C) renal fascia.   D) basement membrane.

Answer: C
Diff: 2   *Page Ref: 849*

24) The mechanism of water reabsorption by the renal tubules is:

A) active transport.   B) osmosis.

C) solvent drag.   D) cotransport with sodium ions.

Answer: B
Diff: 2   *Page Ref: 855*

25) Most electrolyte reabsorption by the renal tubules:

A) is T_m limited.

B) is in the distal convoluted tubule.

C) is hormonally controlled in distal tubule segments.

D) is completed by the time the loop of Henle is reached.

Answer: C
Diff: 2   *Page Ref: 855*

26) The macula densa cells respond to:

A) aldosterone.   B) antidiuretic hormone.

C) changes in pressure in the tubule.   D) changes in osmolarity of the filtrate.

Answer: D
Diff: 2   *Page Ref: 849*

27) Which of the following is not reabsorbed by the proximal convoluted tubule?

A) Na^+ B) K^+ C) glucose   D) creatinine

Answer: D
Diff: 2   *Page Ref: 855–856*

28) The fluid in the glomerular (Bowman's) capsule is similar to plasma except that it does not contain a significant amount of:

A) glucose.   B) hormones.   C) electrolytes.   D) plasma protein.

Answer: D
Diff: 2   Page Ref: 850

29) Alcohol acts as a diuretic because it:

A) is not reabsorbed by the tubule cells.

B) increases the rate of glomerular filtration.

C) increases secretion of ADH.

D) inhibits the release of ADH.

Answer: D
Diff: 2   Page Ref: 863

30) The function of angiotensin II is to:

A) constrict arterioles and increase blood pressure.

B) decrease the production of aldosterone.

C) decrease arterial blood pressure.

D) decease water absorption.

Answer: A
Diff: 2   Page Ref: 853

31) An important characteristic of urine is its specific gravity or density, which is:

A) 1.041–1.073.   B) 1.001–1.035.   C) 1.030–1.040.   D) 1.00–1.015

Answer: B
Diff: 2   Page Ref: 864

32) Place the following in correct sequence from the formation of a drop of urine to its elimination from the body. 1. major calyx 2. minor calyx 3. nephron 4. urethra 5. ureter 6. collecting duct

A) 3, 1, 2, 6, 5, 4   B) 6, 3, 2, 1, 5, 4   C) 2, 1, 3, 6, 5, 4   D) 3, 6, 2, 1, 5, 4

Answer: D
Diff: 2   Page Ref: 842–843

33) Select the correct statement about the nephron.

A) The parietal layer of the glomerular capsule is simple squamous epithelium.

B) The glomerulus is correctly described as the proximal end of the proximal convoluted tubule.

C) Podocytes are the branching epithelial cells that line the tubules of the nephron.

D) Filtration slits are the pores that give fenestrated capillaries their name.

Answer: A
Diff: 2   Page Ref: 843–845

34) What would happen if the capsular hydrostatic pressure were increased above normal?

A) Net filtration would increase above normal.

B) Net filtration would decrease.

C) Filtration would increase in proportion to the increase in capsular pressure.

D) Capsular osmotic pressure would compensate so that their filtration would not change.

Answer: B
Diff: 2   Page Ref: 850

35) Which of the following is not a part of the juxtaglomerular apparatus?

A) JG cells   B) macula densa   C) podocyte cells   D) lacis cells

Answer: C
Diff: 2   Page Ref: 847–849

36) Tubular reabsorption:

A) includes substances such as creatinine.

B) by active mechanisms usually involves movement against an electrical and/or chemical gradient.

C) by passive processes requires ATP to move solutes from the interior of the tubule to the blood.

D) is a way for the body to get rid of unwanted waste.

Answer: B
Diff: 2   Page Ref: 853–858

37) Which statement is true about urine?

A) Urine is usually slightly alkaline.

B) Urine has an ammonialike odor when fresh.

C) Urine has nitrogenous waste such as urea and uric acid.

D) Urine has a yellow color due to the presence of hemoglobin.

Answer: C
Diff: 2   Page Ref: 863–864

38) Reabsorption of high levels of glucose and amino acids in the filtrate is accomplished by:

A) facilitated diffusion.   B) passive transport.

C) countertransport.   D) active transport.

Answer: D
Diff: 2   Page Ref: 855

39) While the kidneys process about 180 L of blood–derived fluids daily, the amount that actually leaves the body is:

A) 50%, or 90 L.   B) all of the 180 L.   C) 1%, or 1.5 L.   D) 100 L.

Answer: C
Diff: 2   Page Ref: 849

40) The factor favoring filtrate formation at the glomerulus is:

A) the colloid osmotic pressure of the blood.   B) the glomerular hydrostatic pressure.

C) the capsular hydrostatic pressure.   D) None of the above are correct.

Answer: B
Diff: 3   Page Ref: 850

41) If the T_m for a particular amino acid is 120 mg/100 ml and the concentration of that amino acid in the blood is 230 mg/100 ml, the amino acid:

A) will be actively secreted into the filtrate.

B) will be completely reabsorbed by the tubule cells.

C) will appear in the urine.

D) Only A and C are correct.

Answer: C
Diff: 3   Page Ref: 855

42) If one says that the clearance value of glucose is zero, what does this mean?

A) No glucose is filtered out of the blood.

B) All of the glucose is filtered out.

C) Normally all the glucose is reabsorbed.

D) The clearance value of glucose is low but small amounts are lost in the urine.

Answer: C
Diff: 3   Page Ref: 863

43) Excretion of dilute urine requires:

A) relative permeability of the distal tubule to water.

B) impermeability of the collecting tubule to water.

C) transport of sodium and chloride ions out of the descending loop of Henle.

D) the presence of ADH.

Answer: B
Diff: 3   Page Ref: 861

44) As the renal artery approaches the kidney, it branches to supply the renal tissue. Place the following in correct sequence starting from the renal artery. 1. segmental 2. interlobular 3. arcuate 4. interlobar

A) 1, 4, 3, 2   B) 3, 1, 4, 2   C) 1, 2, 3, 4   D) 1, 4, 2, 3

Answer: A
Diff: 3   Page Ref: 843

45) In the ascending limb of the loop of Henle:

A) the thin segment is freely permeable to water.

B) the thick segment is permeable to water.

C) the thin segment is not permeable to sodium and chloride.

D) the thick segment moves ions out into interstitial spaces for reabsorption.

Answer: D
Diff: 3   *Page Ref: 857*

46) The disruption in homeostasis known as pyelitis is:

A) a virus that appears only in children because of poor hygiene.

B) the aftermath of a severe upper respiratory infection.

C) an infection of the renal pelvis and calyces.

D) more prevalent in the elderly.

Answer: C
Diff: 3   *Page Ref: 843*

47) Which statement is correct?

A) Reabsorption of water is hormonally controlled.

B) Normal filtrate contains a large amount of protein.

C) Most of the water passing through the kidney is eliminated as urine.

D) The excretion of sodium ions is one of the mechanisms that maintains the pH balance of the blood.

Answer: A
Diff: 3   *Page Ref: 861–862*

Clinical Questions

1) An older man sees his doctor for severe pain in his lower abdominal or flank area, elevated temperature, and nausea. Exhaustive tests rule out abdominal obstructions and infections. X rays indicate a shadow on his right ureter. Diagnose his problem. Give suggested treatment and prognosis.

Answer: The symptoms indicate a kidney stone that has been passed into the ureter. Treatment would be IV therapy to flush the stone out, surgery, or ultrasound waves to shatter the calculi. The prognosis is for complete recovery. There is a possibility of kidney stones forming again.
Diff: 4   *Page Ref: 865*

2) Eleven-year-old Harry is complaining of a severe sore throat and gets to stay home from school. His pediatrician prescribes a course of broad-spectrum antibiotics, and Harry feels much better within a few days. However, some two weeks later, Harry has a dull, bilateral pain in his lower back and his urine is a smoky brown color. On the basis of Harry's signs and symptoms, diagnose his condition and indicate the relationship (if any) between his present condition and his earlier sore throat.

Answer: Harry is showing the symptoms of kidney inflammation. The smoky brown color of the urine indicates the presence of blood or bile. Kidney inflammations usually result from infections either of the lower urinary tract or, in Harry's case, from his earlier infection of a sore throat. The kidney inflammation is called either pyelitis (involves only the renal pelvis and calyces) or pyelonephritis (affects the whole kidney).

Diff: 5   Page Ref: 843

3) Ellen, a 47-year-old woman who has suffered kidney disease for several years, has been diagnosed with proteinuria. Her legs and feet are so swollen that she has difficulty walking. Her hands and her left arm are also swollen. What is proteinuria, and could this condition be playing a role in her swollen limbs?

Answer: Proteinuria is a condition in which the permeability of the glomerular capillaries is increased to such an extent that large amounts of plasma proteins (mostly albumin) pass into the glomerular filtrate and are excreted in the urine. If the condition is severe, the loss of plasma proteins may decrease osmotic pressure substantially. When this happens there is a tendency for fluid to leave the systemic blood vessels and enter the tissue space. This is the reason for Ellen's swollen limbs.

Diff: 5   Page Ref: 864

4) Rachael has been complaining of frequent and burning urination. She also reported seeing some blood in her urine. Her physician suspects cystitis. What is cystitis, and how can it cause these symptoms?

Answer: It is possible that Rachael has cystitis, a condition in which the mucous membrane lining the bladder becomes swollen and bleeding occurs. This condition is caused by bacterial invasion of the bladder or by chemical or mechanical irritation.

Diff: 5   Page Ref: 867

CHAPTER 25   Fluid, Electrolyte, and Acid–Base Balance

Fill-in-the-Blank/Short Answer Questions

Fill in the blank or provide a short answer:

1) _____ occurs when carbon dioxide is eliminated faster than it is produced.

   Answer: Respiratory acidosis
   Diff: 1   Page Ref: 891

2) The female hormone _____ seems to decrease sodium reabsorption, thus promoting sodium and water loss by the kidney.

   Answer: progesterone
   Diff: 1   Page Ref: 882–883

3) Water hydration is also called _____.

   Answer: water intoxication
   Diff: 1   Page Ref: 876

4) The preferred intracellular negative ion is _____.

   Answer: phosphate
   Diff: 1   Page Ref: 872

5) The most important ECF buffer of HCl is _____.

   Answer: sodium bicarbonate
   Diff: 1   Page Ref: 886

6) The most important hormone that regulates calcium ions in the body is _____.

   Answer: PTH
   Diff: 1   Page Ref: 884

7) Molecules that can act reversibly as acids or bases depending upon the pH of their environment are called _____.

   Answer: amphoteric
   Diff: 1   Page Ref: 887

8) The breakdown of phosphorus-containing proteins releases _____ acid.

   Answer: phosphoric
   Diff: 1   Page Ref: 887

9) What provides the shortest term mechanism for preventing acid–base imbalances in the body? The longest term mechanism?

Answer: Chemical buffers act within a fraction of a second to resist a pH change. The longest term mechanism is the kidney system, which ordinarily requires from several hours to a day or more to effect changes in blood pH.
Diff: 1   Page Ref: 885–886

10) Arterial blood pH below 7.35 is called _____.

Answer: acidemia
Diff: 2   Page Ref: 885

11) _____ reduces blood pressure and volume by inhibiting nearly all events that promote vasoconstriction and the retention of sodium ions and water.

Answer: Atrial natriuretic peptide
Diff: 2   Page Ref: 882

12) What is the effect of acidosis on the body? Of alkalosis?

Answer: When the body is in acute acidosis, the nervous system becomes so severely depressed that the person goes into a coma and death soon follows. Alkalosis causes overexcitement of the nervous system. Characteristic signs include muscle tetany, extreme nervousness, and convulsions. Death often results from respiratory arrest.
Diff: 3   Page Ref: 892

13) Describe the mechanisms by which the kidneys remove hydrogen ions from the body.

Answer: Virtually all of the H^+ that leaves the body in urine is secreted into the filtrate. The tubule cells, including collecting ducts, appear to respond directly to the pH of the ECF and to alter their rate of H^+ secretion accordingly. The secreted H^+ ions are obtained from the dissociation of carbonic acid within the tubule cells. For each H^+ ion actively secreted into the tubule lumen, one sodium ion is reabsorbed into the tubule cell from the filtrate, thus maintaining the electrochemical balance.
Diff: 3   Page Ref: 888–889

14) Describe the influence of rising PTH levels on bone, the small intestine, and the kidneys.

Answer: Parathyroid hormone (PTH) activates osteoclasts that break down the bone matrix, resulting in the release of Ca^{+2} and PO_4^{3-} to the blood. PTH enhances intestinal absorption of Ca^{+2} indirectly by stimulating the kidneys to transform vitamin D to its active form, which is a necessary cofactor for calcium absorption by the small intestine. PTH increases the reabsorption of calcium by the renal tubules, which simultaneously decreases phosphate ion reabsorption.
Diff: 3   Page Ref: 884

15) When the blood becomes hypertonic (too many solutes), ADH is released. What is the effect of ADH on the kidney tubules?

Answer: The release of ADH causes the kidney tubules to reabsorb excess water, resulting in the excretion of concentrated urine.
Diff: 3   Page Ref: 880–881

16) Why would an infant with colic be suffering from respiratory alkalosis?

Answer: If the infant is uncomfortable and cries forcefully for long periods of time, this would be similar to hyperventilation. Hyperventilation would cause respiratory alkalosis because the infant is losing carbon dioxide rapidly.
Diff: 3   Page Ref: 891

17) How does the respiratory system influence the buffer system of the body?

Answer: The respiratory system maintains a constant bicarbonate level in the bloodstream by outgassing carbon dioxide. In the event of a respiratory problem the bicarbonate system might not be a constant.
Diff: 3   Page Ref: 887–888

18) Identify and describe the operation of the three major chemical buffers of the body.

Answer: The bicarbonate buffer system (carbonic acid plus sodium bicarbonate) acts to tie up the hydrogen ions released by a strong acid, thus converting it to a weaker acid, which lowers the pH only slightly. For a strong base, the carbonic acid will be forced to donate more H^+ to tie up the OH^- released by the base, with the net result of replacement of a strong base by a weak one. Again the pH rise is very small. The phosphate buffer system, composed of the sodium salts of dihydrogen phosphate and monohydrogen phosphate, acts in a similar fashion to the bicarbonate system. NaH_2PO_4 acts as a weak acid; Na_2HPO_4 acts as a weak base. Hydrogen ions released by strong acids are tied up in weak acids; strong bases are converted to weak bases. Amino acids of the protein buffer system release H^+ when the pH begins to rise by dissociating carboxyl groups, or bind hydrogen ions with amine groups to form NH^{3+} when the pH falls.
Diff: 4   Page Ref: 885–887

19) When does a person experience greater thirst, during periods when ADH release is elicited or during periods when aldosterone release is elicited?

Answer: A person experiences greater thirst during periods when ADH release is elicited.
Diff: 3   Page Ref: 879–882

Matching Questions

Match the following:

1) Column 1: Dissociate in water.

Column 2: Electrolytes

Answer: Electrolytes
Diff: 2   Page Ref: 871

2) Column 1: Will not dissolve in water.

Column 2: Nonelectrolytes

Answer: Nonelectrolytes
Diff: 2   Page Ref: 871

3) Column 1: The compartments outside the
            cell.

   Column 2: Extracellular

   Answer: Extracellular
   Diff: 2   *Page Ref: 871*

4) Column 1: Located within the cell.

   Column 2: Intracellular

   Answer: Intracellular
   Diff: 2   *Page Ref: 871*

5) Column 1: Spaces between cells.

   Column 2: Interstitial

   Answer: Interstitial
   Diff: 2   *Page Ref: 871*

Match the following:

6) Column 1: Magnesium excess.

   Column 2: Hypermagnesemia

   Answer: Hypermagnesemia
   Diff: 1   *Page Ref: 878*

7) Column 1: Calcium depletion.

   Column 2: Hypocalcemia

   Answer: Hypocalcemia
   Diff: 1   *Page Ref: 878*

8) Column 1: Sodium excess.

   Column 2: Hypernatremia

   Answer: Hypernatremia
   Diff: 2   *Page Ref: 878*

9) Column 1: Potassium excess.

   Column 2: Hyperkalemia

   Answer: Hyperkalemia
   Diff: 2   *Page Ref: 878*

10) Column 1: Sodium depletion.

    Column 2: Hyponatremia

    Answer: Hyponatremia
    Diff: 2   *Page Ref: 878*

Match the following:

11) Column 1: An atypical accumulation of
             fluid in the interstitial space.

    Column 2: Edema

    Answer: Edema
    Diff: 2   *Page Ref:* 876

12) Column 1: A condition of unusually low
             levels of plasma proteins
             resulting in tissue edema.

    Column 2: Hypoproteinemia

    Answer: Hypoproteinemia
    Diff: 2   *Page Ref:* 877

13) Column 1: A disorder entailing deficient
             mineralocorticoid hormone
             production by the adrenal
             cortex.

    Column 2: Addison's disease

    Answer: Addison's disease
    Diff: 2   *Page Ref:* 877

14) Column 1: Regulates sodium ion
             concentrations in the
             extracellular fluid.

    Column 2: Aldosterone

    Answer: Aldosterone
    Diff: 2   *Page Ref:* 879

15) Column 1: Special neurons in the
             hypothalamus that sense the
             ECF solute concentration and
             trigger or inhibit ADH release
             from the posterior pituitary
             gland.

    Column 2: Osmoreceptors

    Answer: Osmoreceptors
    Diff: 2   *Page Ref:* 880

Match the electrolyte composition for the following:

16) Column 1: Sodium ions are highest in

             _____.

    Column 2: Blood plasma

    Answer: Blood plasma
    Diff: 1   *Page Ref:* 873

17) Column 1: Potassium ions are highest in
_____.

Column 2: Cellular fluid

Answer: Cellular fluid
Diff: 1   Page Ref: 873

18) Column 1: Phosphate ions are highest in
_____.

Column 2: Cellular fluid

Answer: Cellular fluid
Diff: 1   Page Ref: 873

19) Column 1: Bicarbonate ions are highest
in _____.

Column 2: Interstitial fluid

Answer: Interstitial fluid
Diff: 1   Page Ref: 873

20) Column 1: Proteins are highest in
_____.

Column 2: Cellular fluid

Answer: Cellular fluid
Diff: 1   Page Ref: 873

True/False Questions

1) Adipose tissue is one of the most hydrated of all tissues in the human body.

Answer: FALSE
Diff: 1   Page Ref: 871

2) The most abundant cation in intracellular fluid is sodium.

Answer: FALSE
Diff: 1   Page Ref: 877

3) Electrolytes determine most of the chemical and physical reactions of the body.

Answer: TRUE
Diff: 1   Page Ref: 872

4) Water produced by cellular metabolism is called water of andoven.

Answer: FALSE
Diff: 1   Page Ref: 874

5) The thirst center in the brain is located in the hypothalamus.

Answer: TRUE
Diff: 2   Page Ref: 875

6) Dehydration can be caused by endocrine disturbances such as diabetes mellitus or diabetes insipidus.

Answer: TRUE
Diff: 1   Page Ref: 876

7) It is impossible to overhydrate because people need as much water as they can drink to carry out ordinary body functions.

Answer: FALSE
Diff: 1   Page Ref: 876

8) Water imbalance, in which output exceeds intake, causing an imbalance in body fluids, is termed dehydration.

Answer: TRUE
Diff: 1   Page Ref: 876

9) Salts are lost from the body in perspiration, feces, and urine.

Answer: TRUE
Diff: 1   Page Ref: 877

10) Hypoproteinemia reflects a condition of unusually high levels of plasma proteins and causes tissue edema.

Answer: FALSE
Diff: 2   Page Ref: 877

11) While the sodium content of the body may be altered, its concentration in the ECF remains stable because of immediate adjustments in water volume.

Answer: TRUE
Diff: 1   Page Ref: 879

12) Urinary excretion of large amounts of sodium always results in the excretion of small amounts of water as well.

Answer: FALSE
Diff: 1   Page Ref: 879

13) Sodium is pivotal to fluid and electrolyte balance and to the homeostasis of all body systems.

Answer: TRUE
Diff: 1   Page Ref: 877

14) The single most important electrolyte involved in maintaining water balance through urinary output is sodium.

Answer: TRUE
Diff: 1   Page Ref: 878–880

15) When aldosterone release is inhibited, sodium reabsorption cannot occur beyond the collecting tube.

Answer: FALSE
Diff: 3   Page Ref: 879

16) Aldosterone stimulates the reabsorption of sodium while enhancing potassium secretion.

Answer: TRUE
Diff: 3   Page Ref: 879

17) Aldosterone is secreted in response to low extracellular potassium.

Answer: FALSE
Diff: 3   Page Ref: 879

18) Addison's disease is a disorder resulting from a viral infection.

Answer: FALSE
Diff: 3   Page Ref: 880

19) When a person ingests too much beer, ADH is released, and this is the trigger for eliminating the beer.

Answer: FALSE
Diff: 3   Page Ref: 881

20) Neuromuscular function is influenced by serum levels of sodium.

Answer: FALSE
Diff: 1   Page Ref: 884

21) Atrial natriuretic peptide hormone reduces blood pressure and blood volume by inhibiting nearly all events that promote vasodilation and potassium and water retention.

Answer: FALSE
Diff: 1   Page Ref: 882

22) Premenstrual edema may be due to enhanced reabsorption of sodium chloride.

Answer: TRUE
Diff: 3   Page Ref: 883

23) Heavy consumption of salt substitutes high in potassium can present a serious clinical problem.

Answer: TRUE
Diff: 1   Page Ref: 884

24) Hypercalcemia causes muscle tetany.

Answer: FALSE
Diff: 1   Page Ref: 884

25) Chloride is the major anion accompanying sodium in the ECF.

Answer: TRUE
Diff: 1   *Page Ref: 885*

26) The two hormones responsible for the regulation of calcium are pituitary hormone and calcitonin.

Answer: FALSE
Diff: 1   *Page Ref: 884*

27) Calcitonin targets the bones and causes the release of calcium from storage when serum levels are low.

Answer: FALSE
Diff: 2   *Page Ref: 884*

28) The normal pH of blood is 7.4.

Answer: TRUE
Diff: 1   *Page Ref: 884*

29) Most acidic substances (hydrogen ions) originate as by–products of cellular metabolism.

Answer: TRUE
Diff: 1   *Page Ref: 885*

30) Weak acids are able to act as chemical buffering systems for the body because they partially dissociate.

Answer: TRUE
Diff: 2   *Page Ref: 885*

31) The phosphate buffer system is relatively unimportant for buffering blood plasma.

Answer: TRUE
Diff: 1   *Page Ref: 887*

32) The single most important blood buffer system is the bicarbonate buffer system.

Answer: TRUE
Diff: 1   *Page Ref: 886*

33) Individual molecules that cannot act reversibly as acid–base buffers are called amphoteric.

Answer: FALSE
Diff: 1   *Page Ref: 887*

34) One of the most powerful and plentiful sources of buffers is the protein buffer system.

Answer: TRUE
Diff: 1   *Page Ref: 887*

35) As ventilation increases and more carbon dioxide is removed from the blood, the hydrogen ion concentration of the blood decreases.

Answer: TRUE
Diff: 1   *Page Ref: 888*

36) The respiratory system attempts to compensate for metabolic acid–base imbalances, and the kidneys work to correct imbalances caused by respiratory disease.

Answer: TRUE
Diff: 3   *Page Ref: 888*

37) Regulation of the acid–base system is accomplished mainly through respiratory control, and the kidneys also play a small role.

Answer: FALSE
Diff: 2   *Page Ref: 888*

38) Severe damage to the respiratory system rarely will result in acid–base imbalances.

Answer: FALSE
Diff: 1   *Page Ref: 888*

39) Respiratory acidosis results when lungs are obstructed and gas exchange is inefficient.

Answer: TRUE
Diff: 3   *Page Ref: 888*

40) Prolonged hyperventilation can cause alkalosis.

Answer: TRUE
Diff: 2   *Page Ref: 888*

Multiple-Choice Questions

1) Water occupies two main fluid compartments within the body, the intracellular fluid compartment and the extracellular fluid compartment. Which of the following statements is true concerning the volume of intracellular fluid?

A) All of the water is in the intracellular fluid compartment.

B) Approximately two-thirds of the water is in the intracellular fluid compartment.

C) The intracellular fluid compartment changes, so it is impossible to determine the amount of water at any given time.

D) Approximately one-third of the water is in the intracellular fluid compartment.

Answer: B
Diff: 1   *Page Ref: 871*

2) The term *water intoxication* refers to:

   A) the feeling one might have after a long swim.

   B) the unpleasant feeling people have after drinking too much liquor.

   C) a condition that may result from renal insufficiency or drinking extraordinary amounts of water.

   D) a condition that is caused by high levels of sodium in the extracellular fluid compartment.

   Answer: C
   Diff: 1   *Page Ref: 876*

3) Hypoproteinemia is a condition of unusually low levels of plasma proteins. This problem is often characterized by:

   A) tissue edema.   B) extreme weight loss.

   C) extreme weight gain.   D) nerve damage.

   Answer: A
   Diff: 1   *Page Ref: 877*

4) Which of the following hormones is important in the regulation of sodium ion concentrations in the extracellular fluid?

   A) antidiuretic hormone   B) erythropoietin

   C) aldosterone   D) renin

   Answer: C
   Diff: 1   *Page Ref: 879*

5) Atrial natriuretic peptide is a hormone that is made in the atria of the heart. The influence of this hormone is:

   A) to enhance atrial contractions.

   B) to activate the renin–angiotensin mechanism.

   C) to prevent pH changes caused by organic acids.

   D) to reduce blood pressure and blood volume by inhibiting sodium and water retention.

   Answer: D
   Diff: 1   *Page Ref: 882*

6) Respiratory acidosis can occur when:

   A) a person consumes excessive amounts of antacids.

   B) a person's breathing is shallow due to obstruction.

   C) a runner has completed a very long marathon.

   D) the kidneys secrete hydrogen ions.

   Answer: B
   Diff: 1   *Page Ref: 888*

7) Which of the following two organs function as the most important physiological buffer systems?

A) the lungs and the kidneys

B) the adrenal glands and the testes

C) the thyroid gland and the heart

D) the stomach and the liver

Answer: A
Diff: 1   *Page Ref: 887–888*

8) Edema may result from:

A) hyperproteinemia.

B) hindering the flow of water out of the capillaries.

C) decreased blood hydrostatic pressure.

D) lymphatic blockage.

Answer: D
Diff: 1   *Page Ref: 876–877*

9) The dangerous water imbalance condition signaled by hyponatremia, nausea and vomiting, muscular cramping, and cerebral edema, ultimately leading to coma, is:

A) water intoxication.

B) dehydration.

C) oliguria.

D) edema.

Answer: A
Diff: 1   *Page Ref: 876*

10) The fluid link between the external and internal environment is:

A) plasma.

B) intracellular fluid.

C) interstitial fluid.

D) cerebrospinal fluid.

Answer: A
Diff: 1   *Page Ref: 872–873*

11) Whereas sodium is found mainly in the extracellular fluid, most _____ is found in the intracellular fluid.

A) iron   B) chloride   C) potassium   D) magnesium

Answer: C
Diff: 1   *Page Ref: 873*

12) Which of the following describes the distribution of sodium and potassium between cells and body fluids?

A) K^+ mainly in the cells, Na^+ in the body fluids

B) Na^+ mainly in the cells, K^+ in the body fluids

C) equal amounts of each ion in the cells and body fluids

D) little of either in the cells, but large amounts of each in the body fluids

Answer: A
Diff: 1   *Page Ref: 873*

13) The single most important factor influencing potassium ion secretion is:

    A) the potassium ion content in the renal tubule cells.

    B) pH of the ICF.

    C) intracellular sodium levels.

    D) potassium ion concentration in blood plasma.

    Answer: D
    Diff: 1   Page Ref: 883

14) The term *alkaline reserve* is used to describe the _____ buffer system.

    A) phosphate   B) hemoglobin   C) bicarbonate   D) protein

    Answer: C
    Diff: 1   Page Ref: 886

15) A falling blood pH and a rising partial pressure of carbon dioxide, occurring due to pneumonia or emphysema, indicates:

    A) respiratory acidosis.   B) respiratory alkalosis.

    C) metabolic acidosis.   D) metabolic alkalosis.

    Answer: A
    Diff: 1   Page Ref: 891

16) The movement of fluids between cellular compartments:

    A) requires active transport.

    B) is regulated by osmotic and hydrostatic forces.

    C) requires ATP for the transport to take place.

    D) involves filtration.

    Answer: B
    Diff: 1   Page Ref: 872

17) Electrolyte balance:

    A) refers to the phosphate balance in the body.

    B) may be disturbed due to higher loss of electrolytes on hot days.

    C) is usually difficult to maintain.

    D) can be disrupted because water is not free to move between cells and capillaries.

    Answer: B
    Diff: 1   Page Ref: 877–879

18) Parathyroid hormone:

    A) is the most important control of calcium homeostasis.

    B) activates osteoblasts that deposit ionic calcium in bone.

    C) prevents excess calcium absorption by deactivating vitamin D in the small intestine.

    D) decreases renal absorption while simultaneously increasing phosphate reabsorption.

    Answer: A
    Diff: 1   Page Ref: 884

19) Chemical buffering systems of the body may include:

   A) phosphate.   B) ammonia.

   C) hydrochloric acid.   D) sodium hydroxide.

   Answer: A
   Diff: 1   Page Ref: 885–887

20) Extracellular fluid in the human body is composed of:

   A) lymph and interstitial fluid.   B) blood plasma.

   C) cerebrospinal fluid.   D) All of the above are correct.

   Answer: D
   Diff: 2   Page Ref: 871

21) Which of the following statements is true regarding fluid shifts?

   A) Nonelectrolytes are the controlling factor in directing fluid shifts.

   B) Electrolytes are not as important as proteins in regulating fluid shifts in the body.

   C) Electrolytes have greater osmotic power than nonelectrolytes and therefore have the greatest ability to cause fluid shifts.

   D) There are always more positive electrolytes than negative in a solution; it is therefore impossible to follow fluid shifts.

   Answer: C
   Diff: 2   Page Ref: 872–874

22) Which of the following hormones is important in stimulating water conservation in the kidneys?

   A) aldosterone   B) thymosin

   C) antidiuretic hormone   D) atrial natriuretic peptide

   Answer: C
   Diff: 2   Page Ref: 880

23) When the pH of the body fluids changes significantly, which of the following compensates for the change?

   A) maintaining a constant breathing rate.

   B) the carbonic acid–bicarbonate buffer system.

   C) buffers of extracellular proteins.

   D) phosphate buffer system.

   Answer: B
   Diff: 2   Page Ref: 887

24) The result of drastic shifts in the blood pH is:

A) that death can occur because the absolute blood pH limits for life are narrow.

B) that nothing happens because the body will compensate.

C) metabolic alkalosis.

D) metabolic acidosis.

Answer: A
Diff: 2   Page Ref: 885, 892

25) The total body water is divided into intracellular and extracellular fluids. Plasma is considered:

A) extracellular.   B) intracellular.   C) interstitial.   D) lymph.

Answer: A
Diff: 2   Page Ref: 871

26) The maintenance of the proper pH of the body fluids may be the result of:

A) the control of respiratory ventilation.

B) the operation of the various buffer systems in the stomach.

C) the active secretion of OH⁻ into the filtrate by the kidney tubule cells.

D) control of the acids produced in the stomach.

Answer: A
Diff: 2   Page Ref: 887

27) Disorders of water balance include:

A) excessive water loss due to excess ADH secretion.

B) hypotonic hydration, in which sodium content is normal but water content is high.

C) edema or tissue swelling, which is usually due to a decreased capillary hydrostatic pressure.

D) excess water in interstitial spaces due to a low level of plasma proteins.

Answer: C
Diff: 2   Page Ref: 876–877

28) The regulation of sodium:

A) is due to specific sodium receptors in the hypothalamus.

B) is linked to blood pressure.

C) involves aldosterone, a hormone that increases sodium excretion in the kidneys.

D) involves hypothalamic osmoreceptor detection of ion concentration.

Answer: C
Diff: 2   Page Ref: 879

29) Select the correct statement about renal mechanisms of acid–base balance.

   A) The kidneys are not able to excrete phosphoric acid.

   B) Excreted hydrogen ions are unbound in the filtrate.

   C) Kidney tubule cells are able to synthesize bicarbonate ion.

   D) The kidneys are the most important mechanism for eliminating all bicarbonate ions.

   Answer: C
   Diff: 2   *Page Ref: 888–891*

30) Blood analysis indicates a low pH, and the patient is breathing rapidly. Given your knowledge of acid–base balance, which of the following is most likely?

   A) respiratory acidosis   B) metabolic acidosis

   C) metabolic alkalosis   D) respiratory alkalosis

   Answer: B
   Diff: 2   *Page Ref: 892*

31) A patient is breathing slowly and blood pH analysis indicates an abnormally high value. What is the likely diagnosis?

   A) respiratory acidosis   B) metabolic acidosis

   C) metabolic alkalosis   D) respiratory alkalosis

   Answer: C
   Diff: 2   *Page Ref: 892*

32) One of the major physiological factors that triggers thirst is:

   A) a dry mouth from high temperatures.   B) becoming overly agitated.

   C) drinking caffeinated beverages.   D) a rise in plasma osmolarity.

   Answer: D
   Diff: 3   *Page Ref: 875*

33) Annie has just eaten a large order of heavily salted french fries, some pickled eggs, and some cheese. How will consuming this much salt affect her physiology?

   A) It will increase the osmolarity of the blood.

   B) There will be a temporary increase in blood volume.

   C) She will experience hypotension.

   D) There will be a shift in the pH of her body fluids to the higher side of the pH scale.

   Answer: B
   Diff: 3   *Page Ref: 879*

34) The most important force causing net water flow across capillary walls is:

   A) osmotic pressure of plasma proteins.   B) hydrostatic pressure of capillary blood.

   C) hydrostatic pressure of interstitial fluid.   D) intracellular hydrostatic pressure.

   Answer: B
   Diff: 3   *Page Ref: 872–873*

35) Assume a condition of metabolic acidosis. Which of the following is true?

  A) Bicarbonate levels in the plasma are low.

  B) The kidneys are reabsorbing bicarbonate at a rapid pace.

  C) The kidneys are adding new bicarbonate ions to the blood to bolster the alkaline reserve.

  D) Both A and C are correct.

  Answer: D
  Diff: 3   *Page Ref: 891–892*

36) Which of the following depend(s) on the presence of electrolytes?

  A) membrane polarity

  B) neuromuscular excitability

  C) maintenance of osmotic relations between cells and ECF

  D) All of the above are correct.

  Answer: D
  Diff: 3   *Page Ref: 877*

37) The regulation of potassium balance:

  A) is not linked to sodium balance.

  B) includes renal secretion, but never absorption.

  C) is accomplished mainly by hepatic mechanisms.

  D) involves aldosterone–induced secretion of potassium.

  Answer: D
  Diff: 3   *Page Ref: 883–884*

38) The respiratory mechanism of acid–base balance:

  A) requires an enzyme within red blood cells that causes the formation of carbonic acid.

  B) includes an increased breathing rate during times of alkalosis.

  C) operates well only within a very narrow margin.

  D) is considered a chemical buffering system.

  Answer: A
  Diff: 3   *Page Ref: 887–888*

Clinical Questions

1) A person is admitted to the hospital in complete collapse. His blood pH is 6.8, and his HCO_3^- is 20 mEq/L. What diagnosis would you give and what prognosis? A medical history reveals that this person is a chronic alcoholic.

  Answer: The pH and bicarbonate levels and the history of alcoholism indicate metabolic acidosis. With a pH below 7.0, the person will go into a coma and death soon follows.
  Diff: 5   *Page Ref: 892*

2) A pregnant woman complains to her doctor that her ankles and feet stay swollen all of the time. She is very worried about this. As her doctor, what would you tell her?

Answer: She is showing edema, an atypical accumulation of fluid in the spaces between cells (interstitial spaces). This is caused by her pregnancy due to a high blood volume that increases capillary hydrostatic pressure and enhances capillary permeability. She should be monitored for the edema during the pregnancy, but it should clear up at the end of the pregnancy.

Diff: 5   *Page Ref: 876*

3) Helen is a 62-year-old smoker. Her physician has diagnosed her as having emphysema that has caused her to hypoventilate. She is tired and sedentary. Besides having difficulty breathing, what other condition is contributing to her tiredness?

Answer: Helen is suffering from respiratory acidosis because she is retaining too much carbon dioxide. Her shallow breathing, due to the damage to her lungs from the disease, is the cause. In order to release the carbon dioxide, one must be able to breathe normally (deep breathing would be optimal).

Diff: 5   *Page Ref: 891*

4) Recently Alex's family noticed that he is craving salt to the point where he uses it excessively on his food. He also has had a need to consume strange substances such as clay and burnt match tips. What might be the cause of this strange behavior?

Answer: Alex may be suffering from Addison's disease, a disorder entailing deficient mineralocorticoid hormone production by the adrenal cortex. Sometimes when the necessary electrolytes are deficient, people crave strange substances such as chalk, clay, starch, or burnt match tips. This unusual habit is called pica.

Diff: 5   *Page Ref: 877*

5) After traveling from Los Angeles to Denver, Claire finds she is not feeling well and checks into a clinic for help. The clinic's diagnosis is respiratory alkalosis. What has caused this problem?

Answer: Respiratory alkalosis is always caused by hyperventilation. Claire is experiencing the effect of the high altitude and was overcompensating or trying to do too much the first day in Denver.

Diff: 5   *Page Ref: 891*

CHAPTER 26   The Reproductive System

Fill-in-the-Blank/Short Answer Questions

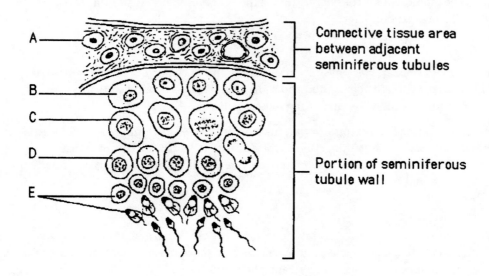

Figure 26.1

Use Figure 26.1 to identify the following:

1) Stem cell.

   Answer: A
   Diff: 2   Page Ref: 905

2) First cells with *n* number of chromosomes.

   Answer: D
   Diff: 2   Page Ref: 905

3) Early spermatids.

   Answer: E
   Diff: 2   Page Ref: 905

4) Only cell not meiotically active.

   Answer: A
   Diff: 2   Page Ref: 905

5) Primary spermatocyte.

   Answer: C
   Diff: 2   Page Ref: 905

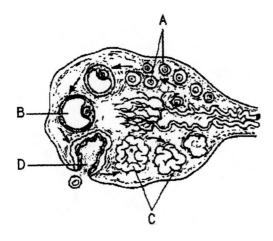

Figure 26.2

Use Figure 26.2 to identify the following:

6) Graafian follicle.

   Answer: B
   Diff: 1   *Page Ref: 910*

7) The stage called ovulation.

   Answer: D
   Diff: 1   *Page Ref: 910*

8) Primary follicles.

   Answer: A
   Diff: 1   *Page Ref: 910*

9) Corpus luteum.

   Answer: C
   Diff: 1   *Page Ref: 910*

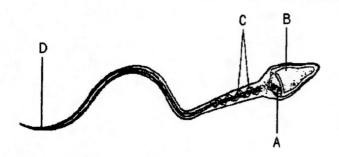

Figure 26.3

Use Figure 26.3 to identify the following:

10) Acrosome.

Answer: B
Diff: 1   *Page Ref: 906*

11) Mitochondria.

Answer: C
Diff: 1   *Page Ref: 906*

12) Midpiece.

Answer: C
Diff: 1   *Page Ref: 906*

13) Area of compacted DNA.

Answer: A
Diff: 1   *Page Ref: 906*

14) Nucleus.

Answer: A
Diff: 1   *Page Ref: 906*

Fill in the blank or provide a short answer:

15) The _____ plexus of testicular veins assists in cooling the testis.

Answer: pampiniform
Diff: 1   *Page Ref: 897*

16) Surgical cutting of the ductus deferens as a form of birth control is called a _____.

Answer: vasectomy
Diff: 1   *Page Ref: 898*

17) The erectile tissue around the urethra is the corpus _____.

Answer: spongiosum
Diff: 1   Page Ref: 898

18) The midpiece of the sperm tail contains mostly _____.

Answer: mitochondria
Diff: 1   Page Ref: 906

19) The _____ cell of the testis nourishes the newly formed sperm cells.

Answer: sustentacular
Diff: 1   Page Ref: 906

20) The suspensory and mesovarium ligaments are part of the _____ ligament.

Answer: broad
Diff: 1   Page Ref: 910

21) A follicle with only small antrums in it would be classified as a _____ follicle.

Answer: secondary
Diff: 1   Page Ref: 919–920

22) The small opening of the uterus that sperm would first enter is called the _____.

Answer: external os
Diff: 1   Page Ref: 912–913

23) The portion of the uterine endometrium that is not sloughed off every month is called the _____.

Answer: stratum basalis
Diff: 1   Page Ref: 913

24) _____ is caused by *Treponema pallidum.*

Answer: Syphilis
Diff: 2   Page Ref: 926

25) What are some risk factors for developing breast cancer?

Answer: Some of the risk factors for developing breast cancer are: (1) early onset of menses and late menopause; (2) first pregnancy late in life or no pregnancies at all; (3) repeated X rays without proper protection against radiation; (4) cigarette smoking and excessive use of alcohol; (5) a high–fat diet; (6) advanced age; (7) familial history of breast cancer and other cancer histories.
Diff: 2   Page Ref: 916–917

26) What is the name given to the female homologue to the penis?

Answer: The female clitoris is homologous to the glans penis of the male. It is homologous in that it contains dorsal erectile columns and can become swollen with blood during tactile stimulation.
Diff: 2   Page Ref: 915

27) Describe the composition and functional roles of semen.

Answer: Semen is a fluid mixture of sperm and accessory gland secretions (prostate, seminal vesicles, and bulbourethral). The liquid provides a transport medium for nutrients and contains chemicals that protect the sperm and facilitate their movements.
Diff: 2   Page Ref: 900

28) Explain the function of the myometrium and endometrium.

Answer: The myometrium plays an active role during childbirth when it contracts rhythmically to force the baby out of the mother's body. The endometrium is the innermost lining of the uterus where the young embryo implants and stays for the rest of its development.
Diff: 2   Page Ref: 913

29) What is the purpose of the male bulbourethral gland?

Answer: Since it releases its contents prior to ejaculation, its function is probably to neutralize the acids in the vagina.
Diff: 2   Page Ref: 900

30) What is the physiological importance of the fact that the male testes descend to reside in the scrotal sac?

Answer: The male testes descend into the scrotal sac so that a fairly constant intrascrotal temperature is maintained. Failure of the testes to descend results in sterility, because production of viable spermatozoa requires a temperature several degrees lower than normal body temperature.
Diff: 3   Page Ref: 896

31) Ovulation occurs when the oocyte is released into the peritoneal cavity. By what means does it usually enter the fallopian tube?

Answer: Fimbriae, that drape over the ovary, become very active close to the time of ovulation and undulate to create currents in the peritoneal fluid. These currents usually carry the oocyte to the uterine tube, where it begins its journey toward the uterus.
Diff: 3   Page Ref: 911

32) Assume that a woman could be an "on-demand" ovulator like a rabbit, in which copulation stimulates the hypothalamic-AP axis and causes LH release and an oocyte was ovulated and fertilized on day 26 of her 28-day cycle. Why would a successful pregnancy be unlikely at this time?

Answer: A successful pregnancy would be unlikely at this time because progesterone levels have fallen, depriving the endometrium of hormonal support. The endometrial cells begin to die and the integrity of the uterus is compromised. The fertilized egg would not be able to implant in the wall.
Diff: 3   Page Ref: 922

Matching Questions

Match the following:

1) Column 1: Where the fetus develops and
grows.

   Column 2: Uterus

   Answer: Uterus
   Diff: 1   Page Ref: 911

2) Column 1: External sac enclosing the
testes.

   Column 2: Scrotum

   Answer: Scrotum
   Diff: 1   Page Ref: 896

3) Column 1: The release of oocyte from
ovary.

   Column 2: Ovulation

   Answer: Ovulation
   Diff: 1   Page Ref: 920

4) Column 1: Erectile tissue in the male.

   Column 2: Corpora cavernosa

   Answer: Corpora cavernosa
   Diff: 1   Page Ref: 898

5) Column 1: Female homologue of the
scrotum.

   Column 2: Labia majora

   Answer: Labia majora
   Diff: 2   Page Ref: 915

Match the following:

6) Column 1: Urethritis in males.

   Column 2: Gonorrhea

   Answer: Gonorrhea
   Diff: 2   Page Ref: 926

7) Column 1: *Treponema pallidum.*

   Column 2: Syphilis

   Answer: Syphilis
   Diff: 2   Page Ref: 926–927

8) Column 1: Human *papillomavirus*.

   Column 2: Genital warts

   Answer: Genital warts
   Diff: 2   *Page Ref: 927*

9) Column 1: Epstein–Barr virus.

   Column 2: Genital herpes

   Answer: Genital herpes
   Diff: 2   *Page Ref: 927*

10) Column 1: Organism responsible for approximately half of the diagnosed cases of pelvic inflammatory disease.

    Column 2: Chlamydia

    Answer: Chlamydia
    Diff: 2   *Page Ref: 927*

True/False Questions

1) The Leydig cells produce androgens (most importantly, testosterone), which are secreted into the surrounding interstitial fluid.

   Answer: TRUE
   Diff: 1   *Page Ref: 897*

2) It is necessary for the testes to be kept below body temperature.

   Answer: TRUE
   Diff: 1   *Page Ref: 896*

3) The hormone oxytocin combines with enzymes in semen to enhance sperm motility.

   Answer: FALSE
   Diff: 1   *Page Ref: 900*

4) When a couple is having difficulty conceiving a child, it is necessary to investigate the sperm of the male.

   Answer: TRUE
   Diff: 1   *Page Ref: 907*

5) The amount of testosterone and sperm produced by the testes is dependent on the influence of FSH alone.

   Answer: TRUE
   Diff: 1   *Page Ref: 907*

6) Ovarian follicles contain mature eggs.

Answer: FALSE
Diff: 1   *Page Ref: 910*

7) Sexually transmitted diseases are the most important cause of reproductive disorders.

Answer: TRUE
Diff: 1   *Page Ref: 926–927*

8) Reproduction is not possible in males or females until one year after puberty has begun.

Answer: FALSE
Diff: 1   *Page Ref: 920*

9) Pain during ovulation is called dysmenorrhea.

Answer: FALSE
Diff: 1   *Page Ref: 920*

10) A human egg or sperm contains 23 pairs of chromosomes.

Answer: TRUE
Diff: 1   *Page Ref: 901*

11) The Pap smear is a test to detect cancerous changes in cells of the cervix.

Answer: TRUE
Diff: 1   *Page Ref: 913*

12) The adenohypophyseal hormone that triggers ovulation is estrogen.

Answer: FALSE
Diff: 1   *Page Ref: 920*

13) The female hormone corresponding to the male ICSH is FSH.

Answer: FALSE
Diff: 1   *Page Ref: 907*

14) The male urethra serves the urinary system only.

Answer: FALSE
Diff: 1   *Page Ref: 899*

15) Both tetrads and crossovers are seen during meiosis.

Answer: TRUE
Diff: 1   *Page Ref: 904*

16) Failure to attain erection is called impotence.

Answer: TRUE
Diff: 1   *Page Ref: 900*

17) Ovulation occurs near the end of the ovarian cycle.

Answer: FALSE
Diff: 1   *Page Ref: 920*

18) The corpus luteum secretes progesterone only.

Answer: FALSE
Diff: 1   *Page Ref: 920*

19) Female orgasm is required for conception.

Answer: FALSE
Diff: 1   *Page Ref: 926*

20) The first sign of puberty in females is budding breasts.

Answer: TRUE
Diff: 1   *Page Ref: 920*

21) The primary function of the testes is to produce testosterone.

Answer: FALSE
Diff: 2   *Page Ref: 897–898*

22) The stage in meiosis where chromosomal exchange takes place is telophase.

Answer: FALSE
Diff: 2   *Page Ref: 903–904*

23) The diamond-shaped area between the anus and clitoris in the female is the vulva.

Answer: FALSE
Diff: 2   *Page Ref: 915*

24) The soft mucosal lining of the uterus is the endometrium.

Answer: TRUE
Diff: 2   *Page Ref: 913*

25) A scrotal muscle that contracts in response to cold environmental temperature is the cremaster.

Answer: TRUE
Diff: 2   *Page Ref: 896*

26) The secretions of the bulbourethral glands neutralize traces of acidic urine in the urethra and serve as a lubricant during sexual intercourse.

Answer: TRUE
Diff: 2   *Page Ref: 900*

27) The zona pellucida is formed as the follicle becomes a secondary follicle.

Answer: TRUE
Diff: 2   Page Ref: 920

28) The molecule that enhances the ability of testosterone to promote spermatogenesis is inhibin.

Answer: FALSE
Diff: 3   Page Ref: 907

Multiple-Choice Questions

1) The dartos and cremaster muscles are important to the integrity of the male reproductive system. Which of the following is true about the role they play?
   A) They contract to push sperm along the ductus deferens.
   B) They regulate the temperature of the testes.
   C) They are responsible for penile erection.
   D) They contract to allow ejaculation.

Answer: B
Diff: 1   Page Ref: 896

2) The ability of sperm cells to move along the ductus deferens is due to:
   A) gravity.   B) peristaltic contractions.
   C) enzymatic activity.   D) hormonal action.

Answer: B
Diff: 1   Page Ref: 898

3) The ability of a male to ejaculate is due to the action of:
   A) detumescence.   B) the dartos muscle.
   C) leutinizing hormone.   D) the bulbospongiosus muscles.

Answer: D
Diff: 1   Page Ref: 901

4) The most important risk for testicular cancer in young males is:
   A) smoking.   B) a diet high in fat.
   C) nondescent of the testes.   D) sexually transmitted diseases.

Answer: C
Diff: 1   Page Ref: 898

5) Which of the following glands are responsible for 60% of the synthesis of semen?
   A) the seminal vesicles   B) the Leydig cells
   C) the prostate   D) the pituitary

Answer: A
Diff: 1   Page Ref: 899

6) Which of the following hormones controls the release of anterior pituitary gonadotropins?

A) LH   B) FSH   C) GnRH   D) testosterone

Answer: C
Diff: 1   Page Ref: 907

7) The primary function of the uterus is to:

A) protect the ovaries.

B) synthesize female hormones.

C) regulate the ovarian and menstrual cycles.

D) receive, retain, and nourish a fertilized ovum.

Answer: D
Diff: 1   Page Ref: 911

8) The corpus luteum is:

A) the ruptured follicle following the ejection of an oocyte from the ovary.

B) the ovarian ligament that anchors the ovary medially to the uterus.

C) the mesovarium.

D) part of the uterine tube.

Answer: A
Diff: 1   Page Ref: 920

9) The structures that receive the ovulated oocyte, providing a site for fertilization, are called:

A) the Graafian follicles.   B) the fallopian tubes.

C) the infundibula.   D) the fimbriae.

Answer: B
Diff: 1   Page Ref: 911

10) Which of the following constitutes the female counterpart of the male scrotum?

A) the clitoris   B) the greater vestibular glands

C) the labia majora   D) the mons pubis

Answer: C
Diff: 1   Page Ref: 915

11) Human egg and sperm are similar in that:

A) about the same number of each is produced per month.

B) they have the same degree of motility.

C) they have the same number of chromosomes.

D) they are about the same size.

Answer: C
Diff: 1   Page Ref: 901

12) The constancy of the chromosome number from one cell generation to the next is maintained through:

   A) mitosis.   B) meiosis.   C) cytokinesis.   D) DNA synthesis.

Answer: B
Diff: 1   Page Ref: 902

13) Fertilization generally occurs in the:

   A) ovary.   B) uterus.   C) vagina.   D) fallopian tubes.

Answer: D
Diff: 1   Page Ref: 911

14) Spermiogenesis involves:

   A) the formation of four haploid cells from a spermatogonium.

   B) the movement of sperm in the female genital tract.

   C) the formation of a functional sperm by the stripping away of superfluous cytoplasm.

   D) None of the above are correct.

Answer: C
Diff: 1   Page Ref: 906

15) All of the following can be considered male secondary sex characteristics except the:

   A) development of body hair.

   B) lowering of the voice.

   C) development of testes as opposed to ovaries.

   D) increasing mass of the skeleton.

Answer: C
Diff: 1   Page Ref: 908–909

16) In humans, separation of the cells at the two–cell state following fertilization may lead to the production of twins, which in this case would be:

   A) dizygotic.   B) identical.

   C) fraternal.   D) of different sexes.

Answer: B
Diff: 1   Page Ref: 920

17) Characteristics of the mature sperm include:

   A) the presence of two X chromosomes in approximately half the sperm.

   B) the presence of Y chromosomes in approximately half the sperm.

   C) the absence of an acrosome.

   D) the absence of coiled mitochondria.

Answer: B
Diff: 1   Page Ref: 906

18) Functions of testosterone include:

    A) facilitation of muscle and skeletal growth in mass.

    B) loss of facial hair.

    C) growth of the breasts.

    D) drying of the skin.

    Answer: A
    Diff: 1   Page Ref: 908–909

19) Effects of estrogen include:

    A) increased oiliness of the skin.

    B) deepening of the voice.

    C) growth of the breasts at puberty.

    D) growth of the larynx.

    Answer: C
    Diff: 1   Page Ref: 924

20) Secretion of progesterone stimulates:

    A) contraction of uterine muscles.

    B) preparation of the mammary glands for lactation.

    C) secretory activity of the uterine myometrium.

    D) development of the female secondary sex characteristics.

    Answer: B
    Diff: 1   Page Ref: 924

21) Which of the following statements about spermatozoa is not true?

    A) They contain very little cytoplasm or stored nutrients.

    B) They are sluggish in an alkaline environment.

    C) The acrosome is produced by the Golgi apparatus and contains hydrolytic enzymes.

    D) The sperm midpiece consists of Golgi bodies spiraled tightly around the contractile filaments of the tail.

    Answer: D
    Diff: 1   Page Ref: 901–902

22) The cells that produce testosterone in the testis are called:

    A) spermatocytes.

    B) spermatogonia.

    C) sustentacular cells.

    D) interstitial cells or Leydig cells.

    Answer: D
    Diff: 1   Page Ref: 907

23) The testicular cells that construct the blood–testes barrier are the:

    A) spermatocytes.

    B) spermatogonia.

    C) sustentacular cells.

    D) interstitial cells or Leydig cells.

    Answer: C
    Diff: 1   Page Ref: 907

24) Erection of the penis results from:

A) a sympathetic reflex.

B) parasympathetic activation of the bulbourethral glands.

C) dilation of the veins in the penis.

D) a spinal reflex mediated by the parasympathetic nervous system.

Answer: D
Diff: 1   *Page Ref: 900*

25) Which is not a part of the proliferative phase of the female menstrual cycle?

A) cervical mucus becomes thin and crystalline

B) ovulation

C) corpus luteum

D) development of endometrial cells

Answer: C
Diff: 1   *Page Ref: 922*

26) Select the correct statement about the testis.

A) The testis is surrounded by the tunica vaginalis.

B) Each lobule of the testis contains 4–8 tightly coiled seminiferous tubules.

C) The interstitial cells are responsible for sperm cell maturation and also form the blood–testis barrier.

D) The Sertoli cells secrete testosterone.

Answer: A
Diff: 1   *Page Ref: 896–897*

27) Select the correct statement about male sexual response.

A) Sympathetic impulses are responsible for causing penile arteriolar dilation, resulting in erection.

B) Erection is the result of vascular spaces in the erectile tissues filling with blood.

C) Expansion of the penile tissues results in dilation of the venous outflow.

D) Ejaculation is the result of parasympathetic stimulation.

Answer: B
Diff: 1   *Page Ref: 900–901*

28) The ovaries:

A) are surrounded by the tunica albuginea.

B) are anchored to the uterus by the suspensory ligament.

C) are anchored to the body wall by the ovarian ligament.

D) contain a germinal epithelium from which the gametes arise.

Answer: A
Diff: 1   *Page Ref: 910–911*

29) Select the correct statement about mammary glands.

   A) Mammary glands are modified sebaceous glands.

   B) They have functional, milk–producing, simple alveolar glands.

   C) The breasts of most nonpregnant females are composed of fat and connective tissue.

   D) The pigmented area around the nipple is called the perineum.

   Answer: C
   Diff: 1   *Page Ref: 916*

30) During the secretory phase of the menstrual cycle:

   A) LH reaches its highest levels.   B) progesterone levels are at their highest.

   C) estrogen reaches its highest levels.   D) the Graafian follicle forms.

   Answer: B
   Diff: 1   *Page Ref: 922-924*

31) Select the correct statement about the uterine cycle.

   A) The menstrual phase of the cycle is from day 1 to day 8.

   B) During the secretory phase, estrogen levels are at their highest.

   C) During the proliferative phase, levels of progesterone rise as the follicle begins to produce
      more hormone.

   D) If fertilization occurs, the corpus luteum is maintained by a hormone secreted by the
      developing embryo.

   Answer: D
   Diff: 1   *Page Ref: 922-924*

32) What mechanism divides the testes into lobules?

   A) interstitial spaces   B) seminiferous tubules

   C) the ductus deferens   D) septal extensions of the tunica albuginea

   Answer: D
   Diff: 2   *Page Ref: 896*

33) Which of the following statements is true concerning the mammary glands of both males and
   females?

   A) Both sexes are equally prone to breast cancer.

   B) All lumps identified in breast tissue are malignant.

   C) The only time hormones target breast tissue is during pregnancy and lactation.

   D) The mammary glands are modified sweat glands that are actually part of the
      integumentary system.

   Answer: D
   Diff: 2   *Page Ref: 916*

34) Normally menstruation occurs when:

A) blood levels of FSH fall off.

B) blood levels of estrogen and progesterone decrease.

C) blood levels of estrogen and progesterone increase.

D) the corpus luteum secretes estrogen.

Answer: B
Diff: 2   *Page Ref: 922*

35) The basic difference between spermatogenesis and oogenesis is that:

A) during spermatogenesis two more polar bodies are produced.

B) the mature ovum is n, while the sperm is $2n$.

C) in oogenesis, one mature ovum is produced, and in spermatogenesis four mature sperm are produced from the parent cell.

D) spermatogenesis involves mitosis and meiosis, but oogenesis involves meiosis only.

Answer: C
Diff: 2   *Page Ref: 905, 918*

36) Occasionally three polar bodies are found clinging to the mature ovum. One came from an unequal division of the ovum, but from where did the other two arise?

A) There were originally four polar bodies and one disappeared.

B) One is an undeveloped primary oocyte that failed to mature.

C) The first polar body has also divided to produce two polar bodies.

D) What you really see are two polar bodies and the sperm that will fertilize the egg.

Answer: C
Diff: 2   *Page Ref: 917–919*

37) Which of the following will occur after ovulation?

A) The corpus luteum secretes estrogen only.

B) The endometrium enters its secretory phase.

C) The secretion of anterior pituitary gonadotropins is enhanced.

D) The corpus luteum prepares to become a corpus albicans.

Answer: B
Diff: 2   *Page Ref: 920*

38) The seminal vesicles:

A) produce a yellowish fluid rich in fructose.

B) produce about 90% of the volume of semen.

C) encircle the upper part of the urethra.

D) attach at the base of the penis.

Answer: A
Diff: 2   *Page Ref: 899*

39) Spermatogenesis:

   A) is the process of releasing mature sperm cells into the lumen of the seminiferous tubule.

   B) involves a kind of cell division limited to the gametes.

   C) results in the formation of diploid cells.

   D) uses mitosis to produce gamete cells.

   Answer: B
   Diff: 2   *Page Ref: 901*

40) The brain–testicular axis:

   A) is the tight relationship between the cortex and the control of testicular function.

   B) involves FSH and LH release.

   C) involves posterior pituitary release of regulating hormones.

   D) involves a positive feedback loop control of spermatogenesis.

   Answer: B
   Diff: 2   *Page Ref: 907*

41) Select the correct statement about testosterone control.

   A) GnRh from the hypothalamus causes FSH and LH release from the anterior pituitary.

   B) FSH stimulates testicular production of testosterone.

   C) Inhibin and testosterone exert positive feedback on the hypothalamus and pituitary.

   D) The pineal gland is believed to be the gland that exerts the most influence in testosterone control.

   Answer: A
   Diff: 2   *Page Ref: 907*

42) Which of the following is a correct statement about uterine tubes?

   A) The ampulla is the narrow constricted region.

   B) The infundibulum is the funnel–shaped region near the ovary.

   C) The isthmus is the normal site of fertilization.

   D) The mesometrium supports the uterine tubes along their entire length.

   Answer: B
   Diff: 2   *Page Ref: 911*

43) Select the correct statement about the hormonal events of the ovarian cycle.

   A) Rising levels of estrogen start follicle development.

   B) High estrogen levels result in a surge of LH release.

   C) The follicle begins to secrete progesterone in response to estrogen stimulation.

   D) The LH surge stimulates further development of the secondary oocyte.

   Answer: B
   Diff: 2   *Page Ref: 919–920*

44) Which of these statements about sexually transmitted diseases is false?

   A) Chlamydia is caused by bacteria that can bring on a wide variety of nonfatal but uncomfortable symptoms.

   B) Gonorrhea is caused by a bacteria that can bring on very painful discharges.

   C) Syphilis is caused by a virus that may lead to death if untreated.

   D) Genital herpes is caused by a virus that may lead to cervical cancer.

Answer: D
Diff: 2   Page Ref: 926

45) Meiosis:

   A) produces diploid cells from haploid cells.

   B) is found in prokaryotic and eukaryotic organisms.

   C) is a function of sexual but not asexual reproduction.

   D) occurs in every cell of the human body.

Answer: B
Diff: 3   Page Ref: 902–904

46) Which of the following statements about spermatogenesis is not true?

   A) The spermatogonium forms the primary spermatocyte.

   B) The primary spermatocyte forms two secondary spermatocytes.

   C) The secondary spermatocytes each form two spermatids.

   D) Each spermatid forms two sperm.

Answer: D
Diff: 3   Page Ref: 904

47) A boy who has not passed through puberty sustains an injury to his anterior pituitary such that FSH is no longer released, but LH is normal. After he grows to maturity, one would expect that he would:

   A) be sterile.

   B) not develop secondary sex characteristics.

   C) be impotent (unable to have an erection).

   D) have impaired function of interstitial cells.

Answer: A
Diff: 3   Page Ref: 907

48) Which of the following statements about the female reproductive process is not true?

   A) Fertilization usually occurs in the fallopian tube.

   B) Ovulation usually occurs 14 days after the beginning of menses.

   C) Rebuilding the endometrium is under the control of prolactin.

   D) The monthly discharge of the uterus (menses) is initiated by the fall in secretion of female hormones.

Answer: C
Diff: 3   Page Ref: 920–924

49) A low secretion of luteinizing hormone (LH) in the normal male adult would cause:

A) decreased testosterone secretion.

B) excessive beard growth.

C) increased spermatogenesis.

D) shrinkage of the anterior pituitary gland.

Answer: A
Diff: 3   Page Ref: 907

50) All of the following statements referring to the uterine cycle are true except:

A) FSH and LH directly promote development of the uterine endometrium.

B) Estrogen is secreted by the developing follicle in the follicular phase of the cycle.

C) The corpus luteum is formed from the ruptured follicle after ovulation.

D) A fall in the levels of ovarian hormones signals menstruation.

Answer: A
Diff: 3   Page Ref: 922-923

51) Which of the following phases or processes in the monthly reproductive cycle of the female occur simultaneously?

A) maximal LH secretion and menstruation

B) maximal steroid secretion by the corpus luteum and menstruation

C) early follicular development and the secretory phase in the uterus

D) regression of the corpus luteum and a decrease in ovarian progesterone secretion

Answer: D
Diff: 3   Page Ref: 920-924

52) The duct system of the male reproductive system includes:

A) the epididymis, a tightly coiled tube about 6 inches long.

B) the urethra, which is divided into four anatomical areas.

C) the ductus deferens, a duct that runs from the testis up into the pelvic cavity.

D) None of the above are correct.

Answer: C
Diff: 3   Page Ref: 898-899

Clinical Questions

1) Teresa has been complaining of severe abdominal pain, vaginal discharge, and a low–grade fever. She claims that she does not have a sexually transmitted disease, although the symptoms sound positive. What might be the doctor's diagnosis, and how should the condition be treated?

Answer: The symptoms sound like pelvic inflammatory disease, a collective term for any extensive bacterial infection of the pelvic organs, especially the uterus, uterine tubes, or ovaries. PID is most commonly caused by the bacterium that causes gonorrhea, but any bacterium can trigger the infection. Perhaps Teresa was not sexually active and the bacterium was introduced in some way other than through intercourse. Early treatment should include antibiotics (tetracycline or penicillin).

Diff: 3   Page Ref: 911

2) A 38-year-old male is upset about his low sperm count and visits a "practitioner" who commonly advertises his miracle cures of sterility. In point of fact, the practitioner is a quack who treats conditions of low sperm count with megadoses of testosterone. Although his patients experience a huge surge in libido, their sperm count is even lower after hormone treatment. Explain why.

   Answer: Megadoses of testosterone would inhibit hypothalamic release of GnRH and may act directly on the anterior pituitary to inhibit gonadotropin (FSH) release. Spermatogenesis is inhibited in the absence of FSH stimulation.
   Diff: 3   *Page Ref: 907*

3) Mr. and Mrs. John Takahama, a young couple who had been trying unsuccessfully to have a family for years, underwent a series of tests with a fertility clinic to try to determine the problem. Mr. Takahama was found to have a normal sperm count, and the sperm morphology and motility was normal. (1) If his count had been low, what type of information should be collected to determine the cause of the low count? Mrs. Takahama's history sheet revealed that she had two episodes of PID during her early 20s, and the time span between successive menses ranged from 21 to 30 days. She claimed that her family was "badgering" her about not giving them grandchildren and that she was frequently despondent. A battery of hormonal tests was ordered, and Mrs. Takahama was asked to perform a cervical mucus test and daily basal temperature recordings. Additionally, gas was blown through her uterine tubes to determine their patency. Her tubes proved to be closed and she was determined to be anovulatory. (2) What do you suggest might have caused the closing of her tubes? Which of the tests done or ordered would have revealed her anovulatory condition?

   Answer: (1) If his count had been low, he should have been checked for anatomical obstructions or hormonal imbalances. (2) Her tubes were probably scarred by PID. Hormonal testing and the daily basal temperature recordings would have indicated her anovulatory condition.
   Diff: 3   *Page Ref: 907, 911*